Atomic Spectra

and

Atomic Structure

Atomic Spectra
and
Atomic Structure

BY

Gerhard Herzberg

Research Professor of Physics
University of Saskatchewan

TRANSLATED
WITH THE CO-OPERATION OF THE AUTHOR

BY

J. W. T. Spinks

Professor of Physical Chemistry
University of Saskatchewan

NEW YORK
DOVER PUBLICATIONS
1944

Library of Congress Catalog Card Number: 45-4509

Manufactured in the United States of America

Dover Publications, Inc.

180 Varick Street

New York 14, N. Y.

Preface to Second Edition

THE present edition of this work contains a number of corrections and additions; Birge's new set of fundamental constants has been adopted throughout, and various tables, especially the table of ionization potentials, have been brought up to date.

The author is indebted to Professor J. W. Ellis of the University of California at Los Angeles for a list of errors and corrections; several of the author's students have also been helpful in pointing out certain mistakes.

The author is grateful to Dover Publications for their initiative and interest in making this book available again in a revised photo-offset edition in spite of war-time difficulties.

G. H.

SASKATOON, SASK., August, 1944.

Preface

THE present work is the translation of a volume published in German by Theodor Steinkopff about a year ago.[1] *Atomic Spectra and Atomic Structure* constitutes the first part of a more comprehensive course on atomic and molecular spectra which the author has prepared and given recently.

Though in the past few years several excellent accounts have been written on the subject of atomic spectra (cf. bibliography), there is still a need for an elementary introduction that is especially adapted to the beginner in this field and also to those who require a certain knowledge of the subject because of its applications in other fields.

For these two groups of readers the discussion of too many details and special cases does not seem desirable, since it is likely to obscure the fundamentally important points. Consequently, in this book the main stress is laid on the basic principles of the subject. Great pains have been taken to explain them as clearly as possible. To this end numerous diagrams and spectrograms are given as illustrations. Always the experimental results serve as the starting point of the theoretical considerations. Complicated mathematical developments have been avoided. Instead, the results of such calculations have been accepted without proof, reference being given to sources where proof can be found. Throughout the work an effort has been made to emphasize the physical significance of the theoretical deductions.

Rather liberal use has been made of small type in the printing of certain portions of the text. These, together with the footnotes, contain theoretical explanations and details that may very well be omitted in a first reading without interfering with an understanding of the fundamental points. Throughout the book, in making this distinction between small and ordinary type, the author has kept in mind the needs of those readers who wish to obtain a thorough knowledge of only the more important principles. The part printed in ordinary type is self-sufficient and adequate for that purpose.

In view of the applications, particularly to the study of molecular spectra and molecular structure, some points have been more extensively treated than others that might appear more important from the point of view of atomic spectra alone. In general, completeness has not been attempted except in Tables 17 and 18, which give, respectively, nuclear spin values and ionization potentials. In these tables, results published up to the beginning of the present year have been considered.

A discussion of X-ray spectra has been omitted, as one can be found in almost any advanced physics text.

Naturally in the course of the translation the author has used every opportunity to improve the original German presentation. It is believed that in many instances the explanations have been clarified. Also, certain recent findings have been added.

The author is greatly indebted to Dr. J. W. T. Spinks for his willingness to undertake the translation and for his prompt and careful work in carrying it out. He also owes many thanks to Dr. R. N. H. Haslam, who was kind enough to read the entire proof and made numerous and valuable suggestions for improving the presentation. Finally, the author wishes to express his appreciation to Dr. E. U. Condon, Editor of the PRENTICE-HALL PHYSICS SERIES, and the staff of Prentice-Hall, Inc., for their helpful co-operation during the publication of this volume.

G. H.

---

[1] G. Herzberg, Atomspektren und Atomstruktur (Dresden, 1936).

Table of Contents

vii

ERRATA

Page 10. The last number in the first line of the table
should be:
$$1.23954 \times 10^{-4}.$$

Page 35. The clause in the second line of the last paragraph
should be in brackets, thus:
(where $d\,\tau$ is an element of volume)

Page 194. Between the 8th and 9th lines from the bottom,
add:
Results. The nuclear spins obtained by the above
briefly

Page 219. In the first line of Table 20 the numbers .7157 and
16.50, respectively, should be changed to:
0.749 and 17.27

Illustrations

Tables

Introduction

DURING the last few decades the investigation of *atomic and molecular spectra* has had a decisive influence on the development of our present ideas of atomic and molecular structure. This investigation has shown above all that only certain discrete energy states are possible for an atom or molecule. The investigation of atomic spectra in particular, with which we shall occupy ourselves in this book, has given us information about the arrangement and motion (*angular momenta*) of the electrons in an atom. Furthermore, it has led to the discovery of *electron spin* and to a theoretical understanding of the *periodic system* of the elements. The data on the fundamental properties of different atoms obtained by means of spectra form a basis for an understanding of molecule formation and the chemical and physical properties of the elements.

In this book we shall be concerned exclusively with *optical line spectra* in the restricted sense of the term—that is, with atomic spectra in the region from 40Å to the far infrared, and not with X-ray spectra, which extend from approximately 100Å to lower wave lengths. The essential difference between optical line spectra and X-ray spectra is that the former correspond to energy changes of the *outer* electrons of an atom, and the latter to energy changes of the *inner* electrons.

Observation of spectra. The separation of light into its spectral components can be accomplished either by *refraction* or *diffraction*. Both phenomena depend upon the wave length, but in opposite ways: the greater the wave length, the *greater* is the *diffraction* of light; but the greater the wave length, the *smaller* is the *refraction* of light. For the separation of light by diffraction, gratings are used; for separation by refraction, prisms. Both methods may be

1

employed except in the region below 1250 Å, where a grating is necessary. The prism method has the advantage of greater light intensity, whereas the grating method generally affords greater resolving power.[1] The construction and use of spectroscopes and spectrographs will not be dealt with here. Information on these topics is given in bibliography references at the end of this book: (1a), (2a), (3), (4), (11), (14).

Spectra in the far infrared can be investigated only with thermopiles or bolometers; however, below 13,000 Å photographic plates are generally used. By using a photographic plate a large region of the spectrum may be obtained at one time.

Lenses, prisms, and windows of glass can be used only in the region from 3μ to 3600 Å. At lower wave lengths, glass absorbs light almost completely and this necessitates the use of quartz or fluorite. Quartz begins to absorb appreciably at 1800 Å, and therefore fluorite must be used below this wave length. Fluorite itself begins to absorb strongly at 1250 Å, so that below this wave length only reflection gratings can be used, with complete exclusion of lenses and windows.[2] Since air absorbs strongly at 1900 Å, the whole spectrograph must be evacuated for photographs below this wave length. Also, in this region the gelatin on the photographic plates absorbs, and makes necessary the use of specially prepared plates.[3]

Light sources. There are many possibilities for the production of light for spectroscopic investigations. The principal ones are *temperature radiation* and all kinds of *luminescence*—electroluminescence, chemiluminescence, and fluorescence.

In *temperature radiation* of gases, the atoms or molecules are excited to light emission by collision with other atoms or

---

[1] Shortly before the short wave-length limit of transmission, a prism can in some cases provide a greater resolving power than a grating.

[2] Melvin (40) has recently found that LiF transmits down to 1080 Å.

[3] These difficulties disappear for the very penetrating X-rays below 4 Å.

molecules, the necessary energy being derived from the kinetic energy of the colliding particles. Therefore a high temperature is required. Such emission occurs, for example, in flames, although it is then often mixed with chemiluminescence. Excitation of gases by high temperature alone is obtained, however, in any electric furnace of sufficiently high temperature—for example, in the King furnace.

Luminescence includes all forms of light emission in which kinetic heat energy is not essential for the mechanism of excitation. *Electroluminescence* includes luminescence from all kinds of electrical discharges—such as sparks, arcs, or Geissler tubes of different kinds operating on direct or alternating current of low or high frequency. Excitation in these cases results mostly from electron or ion collision; that is, the kinetic energy of electrons or ions accelerated in an electric field is given up to the atoms or molecules of the gas present and causes light emission. *Chemiluminescence* results when energy set free in a chemical reaction is converted to light energy (see Chapter VI). The light from many chemical reactions (for example, $Na + Cl_2$) and from many flames is of this type. *Photoluminescence*, or *fluorescence*, results from excitation by absorption of light (for example, in fluorescein, iodine vapor, sodium vapor, and so on). The term *phosphorescence* is usually applied to luminescence which continues after excitation by one of the above methods has ceased.

Emission and absorption. By any of the foregoing methods, characteristic *emission* spectra can be obtained for each substance. They usually vary for a given substance according to the mode of excitation.[4]

To obtain the *absorption* spectrum of a substance, light with a continuous spectrum (as that from a filament lamp) is passed through an absorbing layer of the substance being

---

[4] Conversely, conclusions as to the mode of excitation may be drawn from the kind of spectrum observed.

investigated and is then analyzed with a spectrograph. We obtain light lines (absorption lines) or bands on a dark background on the photographic plate.[5] (See Fig. 2.) The intensity of the absorption can be altered by varying the thickness of the absorbing layer, or, in the case of gases, by changing the pressure.

Examples. Examples of simple and complicated optical line spectra are given in Figs. 1, 2, 3, 4, 5, 6. In the spectra of H, Na, and Mg (Figs. 1–4), *regularities* are immediately apparent, whereas with Hg and Fe such regularities are not easily recognizable. Actually, both the complicated and the simple spectra consist of *series* of lines, or series of line groups (cf. the figures), whose separation and intensity decrease regularly toward shorter wave lengths. When the number of these series is large, a complicated spectrum results. Two such series are indicated in the Hg spectrum (Fig. 5). Fig. 7 shows a typical example of a *band spectrum* (PN) for comparison with the line spectra. It obviously shows a completely different type of regularity. This difference led quite early to the assumption that *line spectra are emitted or absorbed by atoms, band spectra by molecules.* This assumption has in the course of time been completely justified, notably by the fact that with it all the details of a spectrum can be explained satisfactorily. It has also been independently verified by the experiments of W. Wien on canal rays, and by the determination of line width, which, as a result of the Doppler effect, depends on mass.

Spectral analysis. As already stated, each chemical element gives rise to a characteristic line spectrum by suitable excitation (flame, arc, spark, electric discharge). Conversely, the appearance of a line spectrum can be used as an analytical test for the presence of an element—a test which has the advantage that extraordinarily small amounts of an element can be detected. This method of analysis,

---

[5] Obviously, the reverse holds for visual observation—dark lines appear on a light background.

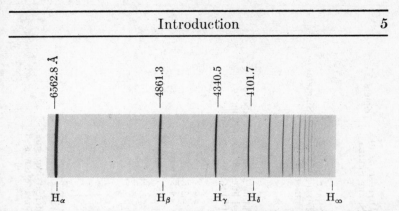

Fig. 1. Emission Spectrum of the Hydrogen Atom in the Visible and Near Ultraviolet Region [Balmer series, Herzberg (41)]. H_∞ gives the theoretical position of the series limit.

Fig. 2. Absorption Spectrum of the Na Atom [Kuhn (42)]. The spectrogram gives only the short wave-length part, starting with the fifth line of the principal series. The lines appear as bright lines on a dark continuous background, just as on the photographic plate.

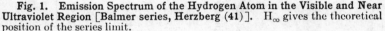

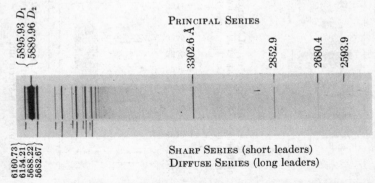

Fig. 3. Emission Spectrum of the Na Atom (Arc with One Na Electrode). Three series can be clearly recognized; one of them, the principal series, coincides with the absorption series of Fig. 2.

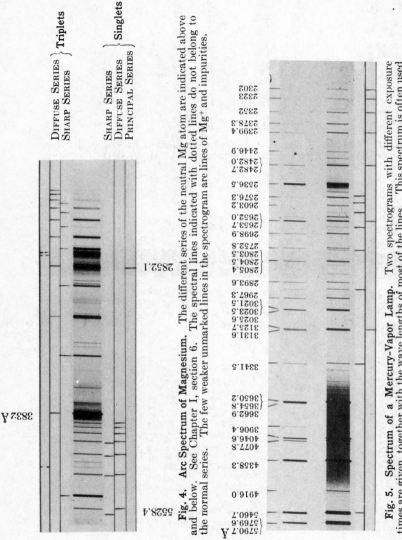

DIFFUSE SERIES ⎱ Triplets
SHARP SERIES ⎰

SHARP SERIES ⎱
DIFFUSE SERIES ⎰ Singlets
PRINCIPAL SERIES ⎰

Fig. 4. Arc Spectrum of Magnesium. The different series of the neutral Mg atom are indicated above and below. See Chapter I, section 6. The spectral lines indicated with dotted lines do not belong to the normal series. The few weaker unmarked lines in the spectrogram are lines of Mg⁺ and impurities.

Fig. 5. Spectrum of a Mercury-Vapor Lamp. Two spectrograms with different exposure times are given, together with the wave lengths of most of the lines. This spectrum is often used as a comparison spectrum.

6

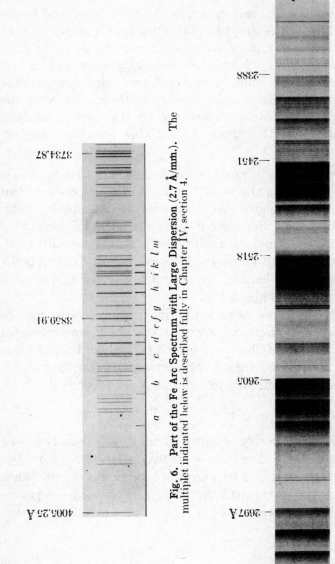

Fig. 6. Part of the Fe Arc Spectrum with Large Dispersion (2.7 Å/mm.). The multiplet indicated below is described fully in Chapter IV, section 4.

a   b   c   d   e f g   h i k   l m

3734.87

3859.91

4005.25 Å

Fig. 7. Band Spectrum of the PN Molecule [Curry, Herzberg, and Herzberg (43)].

2388

2451

2518

2605

2697 Å

7

called *spectral analysis*, has recently been considerably developed [see bibliography: (15), (16), (17), (18), (19)], but the results will not be discussed here. Rather, we shall concern ourselves with the *structure* of atomic spectra and the conclusions which can be drawn regarding atomic structure. However, a knowledge of the structure of the spectrum is of some importance to the spectro-analyst, particularly in the choice of suitable lines for spectro-analytical tests.

Units. In the infrared, wave lengths are usually measured in terms of μ: $1\mu = 10^{-3}$ mm. In the ordinary optical region, wave lengths are measured in Ångstrom units: $1\text{Å} = 10^{-8}$ cm. For wave lengths above 2000Å, the value in air under standard conditions, λ_{air} [6] is generally used, while λ_{vac} is usually employed for wave lengths below 2000Å since these wave lengths are almost always measured with a vacuum spectrograph.

For the purpose of investigating regularities in spectra and their connection with atomic structure, it is very helpful to use, instead of the wave length of a given line, the *frequency* or a value that is proportional to the frequency. The frequency (number of vibrations per second) is:

$$\nu' = \frac{c_{\text{air}}}{\lambda_{\text{air}}} = \frac{c_{\text{vac}}}{\lambda_{\text{vac}}}$$

where c is the velocity of light. That is, ν' is usually a very large number. (For $\lambda_{\text{vac}} = 1000\text{Å}$, $\nu' = 3 \times 10^{15}$.) Because of this and also because the accuracy of λ sometimes is markedly greater than that of c, *wave numbers* are generally used in spectroscopy:

$$\nu = \frac{\nu'}{c_{\text{vac}}} = \frac{1}{\lambda_{\text{vac}}} = \frac{1}{n_{\text{air}}\lambda_{\text{air}}}$$

---

[6] When n is the refractive index of air for the wave length concerned,

$$\lambda_{\text{air}} = \frac{\lambda_{\text{vac}}}{n}$$

Therefore λ_{air} is somewhat smaller than λ_{vac}.

where n_{air} is the refractive index for the wave length considered. The value ν is simply the *reciprocal of the wave length in vacuo*—that is, the number of waves in 1 cm. in vacuo. (Dimensions, cm^{-1}; for $\lambda_{vac} = 1000$ Å, $\nu_{vac} = 100,000$ cm^{-1}.) In order to obtain the vacuum wave number, we must first convert the wave length in air to the wave length in vacuo by multiplying by n_{air}, and then take the reciprocal value. This computation is much simplified by using such tables as the Kayser *Tabelle der Schwingungszahlen* (21).

As will be further explained in Chapter I, the frequency ν' and the energy E of a light quantum are related by the fundamental equation $E = h\nu'$, where h is Planck's constant ($h = 6.624 \times 10^{-27}$ erg sec.). The frequency or the wave number can therefore serve as a measure of the energy. When a single atom or molecule emits light of wave number ν, the emitted light quantum has an energy $E = h\nu' = hc\nu$. Therefore 1 cm^{-1} is equivalent to 1.9858×10^{-16} ergs per molecule. If we consider the elementary act for one mol instead of a single atom or molecule, we must multiply by the number of molecules in one mol, $N = 6.0228 \times 10^{23}$. Then 1 cm^{-1} is equivalent to 11.960×10^{7} ergs per mol, or 2.8575 cal. per mol. using the chemical atomic weight scale.

Finally we must mention the electron-volt, which is very widely used in atomic physics. One electron-volt is the energy of an electron which has been accelerated through a potential of 1 volt.[7] The kinetic energy acquired by an electron of charge e falling through a potential V (in electrostatic units) is eV ergs. With $e = 4.8025 \times 10^{-10}$ electrostatic units and one volt $= 1/299.776$ electrostatic units, it follows that one electron-volt is equivalent to 1.6020×10^{-12} ergs per molecule, which corresponds to 8067.5 cm^{-1} or 23,053 cal. per mol. All these conversion factors are collected together in Table I.

---

[7] The *volt* used here is the absolute volt, which differs slightly from the international: 1 volt$_{int}$ = 1.00034 volt$_{abs}$.

TABLE 1

CONVERSION FACTORS OF ENERGY UNITS

Unit	cm^{-1}	ergs/molecule	cal./mol$_{chem}$	electron-volts
1 cm^{-1}........	1	1.9858×10^{-16}	2.8575	1.23954×10^{-4}
1 erg/molecule .	5.0358×10^{15}	1	1.4390×10^{16}	6.2421×10^{11}
1 cal./mol$_{chem}$ ..	0.34996	6.9494×10^{-17}	1	4.3379×10^{-5}
1 electron-volt .	8067.5	1.60203×10^{-12}	23053	1

The values for e, h, N and c are taken from Birge (144). These values differ rather considerably from those used in the original printing of this book; but they are only insignificantly different from those used in the author's Molecular Spectra and Molecular Structure I: Diatomic Molecules.

CHAPTER I

The Simplest Line Spectra and the Elements of Atomic Theory

1. The Empirical Hydrogen Terms

The Balmer series and the Balmer formula. The simplest line spectrum is that of the H atom, which is itself the simplest atom (see Fig. 1). This spectrum consists, in the visible and near ultraviolet, of a series of lines whose separation and intensity decrease in a perfectly regular manner toward shorter wave lengths. Similar series are emitted by the alkali atoms, though in greater number and overlapping one another (see Fig. 3). The spectra of all the other elements likewise consist of such series, which, however, on account of much overlapping, are not always so easily recognizable.

The apparent regularity of the so-called hydrogen series was first mathematically formulated by Balmer. He found that the wave lengths of the lines could be represented accurately by the formula:

$$\lambda = \frac{n_1{}^2}{n_1{}^2 - 4} G$$

where $n_1 = 3, 4, 5, \cdots$, and G is a constant. The equation is now generally written in the form:

$$\nu = R \left(\frac{1}{2^2} - \frac{1}{n_1{}^2} \right)$$

where ν is the wave number of the line (see Introduction, p. 8). In this equation a single constant R, the Rydberg constant, appears and has the value 109,677.581 cm^{-1} (= 13.595 volts).[1] In spite of the simplicity of the formula, extraordinarily close agreement is obtained between experi-

---

[1] Cf. Birge (145).

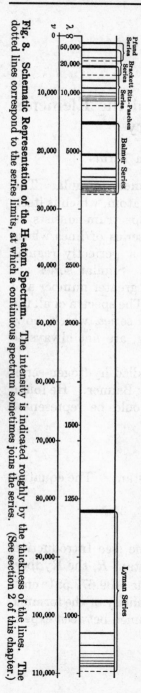

mental and calculated values, the agreement being within the limits of spectroscopic accuracy ($1 : 10^7$).

Other hydrogen series. When the number 2 in the Balmer formula is replaced by $n_2 = 1, 3, 4, 5, \cdots$, and n_1 is allowed to take the values $2, 3, \cdots; 4, 5, \cdots; 5, 6, \cdots; 6, 7, \cdots$, respectively, other series of wave numbers or wave lengths are obtained. The spectral lines of H corresponding to these series have actually been observed and are found to have exactly the predicted wave lengths. The first series ($n_2 = 1$) was discovered by Lyman in the far ultraviolet; the others, in the infrared, by Paschen ($n_2 = 3$), Brackett ($n_2 = 4$), and Pfund ($n_2 = 5$).

All these line series of the H atom can be represented by one formula:

$$\nu = \frac{R}{n_2{}^2} - \frac{R}{n_1{}^2} \qquad (\mathbf{I, 1})$$

where n_2 and $n_1 > n_2$ are integers, and n_2 is constant for a given series. With increasing values of the order number n_1, ν approaches a limit $\nu_\infty = R/n_2{}^2$. That is, the separation of consecutive members of a given series decreases so that ν cannot exceed a fixed limit, the *series limit*. In principle, an infinite number of lines lie at the series limit.

Fig. 8 gives a schematic representation of the complete H spectrum.

Representation of spectral lines by terms. According to formula

(I, 1) the wave number of any line of the H-atom spectrum is the difference between two members of the series, $T(n) = R/n^2$, having different values of n. These members are called *terms*. The lines of other elements also can be represented as the *difference between two such terms*. This conclusion follows empirically from the fact that they likewise form series. Therefore, quite generally the formula for the wave number of a line is:

$$\nu = T_2 - T_1 \qquad \text{(I, 2)}$$

However, the term T usually has a somewhat more complicated form than that for the H spectrum. In addition, the first and second members of the formula are obtained from *different* term series (see below).

The converse of the fact that each spectral line can be represented as the difference between two terms is embodied in the *Rydberg-Ritz combination principle*, which states that, with certain limitations, the difference between *any* two terms of an atom gives the wave number of a spectral line of the atom. For example, the difference between $T(4)$ and $T(10)$ for hydrogen gives the sixth line of the Brackett series.

2. The Bohr Theory of Balmer Terms

The fundamental relation between the terms of an atom and its structure was first recognized by Bohr. Even though the Bohr theory is now extended and altered in some essential respects by the new wave or quantum mechanics, we must deal with it briefly at this point, since a knowledge of this theory considerably simplifies an understanding of modern theories. In fact, a number of phenomena in spectroscopy can be dealt with by using the Bohr theory alone.

Basic assumptions. According to the Rutherford-Bohr theory, the atom consists of a heavy nucleus with a charge Ze, about which Z electrons rotate. (Z = the ordinal number in the periodic system of the elements—that is, the atomic number.) In order to explain the characteristic light emission by atoms, Bohr proposed two basic assumptions. (1) Of the infinite number of orbits of an electron about an atomic nucleus, which are possible according to classical mechanics, *only certain discrete orbits* actually occur. These fulfill certain quantum conditions. Furthermore, in contradiction to the classical Maxwell theory, the electron, in spite of accelerated motion, emits no electromagnetic waves (light) while in one of these discrete orbits. (2) Radiation is emitted or absorbed by a *transition of the electron from one quantum state to another*—by a *quantum jump*—the energy difference between the two states being emitted or absorbed as a light quantum of energy $h\nu'$ (h = Planck's constant, ν' = frequency). The light quantum is emitted when the atom goes from a state of higher energy to one of lower energy, and is absorbed in the converse case (conservation of energy). The relation $h\nu' = E_{n_1} - E_{n_2}$ therefore holds, E_{n_1} and E_{n_2} being the energies of the upper and lower states, respectively. This relation is the *Bohr frequency condition*. The index n of E distinguishes the different orbits and their energy values from one another.

The wave number of the emitted or absorbed light is obtained from the frequency condition:

$$\nu = \frac{\nu'}{c} = \frac{E_{n_1}}{h \cdot c} - \frac{E_{n_2}}{h \cdot c} \qquad (I, 3)$$

From the similarity between equations (I, 2) and (I, 3)—in both cases ν is the difference between two quantities which can take only discrete values, that is, which can be numbered by integers—we see that, apart from a factor, the terms of equations (I, 1) and (I, 2) are equal to the energies of the quantum states. The E values contain an arbitrary additive constant. If we take the additive constant so that $E = 0$ when the electron is completely removed from the nucleus, the energy values of the different quantum states will be negative, since, by the return of an electron to such a state, energy will be liberated. (A positively charged nucleus attracts electrons.) The terms in (I, 1) and (I, 2) are positive quantities (for hydrogen, $T = R/n^2$). Therefore

$$T_1 = -\frac{E_{n_1}}{h \cdot c}, \qquad T_2 = -\frac{E_{n_2}}{h \cdot c}$$

Here $- E = W$ is the work that must be done in order to remove an electron from a given orbit to infinity (separation energy). Apart from the factor hc, the terms are therefore equal to the separation energies of the electron in the given states. For the lowest state of the atom, the *ground state*, the separation energy is called the *ionization energy*, or the *ionization potential*, which accordingly is equal to the largest term value of the atom. Similarly, apart from the factor hc, the term *differences* are equal to the energy differences of the given atomic states.

This connection between term values and energies is shown‧experimentally in the work of Franck and Hertz. They observed that, when collisions between electrons and atoms take place, an inelastic collision—that is, an energy transfer from the electron to the atom—can occur when, and only when, the kinetic energy of the electron is greater than that calculated from the term difference for the transition of the atom from the ground state into an *excited* state. The amount of energy lost by the electron is exactly equal to the excitation energy of the atom as calculated from the spectrum. Furthermore, after such a collision, there can be observed the emission of a spectral line corresponding to the transition from the excited state to the ground state. [Cf. Geiger-Scheel (1*c*).]

Electron orbits in the field of a nucleus with charge *Ze*. Taking first the simplest case, in which the orbits are *circles* of radius r, we apply Newton's fundamental law: force = mass × acceleration. Here the force is Coulomb's attraction Ze^2/r^2; the acceleration is the centripetal acceleration v^2/r. Hence

$$\frac{Ze^2}{r^2} = \frac{mv^2}{r} \quad \text{or} \quad r = \frac{Ze^2}{mv^2} \qquad \textbf{(I, 4)}$$

where m and v are, respectively, the mass and the velocity of the electron. Thus far we have applied only classical mechanics, which leads to the conclusion that every value of r is possible, depending on the value of v.

According to Bohr (see earlier text), only certain orbits actually do occur and these are selected by the *postulate that the angular momentum mvr is an integral multiple of h/2π;* that is,

$$mvr = n \frac{h}{2\pi}, \qquad \text{where } n = 1, 2, 3, \cdots \qquad \text{(I, 5)}$$

This is an assumption which cannot be further justified. Here n is called the *principal quantum number.* For a given value of n, the values of r and v are now unambiguously fixed by equations (I, 4) and (I, 5). For r, we obtain:

$$r = n^2 \frac{h^2}{4\pi^2 m e^2 Z} \qquad \text{(I, 6)}$$

It is apparent that the radii of the possible orbits are proportional to n^2.

In Fig. 9, for the case of hydrogen ($Z = 1$), the first few orbits from $n = 1$ to $n = 4$ are drawn to scale. For the smallest possible orbit; that is, with $n = 1$:

$$r = \frac{h^2}{4\pi^2 m e^2} = a_\text{H} = 0.529\text{Å}$$

This radius is of the same order of magnitude as the radius of the atom given by kinetic theory.

There are three *refinements* of this simplified theory.

(1) In reality the electron revolves, not about the nucleus itself, but about the *common center of gravity;* also, the nucleus revolves about that center. Therefore the mass of the nucleus enters into the equations. It may be shown [cf. Sommerfeld (5a)] that equation (I, 6) still holds if m is replaced by the so-called *reduced mass:*

$$\mu = \frac{mM}{m + M}$$

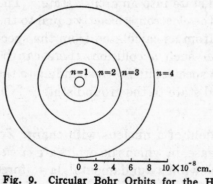

0   2   4   6   8 10×10^{-8} cm.

Fig. 9.   Circular Bohr Orbits for the H Atom ($n = 1$ to $n = 4$).

where M is the mass of the nucleus. Here μ is approximately equal to m because $M/(m + M)$ is very nearly equal to 1. ($m = 9.1066 \times 10^{-28}$ gm. and, for hydrogen, $M = 1.6725 \times 10^{-24}$ gm.)

(2) In general, not only circular orbits but also *elliptical orbits* are possible (compare above). Evidently the one condition mentioned above is not sufficient to fix unambiguously both axes of the ellipse. Therefore Sommerfeld introduced a new and more general postulate than the original one of Bohr—namely, for the stationary states the so-called *action integral* $\oint p_i \, dq_i$ extended over one period of the motion must be an integral multiple of h.

$$\oint p_i \, dq_i = n_i h \qquad \textbf{(I, 7)}$$

Here n_i is a whole number, p_i any *generalized*[2] momentum which depends on the corresponding co-ordinate q_i. This postulate implies the previous one: If $dq_i = d\varphi$ where φ is the angle of rotation, then $p_i = p_\varphi$, the angular momentum of the system. According to classical mechanics, the angular momentum of any isolated system is a constant. Therefore

$$\oint p_\varphi \, d\varphi = p_\varphi \int_0^{2\pi} d\varphi = 2\pi p_\varphi = n_\varphi h; \quad n_\varphi = 1, 2, 3, \cdots \quad \textbf{(I, 8)}$$

that is, as before, the angular momentum is an integral multiple of $h/2\pi$. However, for an ellipse, r is not constant and therefore we have from (I, 7) an additional condition:

$$\oint p_r \, dr = n_r \cdot h; \qquad n_r = 0, 1, 2, \cdots \quad \textbf{(I, 9)}$$

where p_r is the linear momentum in the direction of r. Here n_r is called the *radial quantum number;* n_φ, which will henceforth be replaced by k, is called the *azimuthal quantum number.* Just as previously by (I, 5) the continuous range of r values was reduced to (I, 6), now, by conditions (I, 8) and (I, 9), the possible values of the major and minor axes

---

[2] This term is not defined here because it is not particularly essential for the following considerations. For a complete explanation, the reader is referred to the texts on advanced dynamics.

of the elliptical orbits are reduced to the following [cf. (5a), (10)]:

$$a = \frac{h^2}{4\pi^2\mu e^2} \cdot \frac{n^2}{Z} = \frac{a_\mathrm{H}}{Z} \cdot n^2$$

$$b = \frac{h^2}{4\pi^2\mu e^2} \cdot \frac{nk}{Z} = \frac{a_\mathrm{H}}{Z} \cdot nk \qquad\qquad \text{(I, 10)}$$

where the *principal quantum number* n is now defined as $n = k + n_r$. Here k may take the values $1, 2, \cdots n$ ($k = 0$ was considered impossible in this theory since for zero angular momentum the electron would have to traverse the nucleus). Consequently $n \geqq k$. For $n = k$, $a = b$; in other words, we have the circular orbits discussed in connection with Fig. 9 (with the same meaning for n). From relation (I, 10) it follows that $a/b = n/k$. The principal quantum number n is thus a measure of the major axis of the elliptical orbit, whereas the azimuthal quantum number is a

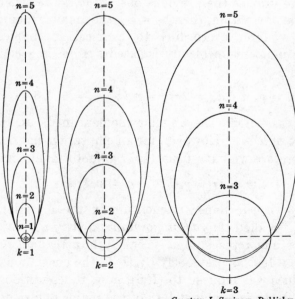

Courtesy J. Springer, Publisher.

Fig. 10.   Elliptical Bohr-Sommerfeld Orbits for the H Atom with $k = 1$, 2, and 3 [from Grotrian (8)].   The positive nucleus is at the focus O of the ellipse.   The energy difference between orbits with equal n but different k is very small.   The smallest value of n for a given k is $n = k$.   Same scale as in Fig. 9.

measure of the minor axis. On the other hand, according to (I, 8), $k(= n_\varphi)$ gives the *angular momentum* of the atom in the specified state *in units* $h/2\pi$. Fig. 10 shows the elliptical orbits (drawn to scale) for hydrogen, with various n values, for $k = 1, 2$, and 3.

(3) Sommerfeld also applied *relativistic mechanics* to the motion of the electron. He found that the orbit is an ellipse, the axis of which rotates uniformly and slowly about the center of gravity (rosette motion) instead of remaining stationary.

Energy of Bohr's orbits (Balmer terms). For circular orbits, the total energy is:

$$E = \text{potential energy} + \text{kinetic energy} = -\frac{Ze^2}{r} + \frac{1}{2}mv^2$$

Using formula (I, 4), we obtain:

$$E = -\frac{Ze^2}{r} + \frac{Ze^2}{2r} = -\frac{Ze^2}{2r}$$

This equation holds also when the motion of the nucleus is considered. Substituting from (I, 6) the value for r and using μ instead of m, we obtain:

$$E_n = -\frac{2\pi^2\mu e^4}{h^2} \cdot \frac{Z^2}{n^2} \qquad \text{(I, 11)}$$

The same expression is obtained for the energy of the elliptical orbits [cf. Sommerfeld (5a)]. Thus the energy does not depend on the azimuthal quantum number k—that is, on the minor axis of the ellipse.

However, if relativity is also considered, a very slight dependence on k results—namely (as found by Sommerfeld),

$$E_{n, k} = -\frac{2\pi^2\mu e^4}{h^2} \cdot \frac{Z^2}{n^2}\left[1 + \frac{\alpha^2 Z^2}{n}\left(\frac{1}{k} - \frac{3}{4n}\right) \right] \qquad \text{(I, 12)}$$

where $\alpha = 2\pi e^2/hc = 7.2977 \times 10^{-3}$ is the so-called Sommerfeld *fine structure constant.*[3]

The second term in brackets is very small because of the term α^2; hence, for most purposes the simplified formula (I, 11) may be used. The state of lowest energy evidently

---

[3] Further terms with α^4, etc., are included in the exact formula, but are usually negligibly small.

has $n = 1$. This state, according to Bohr's theory, is the stable ground state of the hydrogen atom (smallest orbit in Fig. 9).

From equation (I, 11) and Bohr's frequency condition (I, 3), it follows that the *wave numbers of the emitted spectral lines* are given by:

$$\nu = \frac{1}{hc}(E_{n_1} - E_{n_2}) = \frac{2\pi^2\mu e^4}{ch^3} \cdot Z^2 \left(\frac{1}{n_2^2} - \frac{1}{n_1^2}\right) \quad \text{(I, 13)}$$

where n_1 and n_2 are the principal quantum numbers of the upper and lower states.

The formal agreement of this formula with the empirical Balmer formula (I, 1) for the hydrogen series is obvious. By substituting the known values of μ, e, c, h, and Z in the numerical factor of equation (I, 13), we obtain the Rydberg constant R, which formerly had been obtained purely empirically from the Balmer spectrum. For hydrogen $R = 2\pi^2\mu e^4/ch^3$, and the agreement between the calculated and observed values is as close as can be expected from the accuracy with which the above constants are known. The formula for the Balmer series is obtained from (I, 13) by using $n_2 = 2$. This series thus results from the transitions of the hydrogen atom from different higher energy states with $n_1 = 3, 4, \cdots$, to the state $n_2 = 2$. In the remaining hydrogen series the lower state has a different principal quantum number. (See also Fig. 12 and discussion in section 3 of this chapter.)

Spectra of hydrogen-like ions. Taking $Z = 2$ in (I, 13) gives the spectrum which would be emitted by an electron moving about a nucleus with charge 2; that is, the spectrum of He^+. Analogously, for $Z = 3$ and $Z = 4$, we obtain the spectra of Li^{++} and Be^{+++}. The general formula is:

$$\nu = RZ^2 \left(\frac{1}{n_2^2} - \frac{1}{n_1^2}\right), \quad \text{where } R = \frac{2\pi^2\mu e^4}{ch^3} \quad \text{(I, 14)}$$

The mass of the nucleus enters into R because of the dependence of R on μ. Substituting μ, we obtain:

$$R = R_\infty \left(\frac{M}{M + m} \right)$$

where R_∞ is the value of R obtained for an infinitely heavy nucleus—that is, when m is used instead of μ in the formula for R (I, 14). It follows that R varies slightly for He, Li, and Be. The values for R, calculated from R_H by using accurate values for the masses [see Bethe (48)], are given in the second column of Table 2.

TABLE 2

RYDBERG CONSTANTS AND FIRST MEMBERS OF LYMAN SERIES FOR HYDROGEN–LIKE IONS

Hydrogen-like Ion	R (cm^{-1})	$\nu_{2,1}$ (cm^{-1})	$\lambda_{2,1\,vac}$ (Å)
H	109,677.581	82,259.56	1215.664
He$^+$	109,722.263	329,188.7	303.777
* Li^{++}	109,728.723	740,779.8	134.993
Be^{+++}	109,730.624	1,317,118.1	75.924

* Referring to the isotope of mass 7.

Apart from this small correction and apart from the factor Z^2, corresponding to a strong displacement to shorter wave lengths, the spectra of these ions are identical in all details with the hydrogen-atom spectrum. The third and fourth columns, respectively, of Table 2 give for these ions the calculated wave numbers and wave lengths of the lines corresponding to the first line of the Lyman series ($n = 2 \rightarrow n = 1$).[4] These and other lines indicated by (I, 14) have been found at exactly the calculated positions. From formula (I, 11) it follows that for He$^+$ the separation energy W_1 of the electron from the lowest level (the ionization potential) will be very nearly four times that for the hydrogen atom, where it is equal to $R_H = 13.595$ volts. For Li^{++} it will be nine times as great, and for Be^{+++} sixteen times.

[4] The relativity correction of (I, 12) has been allowed for in the calculation of the table, taking $k = 2$ for the upper state ($k = 1$ would give a slightly different wave number).

Continuum at the series limit. As already stated, the energy of an atomic state is known apart from an additive constant. The latter is chosen so that $E = 0$ when the electron is completely removed from the atom; therefore all stable atomic states will have negative E values. A *positive* value of E would, accordingly, indicate more energy than that for the system with its parts infinitely separated and at rest; that is, the two parts possess relative kinetic energy. They approach or separate with a velocity (kinetic energy) that does not disappear—even at infinity.

According to classical mechanics (disregarding radiation) the electron in this case moves, not in an ellipse, but in a hyperbola. This behavior is similar to that of heavenly bodies that come from space with a great velocity and describe a hyperbolic orbit about the sun as focus (for example, the orbit of a comet). Since, according to the quantum theory, only the periodic motions in the atom are quantized, these hyperbolic orbits can occur without any limitation; in other words, *all positive values of E are possible.* Hence, extending from the limit of the discrete energy levels, there is a continuous region of possible energy values: the discrete term spectrum is followed by a continuous one. Just as in elliptical orbits, according to Bohr (but in contrast to classical theory) electrons will not radiate in hyperbolic orbits. Radiation results only through a quantum jump from such a state of positive energy to a lower state of positive or negative energy. When the relative kinetic energy is ΔE, for a transition to the discrete state n_2, formula (I, 13) changes to:

$$\nu = \frac{R}{n_2{}^2} + \frac{\Delta E}{hc} \qquad (\text{I, 15})$$

As ΔE can take any positive value, the series of discrete lines whose limit is at $R/n_2{}^2$ is followed by a continuous spectrum, a so-called *continuum.* Such a continuum actually occurs with the Balmer series in absorption in the spectra of many fixed stars, and is also observed in emission spectra from artificial light sources [Herzberg (41)]. In absorption, it corresponds to the *separation of an electron* from the atom (photoeffect) with more or less kinetic energy (depending on the distance from the limit); in emission, it corresponds to the *capture of an electron* by a proton, the electron going into the orbit with principal quantum number n_2.

The beginning of the continuum, the series limit, corresponds to the separation or the capture of an electron with zero velocity ($\Delta E = 0$). If the transition takes place from the ground state to the ionized state (absorption in cold gas), *the wave number of the series limit gives directly the separation energy (ionization potential).*

The intensity of the continuum falls off more or less rapidly from the limit. Fig. 11 gives as an illustration the continuum for the Balmer series in emission.

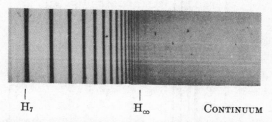

H₇	H∞

H_7 H_∞ CONTINUUM

Fig. 11. Higher Members of the Balmer Series of the H Atom (in Emission) Starting from the Seventh Line and Showing the Continuum [Herzberg (41)]. H_∞ gives the theoretical position of the series limit. The photograph was more strongly exposed than Fig. 1, and consequently some weak molecular lines not belonging to the Balmer series are also present—for example, one in the neighborhood of the position of H_∞.

In Fig. 2 the continuum can be seen beyond the series limit for Na in absorption. The ionization potential for Na may be obtained directly from this limit (5.138 volts).

3. Graphical Representation by Energy Level Diagrams

Energy level diagram and spectrum. Consideration of the hydrogen spectrum and of hydrogen-like spectra has already shown that in a discussion of the spectrum the terms are of far greater importance than the spectral lines themselves, since the latter can always be derived easily from the former. In addition, the representation by terms is much simpler since the number of terms is much smaller than the number of spectral lines. For example, there is only one series of terms for H, but there is an infinite number of series of lines.

A descriptive picture of the terms and possible spectral lines is obtained by graphical representation in a Grotrian energy level diagram. Fig. 12 shows the energy level diagram for the H atom. The ordinates give the energy,

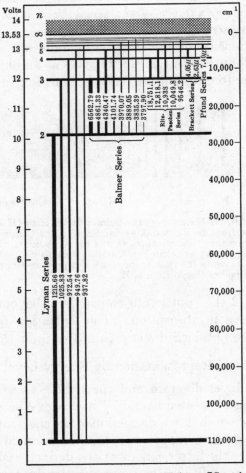

Fig. 12.   Energy Level Diagram of the H Atom [Grotrian (8)].

and the energy levels or terms R_H/n^2 which occur are drawn as horizontal lines. The separation of the levels decreases toward the top of the diagram and converges to a value 0 for $n \to \infty$. Theoretically there is an infinite number of lines in the neighborhood of this point. A continuous term spectrum joins the term series here (indicated by cross-hatching). At the right, the energy scale is given in cm^{-1}, increasing from top to bottom (term values are positive). As previously explained, the value 0 corresponds to the complete separation of proton and electron ($n = \infty$). To the left is a scale in volts beginning with the ground state as zero. This volt scale can be used directly to obtain the excitation potential of a given level by electron collision —that is, the potential through which electrons must be accelerated in order to excite H atoms to a given level on collision (see Franck-Hertz experiment, p. 15).

A spectral line results from the transition of the atom from one energy level to another. Accordingly, this line is represented in the energy level diagram of Fig. 12 by a vertical line joining the two levels. The length of the line connecting the two levels is directly proportional to the wave number of the spectral line (right-hand scale). The thickness of the line gives a rough measure of the intensity of the spectral line. The graphical representation of the different series is readily understood from the figure, as is also the fact that the lines approach a series limit.

The *absorption spectrum* of an atom at not too high a temperature consists of those transitions which are possible from the lowest to higher states. Fig. 12 shows that for H atoms this spectrum is the Lyman series with a continuum starting at the series limit (see above). In general, therefore, H atoms will not absorb at longer wave lengths than 1215.7Å.[5]

---

[5] The appearance, in absorption in some stellar spectra, of the Balmer series whose lower state is not the ground state of the atom, is due to the fact that, on account of the high temperature of the stellar atmosphere, a considerable portion of the atoms are in the first excited state.

Since the terms for hydrogen-like ions differ from those of the H atom only by the factor Z^2 (apart from the very small difference in Rydberg constant and relativity correction term), quite analogous energy level diagrams may be drawn for them.   Practically the only difference is a corresponding change in the energy scale.

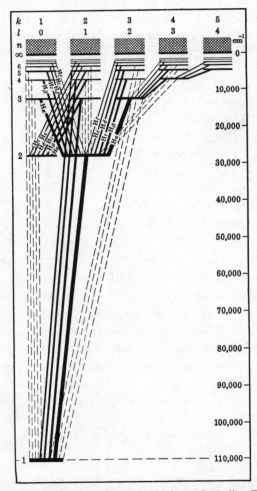

Fig. 13.   Energy Level Diagram of the H Atom, Including Fine Structure [**Grotrian** (8)].   The Balmer series is indicated, as usual, with H_α, H_β, H_γ, and so on.   The broken lines refer to forbidden transitions.

When an atom reaches an excited state by the absorption of light, it can return to a lower state or to the ground state with the emission of light. This is called *fluorescence*. The longest wave length capable of exciting fluorescence is known as the *resonance line* for the atom concerned. Fig. 12 indicates that, for H, this line is the first line of the Lyman series. The resulting fluorescence is called *resonance fluorescence*, or *resonance radiation*.

Consideration of the quantum number k, and the fine structure of the H lines. Each of the simple levels in Fig. 12 with a given value of n actually consists, according to equation (I, 12), of a number of levels lying very close to one another. In the Bohr theory these levels differ in the length of the minor axis of the ellipse—that is, in the azimuthal quantum number k. For a given value of n, n such sub-levels are present. Because of the small value of the factor α^2, the levels lie so close together that their splitting cannot be shown in the figure.

In Fig. 13, therefore, the levels with different k are drawn side by side at the same height, whereas states with equal k and different n are drawn above one another.[6] The number of sub-levels increases with increasing n. According to the Rydberg-Ritz combination principle, each sub-level should be able to *combine* with any other sub-level; in other words, their energy difference should correspond to a spectral line. Consequently each hydrogen line should consist of a number of components corresponding to different possible origins from the various term components.

Selection rule for k. Using spectral apparatus of great resolving power, it has indeed been possible to resolve the Balmer lines and also several He$^+$ lines into a number of components; however, the number of components is much smaller than might be expected on the basis of the combination principle. This discrepancy is due to the fact that

---

[6] Such a group of levels, drawn over one another, corresponds to the group of ellipses with the same value of k in Fig. 10 (p. 18).

the number of possible combinations is limited by certain so-called *selection rules*. Such rules play an equally important rôle in all other spectra. Most of the selection rules are not absolutely rigid, since so-called *forbidden lines* often appear, though very weakly. (See Chapter IV.)

These selection rules can be derived if we take into consideration that, for large quantum numbers, the quantum theory must coincide with the classical theory, and then assume that the rules so derived for large quantum numbers also hold for small quantum numbers (*Bohr's correspondence principle*). The details of this derivation will not be given here. The result, however, is that, in the present case, k may alter only by $+ 1$ or $- 1$. According to this selection rule, in Fig. 13 only those transitions indicated by solid lines between neighboring term series can occur. The combinations indicated by broken lines are *forbidden*. For each line of the Lyman series, there is consequently only one possible origin; for each line of the Balmer series, there are three possible origins; for the Paschen series, five; and so on. However, observations show certain deviations from this theory; for example, there appear certain components which are forbidden according to the k selection rule. This discrepancy was first explained by several new assumptions, which will be discussed in Chapter II, section 2.[7]

In Fig. 13 and similar illustrations that appear later in this book, the wave number of a transition obviously is given, not by the length of the *oblique* line representing it, but by the *vertical* distance between the two levels.

4. Wave Mechanics or Quantum Mechanics

The Bohr theory of the atom gave a surprisingly accurate quantitative explanation of the spectra of atoms and ions with a single electron. But, for atoms with two electrons (He), serious discrepancies with experiment were encountered. Quite apart from these and other discrepancies

---

[7] Extended discussions of the hydrogen fine structure are given by Sommerfeld (5b); Grotrian (8); White (12).

there was the difficulty of understanding the quantum conditions themselves. The attempt to solve this problem found expression in *wave mechanics* (De Broglie, Schrödinger) and *quantum mechanics* (Heisenberg, Born, Jordan, Dirac), which were put forward almost simultaneously and proved to be different mathematical formulations of the same physical theory. In the following discussion the wave mechanical formulation will be principally used wherever the Bohr theory proves inadequate.

Only a brief and necessarily incomplete account of the elements of wave mechanics will be given here. For further details one of the numerous texts in the bibliography should be consulted.

Fundamental principles of wave mechanics. According to the fundamental idea of De Broglie, *the motion of an electron or of any other corpuscle is associated with a wave motion of wave length:*

$$\lambda = \frac{h}{mv} \qquad (I, 16)$$

where h = Planck's constant, m = mass, and v = velocity of the corpuscle. For an electron, replacing these symbols with numerical values, we obtain:

$$\lambda = \frac{12.263}{\sqrt{V}} \text{ Å} \qquad (I, 17)$$

where V = electron energy in volts $\left(\frac{V}{300} = \frac{1}{2} \frac{m}{e} v^2 \right)$. For example, for electrons of 100-volt energy the De Broglie wave length is 1.226Å.

In order to calculate the motion of an electron, we must *investigate the accompanying wave motion* instead of using classical point mechanics. However, classical mechanics can be applied to the motion of larger corpuscles for the same reason that problems in geometric optics can be calculated on the basis of rays, whereas actually the problems deal with waves. Wave mechanics corresponds to wave optics. Accordingly, if we use appropriate wave lengths, we should expect *diffraction phenomena also for corpuscular rays.* From formula (I, 17), electrons with not too great energy should have a wave length of the same order as X-rays. The above prediction by De Broglie was

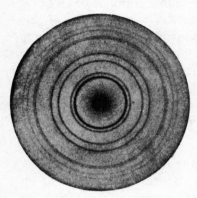

confirmed in experiments first carried out by Davisson and Germer. The experiments show the correctness of De Broglie's fundamental principles. Fig. 14 is an example of diffraction rings produced by the passage of a beam of electrons through a silver foil. Diffraction takes place at the individual silver crystals. The figure agrees in all details with a Debye-Scherrer X-ray photograph. Stern and his coworkers also have shown that analogous diffraction phenomena are exhibited by atomic and molecular rays.

Fig. 14. Photograph of Electron Diffraction by a Silver Foil. Electrons with a velocity of 36,000 volts, corresponding to a wave length of 0.0645 Å, were used in the experiment [after Mark and Wierl (49)].

According to De Broglie, the frequency ν' of the vibrations may be calculated from the Planck relation

$$E = h\nu' \qquad \text{(I, 18)}$$

where E is the energy of the corpuscle.

For a given mode of motion it is necessary to decide whether we are dealing with *progressive* or *standing* waves. Progressive waves correspond to a simple *translational motion* of the corpuscles considered (potential energy $V = 0$). In this case, just as for waves propagated in a very long string, any frequency is possible for the wave motion—that is, any energy values are possible for the corpuscle. However, when the corpuscle takes up a *periodic motion* as a result of the action of a field of force (potential energy $V < 0$) and has not sufficient energy to escape from this field (for example, circular motion or oscillatory motion about an equilibrium point), the wave returns to its former path after a certain number of wave lengths.

Fig. 15 shows this behavior diagrammatically for a circular motion. The waves which have gone around 0, 1, 2, $\cdots$ times overlap and will, in general, destroy one another by interference (dotted waves in Fig. 15). Only in the

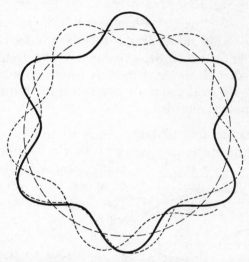

Fig. 15. De Broglie Waves for the Circular Orbits of an Electron about the Nucleus of an Atom (Qualitative). Solid line represents a stationary state (standing wave); dotted line, a quantum-theoretically impossible state (waves destroyed by interference).

special case where the frequency of the wave and, therefore, the energy of the corpuscle are such that an *integral* number of waves just circumscribe the circle (solid-line wave) do the waves which have gone around 0, 1, 2, $\cdots$ times reinforce one another so that a standing wave results. This standing wave has fixed *nodes*, and is analogous to the standing waves in a vibrating string which are possible only for certain definite frequencies, the fundamental frequency and its overtones (cf. Fig. 16). It follows, therefore, that *a stationary mode of vibration, together with a corresponding state of motion (orbit) of the corpuscle, is possible only for certain energy values (frequencies).*   For all other energy values (frequencies), the waves destroy one another by interference, and consequently, if we assume the relation between wave and corpuscle indicated by the observed diffraction phenomena, there is no motion of the corpuscle corresponding to such energy values.   Even quantitatively the results are the same as in Bohr's theory; namely, the interference condition in Fig. 15 is evidently

$$n\lambda = 2\pi r, \qquad \text{where } n = 1, 2, 3, \cdots$$

With (I, 16) this result leads directly to Bohr's original quantum condition (I, 5), from which the Balmer terms were derived.   However, here this condition and, with it, Bohr's discrete stationary states result quite naturally from the interference conditions.

Mathematical formulation.   In order to determine more rigorously the stationary energy states or stationary wave states, we must set up the *wave equation* (Schrödinger) just as in the case of the vibration of a string. Let Ψ be the wave function which is analogous to the displacement y of a vibrating string from its equilibrium position. (In a later paragraph we shall deal with the physical meaning of Ψ.) Since we are dealing with a wave motion, Ψ varies periodically with time at every point in space.

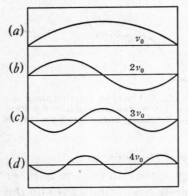

(a) v_0
(b) $2v_0$
(c) $3v_0$
(d) $4v_0$

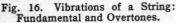

Fig. 16.   Vibrations of a String: Fundamental and Overtones.

We can therefore write:

$$\Psi = \psi \cos (2\pi v't) \qquad \text{or} \qquad \psi \sin (2\pi v't)$$

These expressions are combined in the usual convenient form:

$$\Psi = \psi \cdot e^{-2\pi i v't} \qquad \text{(I, 19)}$$

Here ψ depends only upon the position (x, y, z) and gives the amplitude of the standing wave at this point. For the vibrating string the corresponding amplitude functions are shown in Fig. 16.

Schrödinger's differential equation for the amplitude ψ of the atomic wave function is:

$$\frac{\partial^2 \psi}{\partial x^2} + \frac{\partial^2 \psi}{\partial y^2} + \frac{\partial^2 \psi}{\partial z^2} + \frac{8\pi^2 m}{h^2}(E - V)\psi = 0 \qquad \textbf{(I, 20)}$$

In this equation, m is the mass of the particle, E the total energy, and V the potential energy. *This Schrödinger equation replaces the fundamental equations of classical mechanics for atomic systems.* The frequency ν' of the vibrations in (I, 19) is obtained from the fundamental assumption (I, 18):

$$E = h\nu'$$

and hence we can also write:

$$\Psi = \psi e^{-2\pi i (E/h) t} \qquad \textbf{(I, 21)}$$

When it is assumed, similar to the case of the vibrating string, that ψ is everywhere *single valued, finite, and continuous, and vanishes at infinity,* then the *Schrödinger equation* (I, 20) *is soluble, not for unrestricted values of E, but only for specified values of E,* the so-called *eigenvalues.* The corresponding wave functions are called the *eigenfunctions* of the problem. They represent the stationary states for which the wave motion is not everywhere destroyed by interference. The discrete energy values of an atom which are experimentally observed in the spectrum appear here as the eigenvalues of the atomic wave equation.

Without the above boundary conditions the wave equation could be solved for any value of E (that is, any frequency), but the solution would not be unique. For example, we would obtain different values of ψ for a point according to whether the inclination to a fixed axis were given by the angle φ, or $360° + \varphi$, and so on. The different ψ values at each point would destroy one another by interference (cf., also, Fig. 15 and accompanying discussion).

The amplitude curves (eigenfunctions) for the vibrating string, whose differential equation is much simpler, are represented in Fig. 16. The eigenvalues are the frequencies of the fundamental vibration and its overtones: ν_0, $2\nu_0$, $3\nu_0$, $\cdots$. Other frequencies are impossible.

The eigenfunctions for the wave equation of the H atom are given graphically in Fig. 18 and discussed on page 38.

Equation (I, 20) is, as stated above, the differential equation for the amplitude ψ of the wave function Ψ. The wave equation for Ψ itself, which contains both the spatial co-ordinates and the time, is:

$$- \frac{h^2}{8\pi^2 m} \left(\frac{\partial^2 \Psi}{\partial x^2} + \frac{\partial^2 \Psi}{\partial y^2} + \frac{\partial^2 \Psi}{\partial z^2} \right) + V\Psi = \frac{ih}{2\pi} \frac{\partial \Psi}{\partial t} \qquad \textbf{(I, 22)}$$

In all the cases with which we have to deal in the following discussion, this equation can be solved by substituting Ψ from equation (I, 21), which immediately leads to (I, 20) for the amplitude function ψ. Therefore, in the following considerations equation (I, 20) may always be taken as the starting point.

It should be noted that the imaginary quantity i occurs in (I, 22). Hence it is essential, according to (I, 21), for Ψ to be complex. The function $\psi \sin 2\pi(E/h)t$ would *not* solve the time-dependent Schrödinger equation (I, 22).

Equations (I, 20) and (I, 22) refer only to the one-body problem. If the system contains several particles, these equations must be replaced, respectively, by:[8]

$$- \frac{h^2}{8\pi^2} \sum \frac{1}{m_k} \left(\frac{\partial^2 \Psi}{\partial x_k^2} + \frac{\partial^2 \Psi}{\partial y_k^2} + \frac{\partial^2 \Psi}{\partial z_k^2} \right) + V\Psi = \frac{ih}{2\pi} \frac{\partial \Psi}{\partial t} \qquad \textbf{(I, 23)}$$

and

$$\sum \frac{1}{m_k} \left(\frac{\partial^2 \psi}{\partial x_k^2} + \frac{\partial^2 \psi}{\partial y_k^2} + \frac{\partial^2 \psi}{\partial z_k^2} \right) + \frac{8\pi^2}{h^2} (E - V)\psi = 0 \qquad \textbf{(I, 24)}$$

where m_k is the mass of the kth particle whose co-ordinates are x_k, y_k, z_k. Therefore Ψ and ψ are functions of $3N$ co-ordinates—that is, they are functions in $3N$ dimensional space (configuration space) if N is the number of particles.

Physical interpretation of the Ψ function. According to Born, the value of Ψ for a given value of the co-ordinates is related to *the probability that the particle under consideration will be found at the position given by the co-ordinates;* in other words, the probability is given by $|\Psi|^2$ or $\Psi \cdot \Psi^*$ where Ψ^* is the complex conjugate of Ψ. The corresponding relation for light—namely, that the number of light quanta at a

---

[8] For the derivation of these equations, see Sommerfeld (5b).

given point is proportional to the square of the amplitude of the light wave at that point—is readily understood when it is remembered that, according to elementary wave theory, the light intensity is proportional to the square of the amplitude of the light wave and, on the other hand, is naturally proportional to the number of light quanta, since each light quantum contributes $h\nu'$ to the intensity.

When Ψ_1, Ψ_2, Ψ_3, $\cdots$ are eigenfunctions of a vibration problem, $\Psi = \Sigma c_i \Psi_i$ is also a solution of the differential equation. With a vibrating string this means that a number of overtones, and possibly also the fundamental, can be excited at the same time, as is usually the case. On the other hand, when we have $\Psi = \Sigma c_i \Psi_i$ for an atomic system, this does *not* mean that the different characteristic vibrations Ψ_1, Ψ_2, $\cdots$ are excited in one and the same atom with amplitudes c_1, c_2, $\cdots$, but it corresponds to the following state of knowledge concerning the system: The relative probabilities of being in the states given by Ψ_1 or Ψ_2 or $\Psi_3 \cdots$ are in the ratios $|c_1|^2 : |c_2|^2 : |c_3|^2 \cdots$. A given atom can be found in only one state. London (50) expresses this result by saying that the "as well as" of classical physics has become "either . . . or" in quantum mechanics.

From the probability interpretation of $\Psi\Psi^*$ it follows that $\int \Psi\Psi^* \, d\tau = 1$ where $d\tau$ is an element of volume, since the probability that a given particle will be found somewhere in space is 1. The condition previously stated, that Ψ must vanish at infinity and be everywhere finite, also follows from this.[9] Eigenfunctions Ψ_i for which $\int \Psi_i \Psi_i^* \, d\tau \neq 1$ must be divided by a factor so chosen that $\int \Psi_i \Psi_i^* \, d\tau = 1$ (normalization). Likewise, it can readily be shown mathematically that

$$\int \Psi_n \Psi_m^* \, d\tau = 0, \qquad \text{for } n \neq m \qquad \textbf{(I, 25)}$$

That is, eigenfunctions belonging to different eigenvalues are orthogonal to one another. The system of eigenfunctions is therefore a *normalized orthogonal system*.

---

[9] In fact it follows that Ψ must vanish more rapidly at infinity than $1/r$.

The Heisenberg uncertainty principle. The Heisenberg uncertainty principle is very closely related to wave theory. In order to determine as accurately as possible in wave mechanics the velocity or momentum of a particle, the De Broglie wave length must be defined as accurately as possible, since

$$p = mv = \frac{h}{\lambda}$$

This equation is the converse of (I, 16). In order to measure λ accurately, the wave train must be greatly extended, and in the limiting case must be infinitely extended if we wish to give λ or p an absolutely exact value. Then, according to wave mechanics, the position at which the particle under consideration will be found is completely uncertain, since the probability of finding it at a definite point is $\Psi\Psi^*$ and, when the wave is infinitely extended, this quantity has everywhere the same value $\psi\psi^*$. *If then p is exactly measured, the corresponding position will be completely uncertain.*

Conversely, when we wish to define the position of a particle as accurately as possible, the wave function must be so chosen that it differs from zero only at one given point. According to Fourier's theorem, there can be produced a function limited to a small region by the overlapping of sine waves, but only by the overlapping of many waves of *different* wave lengths. In the limiting case (completely defined position), the wave lengths must take all values from 0 to ∞; this makes the wave length and, therefore, the momentum completely uncertain. We arrive then at the law: *Position and momentum cannot be simultaneously measured exactly.* Heisenberg has formulated this relationship somewhat more precisely: When Δq and Δp are the uncertainties with which q and p can be measured simultaneously, the product $\Delta q \cdot \Delta p$ cannot be of a smaller order of magnitude than Planck's quantum of action.

$$\Delta q \cdot \Delta p \gtrsim h \qquad \text{(I, 26)}$$

This holds for any co-ordinate and the corresponding momentum.

The Heisenberg principle will now be verified for a simple case. Consider the diffraction of a matter wave at a slit of width Δq (Fig. 17). Through this slit the position of the particle is known with an accuracy Δq. The point within the slit through which the particle passes is completely uncertain. The particles are deflected by the slit and will form a diffraction pattern on a screen. How a *single* particle behaves behind the slit is, in principle, indeterminate within certain limits. For example, if the particle appears at A, it has acquired an additional momentum Δp in the vertical direction above the original momentum where $\Delta p = p \sin \alpha$. According to the ordinary diffraction theory, the

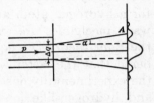

Fig. 17. Diffraction of De Broglie Waves at a Slit (Uncertainty Principle).

diffraction angle α is of the order $\lambda/\Delta q$ (the smaller the slit and the greater the wave length, the greater the diffraction). Substituting, we obtain $\Delta p \sim p\lambda/\Delta q$. But, according to De Broglie, $p\lambda = h$, and therefore $\Delta p \cdot \Delta q \sim h$. Thus, when the position is limited by the slit to a region Δq, the momentum in the same direction is uncertain to at least an extent $\Delta p = h/\Delta q$ since, for each of the points in the diffraction pattern, we can give only the *probability* of the particle's hitting the screen at that point.

Wave mechanics of the H atom. In order to deal in wave mechanics with the H atom or hydrogen-like ions, the Coulomb potential $- Ze^2/r$ must be substituted for V in the wave equation (I, 20). Z is the number of charges on the nucleus (for H, $Z = 1$). The differential equation

$$\frac{\partial^2\psi}{\partial x^2} + \frac{\partial^2\psi}{\partial y^2} + \frac{\partial^2\psi}{\partial z^2} + \frac{8\pi^2 m}{h^2}\left(E + \frac{Ze^2}{r}\right)\psi = 0 \qquad (I, 27)$$

(m = mass of the electron) must then be solved under the conditions that ψ is everywhere single valued, continuous, and finite.

The calculation, which is simple in principle, will not be dealt with here.[10] It gives the result that the differential equation can be solved for all positive values of E but not for all negative values of E. More particularly, it is found

[10] For textbooks on wave mechanics, see bibliography: (5b) and (23) to (32).

that only those negative values of E for which

$$E_n = -\frac{2\pi^2 m e^4}{h^2}\frac{Z^2}{n^2} = \frac{RhcZ^2}{n^2}, \qquad \text{with } n = \text{whole number,}$$

lead to a solution. For all values other than these, the De Broglie waves in a Coulomb field completely destroy one another by interference. Thus the possible energy values for a hydrogen atom and a hydrogen-like ion as given by wave mechanics are exactly the same as those given by the Bohr theory [cf. equation (I, 11)]. It will be remembered that the latter were in quantitative agreement with the experimentally observed spectra of the hydrogen atom and hydrogen-like ions. Making allowance for the fact that the nucleus also moves has the same effect as in the Bohr theory: in the energy formula the reduced mass $\mu = mM/(m + M)$ must be used instead of the electron mass m, where M is the mass of the nucleus. The influence of relativity has been disregarded in (I, 27).

It should perhaps be stated here that, while wave mechanics agrees with the old Bohr theory in this case, it really has made a distinct advance beyond that theory: first, it is in agreement with many experiments which the Bohr theory contradicts; and second, in contrast to the Bohr theory, all the results can be derived from one fundamental assumption (the Schrödinger equation).

To each eigenvalue of the Schrödinger equation—that is, to each stationary energy state—there belongs, in general, more than one eigenfunction. These eigenfunctions are distinguished by two additional quantum numbers l and m, which are always integers. One of them, l, corresponds to the Bohr quantum number k, which was a measure of the minor axis of the elliptical orbit. The quantum number l is called the *azimuthal* quantum number, or the reduced azimuthal quantum number. If the relativity theory is considered, there is also a very small difference in energy for states with different l but equal n. The value of l, together with k, is indicated in the energy level diagram for hydrogen (Fig. 13). For a given value of n, l takes the values $0, 1, 2, \cdots, n - 1$; that is, $l = k - 1$. The quantum number m, called the *magnetic* quantum number, takes the values $-l, -l+1, -l+2, \cdots, +l$ for a given pair of n and l values.　This gives the following scheme:

n	1	2		3			4			
l	0	0	1	0	1	2	0	1	2	3
m	0	0	−1 0 +1	0	−1 0 +1	−2 −1 0 +1 +2	0	−1 0 +1	−2 −1 0 +1 +2	−3 −2 −1 0 +1 +2 +3

Each m value in the last line corresponds to one eigenfunction different from the others.　For each value of n, there are as many different eigenfunctions as there are numbers in the last line below the n value under consideration.

The mathematical form of the eigenfunction is the following:　.

$$\psi_{nlm} = Ce^{-\rho}(2\rho)^l L_{n+l}^{2l+1}(2\rho) P_l^{|m|}(\cos\theta)e^{im\varphi} \qquad \textbf{(I, 28)}$$

referred to a system of polar co-ordinates r (distance from the origin), θ (angle between radius and z-axis), and φ (azimuth of r-z plane, inclination to a fixed plane).　Here ρ is an abbreviation for Zr/na_H; that is, for the lowest state of the H atom ($Z = 1, n = 1$), ρ is equal to the distance from the origin measured in terms of a_H as unit (radius of lowest Bohr orbit = 0.528 Å). $L_{n+l}^{2l+1}(2\rho)$ is a function (*Laguerre polynomial*) of 2ρ; its form depends on n and l. $P_l^{|m|}(\cos\theta)$ is a function of the angle θ (the so-called *associated Legendre polynomial*), and has a different form according to the values of m and l.

The eigenfunctions can be split into two factors, one of which depends only upon the distance r from the origin, and the other only upon the direction in space.　For the values $n = 1, 2, 3$, the dependence on r is shown in Fig. 18 (see p. 40).　For a given value of n, the function shows a different form for different values of l; similarly, it shows a different form for a given value of l and different values of n. The form of the function is, however, independent of m. In Fig. 18 the radius of the corresponding Bohr orbit is represented by a vertical line on the abscissa axis.　In all cases, ψ finally decreases exponentially toward the outside and is already very small at a distance which is, on the average, about twice the radius of the corresponding Bohr orbit.　For $n > 1$, ψ goes once, or more than once, through

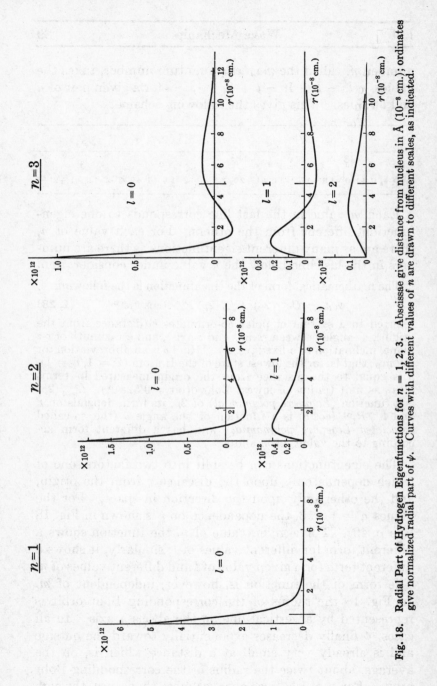

Fig. 18. Radial Part of Hydrogen Eigenfunctions for $n = 1, 2, 3$. Abscissae give distance from nucleus in Å (10^{-8} cm.); ordinates give normalized radial part of ψ. Curves with different values of n are drawn to different scales, as indicated.

the value zero before the exponential decrease sets in; that is, on certain spherical surfaces about the nucleus, the ψ function is always zero. These are the *nodal surfaces of the ψ function* corresponding to the nodes of a vibrating string (see Fig. 16). For $l = 0$, the number of nodal spheres is $n - 1$, as is shown in Fig. 18. Since in these cases the eigenfunctions ψ are also spherically symmetrical,[11] they are represented completely by Fig. 18.

For $l > 0$, the number of nodal spheres is smaller (see Fig. 18) and equals $n - l - 1$. However, new nodal surfaces appear since ψ then depends on direction also. In different directions from the origin the variation with r is the same as in Fig. 18 but the function must be multiplied by a constant factor depending on the direction. For some directions this factor is zero. The resulting nodal surfaces are partly planes through the z-axis, and partly conical surfaces with the z-axis as the axis of the cones. For $l = 3$ and $m = 1$, these nodal surfaces are given in Fig. 19. The variation of the ψ function with direction depends on m and l but not on n. Since the number of nodal surfaces caused by this dependence on direction is l, in all cases the total number of nodal surfaces is $n - 1$.

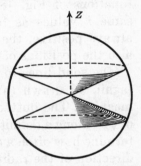

Fig. 19. Nodal Surfaces of the Part of the Hydrogen Eigenfunction Independent of r (for $l = 3$, $m = 1$). The three nodal surfaces are: the plane of the paper, and the two conical surfaces. On the two sides of each nodal surface, ψ has opposite signs.

Thus in quantum mechanics the principal quantum number is given a meaning that is easily visualized—namely, *the total number of nodal surfaces + 1.* The azimuthal quantum number l gives *the number of nodal surfaces going through the mid-point.* It is clear that the number of nodal surfaces can only be integral. Thus while integral quantum

---

[11] In formula (I, 28), $P_l^{|m|} (\cos \theta) e^{im\varphi} = 1$.

numbers are introduced into the Bohr theory as assumptions quite incomprehensible in themselves, they appear in wave mechanics as something quite natural.

As we have seen above, Ψ itself has no immediately apparent physical meaning, but $\Psi\Psi^* = \psi\psi^*$ has. The probability of finding the electron in a volume element $d\tau$ is given by $\psi\psi^* \, d\tau$. The variation of $\psi\psi^*$ is naturally similar to that of ψ (Fig. 18). The dotted curves in Fig. 20 represent, for the same n and l values as in Fig. 18, that part of $\psi\psi^*$ which depends on r (all drawings made to same scale); they represent simply the squares of the corresponding functions of Fig. 18. The zero positions thus lie at the same r values as for ψ. However, since $\psi\psi^* = |\psi|^2$ is always positive, the zero positions are, at the same time, also the positions of the minima of $\psi\psi^*$.

The solid lines in Fig. 20 represent $\psi\psi^*$ *multiplied by* r^2 (again all drawn to same scale). This has the following meaning: The dotted curves of Fig. 20 show the variation of $\psi\psi^*$ along a definite radius vector. If we now wish to determine how often a given r value occurs independent of the direction of the radius vector, we must integrate $\psi\psi^*$ over the whole surface of the sphere for that value of r. This gives a factor proportional to r^2, since the surface of a sphere equals $4\pi r^2$. This is shown by the solid curves of Fig. 20. It is seen from the dotted curves with $l = 0$ that the probability of finding the electron near the mid-point of the atom is greater than at some distance from the mid-point. In spite of this, however, the electron is, on the whole, more often at a point which is some distance from the mid-point, since there are many more possibilities for such a point (all points of the spherical shell of radius r). Therefore the largest maximum in the solid curves of Fig. 20 lies at a noticeable distance from the zero point (origin). The electrons are found most frequently at this distance, the distance of greatest electron probability density, which has approximately the same magnitude as the major semi-axis of the corresponding Bohr orbit (also indicated in Fig. 20). However, according to wave mechanics, any other

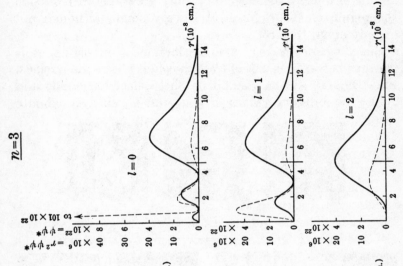

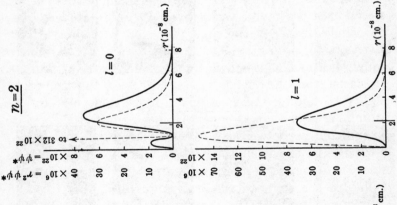

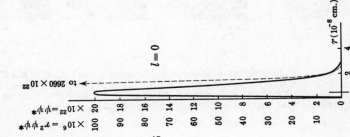

Fig. 20. Probability Density Distribution of the Electron for $n=1$, 2, 3 for the H Atom Plotted as a Function of the Distance r. Dotted curves represent $\psi\psi^*$: solid curves, $r^2\psi\psi^*$. All curves are drawn to the same scale (outer scale for $r^2\psi\psi^*$, inner scale for $\psi\psi^*$). $\psi\psi^*dr$ gives the probability of finding the electron in a volume element $d\tau$ (the dimensions of $\psi\psi^*$ are therefore cm^{-3}); $r^2\psi\psi^*dr$ gives the probability of finding the electron in the spherical shell of thickness dr at a distance r from the midpoint.

43

distances r (even those that are considerably greater) have a probability different from zero. *The electron is, so to speak, smeared out over the whole of space.* However, because of the exponential decrease toward the outside, the probability of finding the electron at any great distance outside the region of the Bohr orbit is very small, although not exactly equal to zero.

Since we no longer have distinct electron orbits, it is perhaps better to speak of *electron clouds* about the nucleus. Fig. 21 is an aid in visualizing these electron clouds and gives, for different values of n, l, and m, an approximate

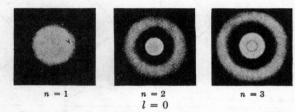

$n = 1$ $n = 2$ $n = 3$
                $l = 0$

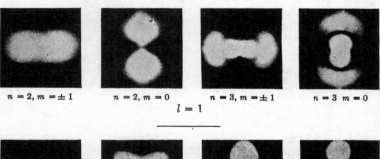

$n = 2, m = \pm 1$ $n = 2, m = 0$ $n = 3, m = \pm 1$ $n = 3$ $m = 0$
                        $l = 1$

$n = 3, m = \pm 2$ $n = 3, m = \pm 1$ $n = 3, m = 0$ $n = 4, m = 0$
                        $l = 2$

Fig. 21. Electron Clouds (Probability Density Distribution) of the H Atom or Hydrogen-like Ions in Different States [after White (51)]. The scale is not uniform for all the figures but decreases with increasing n. States which differ only in the sign of m have the same electron cloud.

picture of what one might expect to see when one is looking at an H atom with an imaginary microscope with enormous magnification.

In the figures, the brightness indicates roughly the density of the electron clouds. These clouds have a rotational symmetry about a vertical axis in the plane of the figure [12] (the z-axis mentioned earlier). The states with $l = 0$ and $n = 1, 2, 3$ are spherically symmetrical. For $n > 1$, alternate light and dark rings appear, corresponding to the above-mentioned nodal spheres of the ψ function. The cloud is subdivided into *spherical shells*.[13] For $l > 0$, one can see in Fig. 21 the nodal cones which, for the particular value $l = 1$, degenerate into a plane perpendicular to the z-axis. Different pictures are obtained for different values of m and equal n and l. With increasing n and l, the pictures become more and more complicated (cf. $n = 4$, $l = 2$, $m = 0$).

However, these are the pictures of the atoms (in particular, the H atom) which, according to our present-day knowledge, we have to use. The term *electron cloud*, which is customarily given to the pictures, must not be interpreted as meaning that, in the case of H for example, one electron occupies at one time the whole of the space occupied by this cloud. On the contrary, in wave mechanics the electron is considered as a *point charge*, and the density of the cloud at a specified point gives only the probability of finding the

---

[12] This results from the fact that the dependence of the wave function ψ on the azimuthal angle φ is given by $e^{im\varphi}$ [equation (I, 28)], which by multiplication with the complex conjugate gives a constant—namely, 1. When it is stated that ψ has nodal planes through the z-axis, this statement holds for the real and imaginary parts of ψ individually, since $\cos m\varphi$ or $\sin m\varphi$ has just $2m$ zero positions in the region 0 to 2π. There are consequently m nodal planes. However, the more accurate theory shows that, in forming $\psi\psi^*$, the complex ψ function must be introduced—not the real or the imaginary part alone (cf. p. 34).

[13] We must emphasize again that, in spite of the greater density at the middle of the cloud (indicated by the greater brightness in Fig. 21), the electron is most often in the outermost spherical shell, since this has a much greater extent. If the electron has $n = 3$, it is, therefore, mostly at a greater distance from the nucleus than it is for $n = 2$ or $n = 1$.

electron at that point.   In order to observe the picture one should, strictly speaking, observe a large number of H atoms in the same state.   Since, however, the orbit of the electron cannot be definitely determined according to wave mechanics, we can in many cases make calculations *as though* the electron were smeared out over the whole space.

According to ordinary wave mechanics, just as in Bohr's theory, the energy of a stationary state for the H atom and hydrogen-like ions depends solely upon n.   States of different l (having different minor axes of the elliptical orbit in the Bohr theory) but equal n have the same energy.   They are *degenerate*.   This degeneracy is, however, removed when we allow for the relativity theory.   A small difference in energy then occurs between states with different l and equal n; this difference, as also in Bohr's theory, gives rise to the *fine structure of the Balmer lines*.   However, a complete agreement of calculated and observed fine structure is obtained only by allowing also for electron spin,[14] which will be discussed in Chapter II.   The degeneracy between states with equal n but different l, which results if the relativity theory or electron spin is not considered, occurs only in the case of a point charge in a pure Coulomb field of force (H atom).   However, in the general case, for example with the alkalis (see section 5 of this chapter), such degeneracy disappears.   States with different l can then have noticeably different energies for the same value of n.   The type of eigenfunction or electron cloud remains the same as in Figs. 18, 20, and 21.   When more electrons are present, to a first very rough approximation, the electron cloud is simply a *superposition* of the probability density distributions of the individual electrons (Fig. 21).

The fact that, for a given n and l, there are still a number of different eigenfunctions according to the value of m (namely, $m = -l, -l+1, -l+2, \cdots, +l$, making

---

[14] The spin also follows as a necessary consequence of Dirac's relativistic wave mechanics.

$2l + 1$ different eigenfunctions) also holds in the general case. Even then these states have exactly equal energies. This is connected with the fact that, when no outer field is present, states with different spatial orientations of the system have equal energy and are degenerate with respect to one another. This is called *space degeneracy*, which we shall discuss in greater detail when dealing with the Zeeman effect (Chapter II).

Neither of these degeneracies occurs for $n = 1$, since then the only possible value for l is $l = 0$, and the only possible value for m is likewise 0. (See scheme, p. 39.)

Momentum and angular momentum of an atom according to wave mechanics. The representations in Fig. 21 give a picture of the probability of finding an electron at a given position in space, or, in other words, the shape of the electron cloud about the nucleus. They tell nothing, however, about the motion of the electron or its *velocity* at different points in space. The Heisenberg uncertainty principle informs us that the simultaneous position and velocity of an electron cannot be given with any desired accuracy—that is, the velocity of the electron cannot be given for each point. However, we can reach at least some conclusions about the velocity or the momentum of the electrons in an atom; for example, we can calculate the *velocity distribution* over the various possible values just as we calculated the probability distribution of the various positions of the electron in the atom (Figs. 20 and 21).

To illustrate, Fig. 22 gives the probability that the electron will have the velocity or the momentum given by the abscissae for the ground state of the H atom ($n = 1$, $l = 0$) and for an excited state ($n = 2$, $l = 0$) [Elsasser (52)]. The curves correspond to the solid curves of Fig. 20. According to Fig. 22, the most frequently occurring velocity in the ground state is 1.2×10^8 cm./sec.; in the first excited state, 0.4×10^8 cm./sec. For the latter state, a velocity of

1.1×10^8 cm./sec. does not occur, although greater and smaller values are both present.

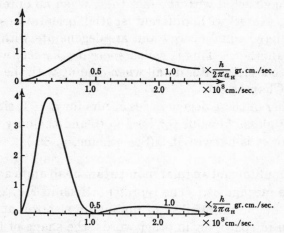

Fig. 22. Probability Distribution of Momentum and Velocity in the States $n = 1$, $l = 0$, and $n = 2$, $l = 0$, of the H Atom. The curves give the square of the momentum wave function given by Elsasser (52). The value of the momentum in units of $h/2\pi a_H = 1.96 \times 10^{-19}$ gr. cm./sec., or the value of the velocity in cm./sec., is shown as abscissae. The ordinate is proportional to the probability of finding the electron in the H atom with the given value of momentum or velocity.

Quite definite statements may be made regarding the *angular momentum* of an atom. The co-ordinate associated with the angular momentum is the angle of rotation. The latter, in contrast to a cartesian co-ordinate, is completely uncertain—a result which follows from the rotational symmetry of the charge distribution. It is, therefore, not in contradiction to the uncertainty principle that the angular momentum corresponding to a given stationary state has an absolutely definite value. Calculation shows that the numerical value of the angular momentum is $\sqrt{l(l + 1)}\, h/2\pi$, or approximately $l(h/2\pi)$. (The approximate value will be used in most of our subsequent considerations.) This fact gives at the same time a descriptive meaning to the quantum number l: *it is the angular momentum of the atom in units of $h/2\pi$.* For $l = 0$, the angular momentum of the atom is zero. That is the reason for introducing l instead of $k - 1$

In the Bohr theory, k represented the angular momentum of the electron in a given orbit; we now represent the angular momentum by $l = k - 1$. While the value $k = 0$ did not occur in the Bohr theory, in wave mechanics the value $l = 0$ (angular momentum $= 0$) does occur and corresponds to $k = 1$. In the Bohr theory, angular momentum $= 0$ meant the so-called pendulum oscillation orbit in which the electron would have had to go through the nucleus, and this was excluded as impossible. Now, an angular momentum equal to zero means simply that the electron cloud does not rotate; the electron does not need to fall into the nucleus because of this. The value $l = 0$ does not mean that absolutely no motion takes place, but only that the motion is not such that an angular momentum results (cf. Fig. 22).

The fact that even in wave mechanics each stationary state of the atom has a perfectly definite angular momentum shows that the atom can still be regarded as consisting of electrons rotating about a nucleus, as in the original Bohr theory. (We must not, however, speak of definite orbits.[15]) Consequently the Bohr theory is adequate in many cases. In particular, we can in many instances use the angular momentum l and the other angular momenta in the same way as in the Bohr theory, the results being confirmed by exact wave mechanical calculations.

In the following discussion the angular momentum *vectors* will be indicated by heavy (boldface) type to distinguish them from the corresponding quantum numbers, printed in regular type. Thus l means a vector of magnitude $\sqrt{l(l + 1)}\, h/2\pi \approx l(h/2\pi)$.

That l is connected with the angular momentum can further be understood from the following. According to De Broglie [equation (I, 16)]:

$$\lambda = \frac{h}{m_e v} = \frac{h}{p} \quad \text{or} \quad p = \frac{h}{\lambda}$$

---

[15] Just because of the fact that φ is quite uncertain, an absolutely definite value can be given to the angular momentum.

where m_e is the electron mass, p the momentum, and λ the corresponding De Broglie wave length. If we wish to introduce the angular momentum p_φ into the De Broglie equation, λ must be measured in the corresponding co-ordinates, that is, the angle of rotation φ. From the expression previously given for the H atom (I, 28), it follows that $\Psi = \psi e^{-2\pi i \nu' t}$ contains the factor $e^{i(m\varphi - 2\pi \nu' t)}$ (m = quantum number). According to the usual wave theory, this factor represents a wave propagated in the direction of increasing or decreasing φ according to the sign of m—that is, a wave which travels around the z-axis with angular velocity $2\pi\nu'/m$. Its wave length is $2\pi/m$, since, when φ increases by $2\pi/m$, $e^{i(m\varphi - 2\pi \nu' t)}$ acquires its original value once more. Substituting this wave length[16] in the expression $p = h/\lambda$ gives as the angular momentum about the z-axis:

$$p_\varphi = m \frac{h}{2\pi}$$

For a given n and l, m can have the values $-l, -l+1, \cdots, +l$. These are, therefore, the angular momenta about the z-axis in units of $h/2\pi$. All of these states have the same energy. This evidently means that the angular momentum itself is $l(h/2\pi)$ and has components equal to $m(h/2\pi)$ along the z-axis, depending on its orientation to this axis. (Cf. Fig. 41, p. 99, in which J replaces l. and M replaces m.) More accurate wave mechanical treatment shows that the angular momentum is $\sqrt{l(l+1)}\, h/2\pi$ and not $l(h/2\pi)$. [Cf. Condon and Shortley (13).] In Chapter II the above relations will be discussed in greater detail.

Transition probabilities and selection rules according to wave mechanics. In wave mechanics, as in the Bohr theory, the transition of an atomic system from one stationary state to another is associated with the emission of light according to the *Bohr frequency condition*. However, this occurrence can be treated from a far more unified viewpoint by wave mechanics (Dirac) than by the Bohr theory. If an atom is in an excited state, the probability of its transition to a lower state can be calculated. The atom remains for a certain time in the upper state (*mean life*). The transition to the lower state follows after a time which is in inverse proportion to the *transition probability:* the greater the probability, the shorter the time. The

---

[16] The magnitude of this wave length can also be immediately obtained when we consider that the real part of the ψ function of the H atom has m nodal planes.

life in a given excited state for the individual atoms varies exactly as do the lives of individual atoms of a given radioactive substance. The mean life is usually of the order of 10^{-8} sec. The intensity of the emission or the absorption of light by a large number of atoms depends on the magnitude of the transition probability. Definite predictions about the polarization of the emitted light can also be made in certain cases [see Condon and Shortley (13)].

Detailed calculations show that, for the H atom and also for more general cases, an important *selection rule* operates —namely, that the intensity is extremely small except when

$$\Delta l = + 1 \quad \text{or} \quad - 1 \qquad (\text{I, 29})$$

That is to say, practically only those states can combine with one another whose l values differ by only one unit. This selection rule corresponds exactly to the earlier selection rule for k. Thus Fig. 13 can be used also for a wave mechanical representation of the transitions for an H atom. There is no selection rule for the quantum number n. Any value of Δn is possible for a transition:

$$\Delta n = 0, 1, 2, 3, \cdots$$

The different values of Δn correspond to the different members of a series.[17]

The simplest classical model capable of radiating electromagnetic waves is an oscillating electric dipole (Hertz oscillator). Electromagnetic waves are radiated with the same period with which the electric charge flows back and forth in such a dipole (for example, in a linear antenna). The intensity of the radiation depends upon the magnitude of the alteration of the dipole moment. The dipole moment is a vector whose components are given, in the case of a system of point charges, by the following expression:[18] $\sum \epsilon_i x_i$, $\sum \epsilon_i y_i$, $\sum \epsilon_i z_i$. According to wave mechanics,

---

[17] For H, a transition with $\Delta n = 0$ would correspond to a transition between fine structure terms with equal n; for $n = 2$, the transition has a wave number of only 0.3 cm^{-1}, or a wave length of about 3 cm. Observations of absorption of this wave length in activated hydrogen are still doubtful [see Betz (53); Haase (140)].

[18] As is well known, the magnitude of the vector is ϵd for two charges ($+ \epsilon$ and $- \epsilon$) separated by a distance d.

the probability density of the electron may be given for any point in the atom. This may, for most practical purposes, be regarded as though, on the average, a certain fraction of the total charge e (given by the probability density) is at the point under consideration. That is, we can treat the atom as though the *electric density* at a point is: $\rho = \epsilon \Psi \Psi^*$. Therefore, in the case of one electron (hydrogen atom) the components of the electric moment for the whole atom for a stationary state n are:

$$P_x = \int \epsilon \Psi_n \Psi_n^* x \, d\tau$$

$$P_y = \int \epsilon \Psi_n \Psi_n^* y \, d\tau$$

$$P_z = \int \epsilon \Psi_n \Psi_n^* z \, d\tau \qquad (I, 30)$$

where $d\tau$ is again an element of volume. Since the nucleus itself is taken as the origin of co-ordinates, its contribution need not be taken into consideration. The integrals are independent of time because the time factors for Ψ_n and Ψ_n^* cancel; on account of the symmetry of the charge distribution, the integrals are actually zero. There is consequently neither a static dipole moment nor one altering with time. This means, in agreement with experiment, that even according to the classical theory the atom does not radiate while in a stationary state; whereas in Bohr orbits it should radiate (if we had not made the additional ad hoc assumption that it does *not* radiate), since the atom with the electron in these orbits has a dipole moment varying with time.

Dirac has shown that the radiation emitted by an atom in the transition from state n to state m may be obtained by replacing $\Psi_n \Psi_n^*$ in equation (I, 30) by $\Psi_n \Psi_m^*$, regarding the resulting P as an electric moment (*transition moment*) and then completing the calculation in the classical manner. Since Ψ_n contains the time factor $e^{-2\pi i (E_n/h) t}$ (I, 21), and Ψ_m^* the time factor $e^{+2\pi i (E_m/h) t}$, $\Psi_n \Psi_m^*$ and $P_x^{nm} = \epsilon \int \Psi_n \Psi_m^* x \, d\tau$ (and correspondingly, P_y^{nm}, P_z^{nm}) are no longer constant in time but have the time factor $e^{-2\pi i [(E_n - E_m)/h] t}$; that is, they vary with just the frequency that would be obtained from the Bohr frequency condition $\nu' = \dfrac{1}{h} (E_n - E_m)$. The result is an emission or absorption of this frequency in a purely classical way. An analogous state of affairs holds for a system containing a number of particles. It is necessary only to sum the integral over the different particles; for example,

$$P_x^{nm} = \sum_k \epsilon_k \int \Psi_n \Psi_m^* x_k \, d\tau \qquad (I, 31)$$

According to what has been said, we can put, for the *variable electric moment associated with the transition from n to m:*

$$P^{nm} = \epsilon R^{nm} e^{-2\pi i [(E_n - E_m)/h]t}.$$ (I, 32)

where R^{nm} is a vector with components

$$R_x{}^{nm} = \int \psi_n \psi_m{}^* x \, d\tau, \quad R_y{}^{nm} = \cdots, \quad R_z{}^{nm} = \cdots$$ (I, 33)

The vector R^{nm} gives the *amplitude* of the vibration *of the transition moment* P^{nm} associated with the transition from n to m.

Remembering that the intensity of light radiated from an atom is equal to the number of transitions per second (that is, the transition probability) multiplied by $h\nu'_{nm}$, we obtain (using the classical formula for the intensity of electromagnetic waves radiated by a vibrating electric dipole) the expression:

$$A^{nm} = \frac{64\epsilon^2 \pi^4}{3h} \nu^3 R^{nm} R^{mn}$$ (I, 34)

for the probability of the transition from n to m where $\nu = \nu'/c$ is the wave number. The transition probability therefore depends upon the quantities R^{nm}. R^{nm} itself is determined by the eigenfunctions of the two states involved [see (I, 33)]. Thus we see that a knowledge of the eigenfunctions is particularly important for the calculation of transition probabilities. The quantities R^{nm} can be arranged in a square array (vertical columns n, horizontal columns m), which is called a *matrix*. R^{nm} are the *matrix elements*. When $R^{nm} = 0$ for a given pair of values of n and m, the transition from n to m is forbidden. Detailed calculation shows that combinations between all states for which l does not differ by ± 1 have $R^{nm} = 0$; that is, the selection rule $\Delta l = \pm 1$ holds. Other selection rules can be similarly derived. Such selection rules always depend upon the symmetry properties of the atomic system under consideration and of the corresponding eigenfunctions. In Chapter II, section 3, the derivation of the selection rules for the magnetic quantum number M will be given as an illustration. (Cf. also p. 68 and p. 154.)

Quadrupole radiation and magnetic dipole radiation. A system of electric charges such as that illustrated in Fig. 23 has no dipole moment ($\sum \epsilon_i x_i = 0$). In spite of this, the system gives an external electric field, which, however, falls off more rapidly with increasing distance than that of the dipole, which itself falls off more rapidly than that of the

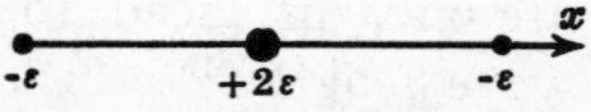

Fig. 23. Example of a Quadrupole.

monopole (the potentials are proportional to $1/r^3$, $1/r^2$, $1/r$, respectively). An assemblage of charges such as that in Fig. 23 is called a *quadrupole*. Its action is characterized by a *quadrupole moment*, which in the above case is given simply by $\sum \epsilon_i x_i^2$, where x is the axis along which the charges are located. It is immediately seen that this expression is *not* zero. In general a quadrupole is more complicated than the one given in Fig. 23, and likewise the quadrupole moment is usually more complex. The general case will not, however, be discussed here.

Just as a variable dipole moment leads to radiation (*dipole radiation*), so also does a variable quadrupole moment lead to radiation (*quadrupole radiation*). The latter is, however, considerably weaker. The transition probability, similarly to the above, is obtained by substituting $\epsilon_i \psi_n \psi_m^* \, d\tau$ for ϵ_i in $\sum \epsilon_i x_i^2$, and integrating. Therefore quadrupole radiation depends upon the integral $\int x^2 \psi_n \psi_m^* \, d\tau$, whereas dipole radiation depends upon $\int x \psi_n \psi_m^* \, d\tau$. Because of this difference, *transitions which are strictly forbidden for dipole radiation may occur—though quite weakly—due to quadrupole radiation.* The ratio of the transition probabilities of ordinary dipole radiation to ordinary quadrupole radiation is found to be about $1 : 10^{-8}$.

Finally, it may happen that, for a transition, the variation of the electric dipole moment will disappear, whereas that of the *magnetic* dipole moment does not (cf. Chapter II, p. 111). According to classical theory, a variable magnetic dipole moment such as that produced, for instance, by an alternating current in a coil gives rise to electromagnetic radiation. Correspondingly, in wave mechanics, it gives rise to a transition probability which may be different from zero even if the ordinary dipole transition probability is zero. Again, the transition probability due to *magnetic dipole radiation* is small compared with that due to electric dipole radiation $(1 : 10^{-5})$.

Actually, cases have been observed in which transitions that are strictly forbidden by the electric dipole selection rules take place due to quadrupole or magnetic dipole radiation. (See Chapter IV.)

5. Alkali Spectra

The principal series. The absorption spectra of alkali vapors (Fig. 2) appear quite similar in many respects to the absorption spectrum of the H atom (Lyman series). They are only displaced, to a considerable extent, toward longer wave lengths.[19] These spectra also consist of a series of lines with regularly decreasing separation and decreasing intensity. This series is called the *principal series.* It

---

[19] We disregard for the moment the splitting of the lines of the heavier alkalis, with which we shall deal in Chapter II. This splitting is still so small for Li that it cannot be noticed with the usual spectroscopic apparatus.

cannot, however, be represented by a formula completely analogous to the Balmer formula. On the other hand, since the lines converge to a limit, we must be able to represent them as differences between two terms. One of these terms is a constant T_{PS} (known as the *fixed term*) and has the frequency of the *series limit*. The other (known as the *running term*) must depend on a running number (order number) m in such a way that the term disappears as $m \to \infty$.

It has been found that the series can be satisfactorily represented with $R/(m + p)^2$ as the running term. R is the Rydberg constant, and p is a constant number < 1; p is called the *Rydberg correction*. It is the correction that, for the alkalis, must be applied to the Balmer term ($p = 0$ gives the Balmer term). The running number m takes values from 2 to ∞. The quantity $n^* = m + p$ is called the *effective principal quantum number*. Thus the formula for the absorption series (principal series) for the alkalis [20] is:

$$\nu = T_{PS} - \frac{R}{(m + p)^2}$$

A continuous spectrum follows at the series limit, as shown in Fig. 2.

Other series. In emission, other series in addition to the principal series may be observed for the alkalis. These series partly overlap one another. Fig. 3 (p. 5) shows the Na emission spectrum. The three most intense of the additional series have been given the names *diffuse, sharp,* and *Bergmann series*. The last is also sometimes called the *fundamental* series. The lines of the diffuse and the sharp series frequently appear diffuse and sharp, as their names indicate. The Bergmann series lies further in the infrared and consequently does not appear in the spectrogram in Fig. 3. The limits of these series and, therefore, their limiting terms differ from the limiting term of the principal

---

[20] This formula does not hold so exactly as that for the H spectrum. More exact agreement with experiment can be obtained by adding to the denominator an additional term which depends on m.

series, but the sharp and the diffuse series have a common limit (see Fig. 3). T_{SS} is the common limiting term for the sharp and the diffuse series; T_{BS}, for the Bergmann series. The running terms are quite analogous to those of the principal series, but the Rydberg correction has a different value for each series. Thus we have:

PRINCIPAL SERIES: $\nu = T_{PS} - \dfrac{R}{(m + p)^2}$ $(m = 2, 3, \cdots)$

SHARP SERIES: $\nu = T_{SS} - \dfrac{R}{(m + s)^2}$ $(m = 2, 3, \cdots)$

DIFFUSE SERIES: $\nu = T_{SS} - \dfrac{R}{(m + d)^2}$ $(m = 3, 4, \cdots)$

BERGMANN SERIES: $\nu = T_{BS} - \dfrac{R}{(m + f)^2}$ $(m = 4, 5, \cdots)$

The values found empirically show that $T_{PS} = R/(1 + s)^2$, $T_{SS} = R/(2 + p)^2$, $T_{BS} = R/(3 + d)^2$; that is, the limiting terms belong to one of the series of running terms. If we put mP as a symbol for $R/(m + p)^2$, mS for $R/(m + s)^2$, and so on, the series may be written:

PRINCIPAL SERIES: $\nu = 1S - mP$ $(m = 2, 3, \cdots)$ **(I, 35)**
SHARP SERIES: $\nu = 2P - mS$ $(m = 2, 3, \cdots)$ **(I, 36)**
DIFFUSE SERIES: $\nu = 2P - mD$ $(m = 3, 4, \cdots)$ **(I, 37)**
BERGMANN SERIES: $\nu = 3D - mF$ $(m = 4, 5, \cdots)$ **(I, 38)**

Theoretical interpretation of the alkali series. From the four series of the alkalis it is evident that four different term series or four sets of energy levels exist, and these can be designated by S, P, D, F. In Fig. 24 these series are given for Li in the manner explained in an earlier section. The ground state of the alkali atom is $1S$, since in absorption only the principal series appears and this has $1S$ as the lower level. The S terms $2S$, $3S$, $\cdots$ follow after it. The lowest P state occurring is $2P$, and it lies above the $1S$ term by an amount equal to the wave number of the first line of the principal series $1S - 2P$. The series of P terms follow after it. The principal series in absorption corresponds to transitions from the ground state to the various P states;

the converse holds for emission. The sharp series corresponds to transitions from the higher S terms to the lowest P state. The lowest D term lies still higher than the lowest P term (namely, by $2P - 3D$), and, analogously, the $4F$ term is higher than $3D$. All term series go to the same limit, whereas of course the line series have different limits (cf. above).

The similarity of this energy level diagram (Fig. 24) to the generalized energy level diagram of H (Fig. 13, p. 26) is obvious. The main difference is that the members of the

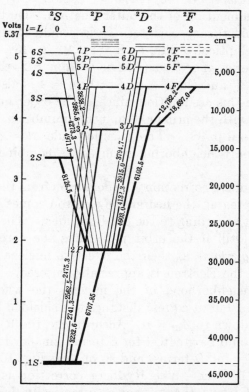

Fig. 24. Energy Level Diagram of the Li Atom [after Grotrian (8)]. The wave lengths of the spectral lines are written on the connecting lines representing the transitions. Doublet structure (see Chapter II) is not included. Some unobserved levels are indicated by dotted lines. The true principal quantum numbers for the S terms are one greater than the empirical running numbers given (see p. 61); for the remaining terms, they are the same.

different adjacent term series no longer have almost exactly the same height. This is to be expected, theoretically, for the terms of a single electron moving in a field which is not the Coulomb field of a point charge. The structure of the alkali spectrum therefore leads to the conclusion that, for the alkali atoms, *a single outer electron moves about an atomic core* [21] whose field shows marked deviations from the Coulomb field of a point charge, which are due to the finite extent of the core. Furthermore, it follows that the *S, P, D, F terms are distinguished* from one another *by the value of the quantum number l* ($l = 0, 1, 2, 3, \cdots$); that is, by the orbital angular momentum of the outer electron. On the basis of the old Bohr theory, each term series would correspond to a series of elliptical orbits, as in Fig. 10 (p. 18). The fact that the series of P terms begins with $m = 2$, the D terms with $m = 3$, and the F terms with $m = 4$ is also in agreement with this assumption, since, if the order number m is identified with the principal quantum number n, m must be $\geqq l + 1$ (see p. 38). The selection rule $\Delta l = \pm 1$ is also fulfilled; only neighboring term series combine with one another.

The Rydberg correction (the deviation from the hydrogen terms) is greater, the nearer the electron comes to the core in its orbit according to the old Bohr idea. The correction is greater still if the orbit penetrates the core (so-called *penetrating orbits*), as then the effective nuclear charge Z_{eff} acting on the electron is appreciably altered. In the immediate neighborhood of the nucleus the whole nuclear charge acts, but at a great distance it is shielded by the core electrons down to $Z_{eff} = 1$. Accordingly, the Rydberg correction should be greatest for S terms, smaller for P terms, still smaller for D terms, and so on (see Fig. 10). This is actually the case. The Rydberg correction is extremely small for F terms; that is, they are practically Balmer terms. In contrast, the Rydberg correction for S terms is so large

---

[21] The stable electron group obtained by removal of the outermost electron or electrons is called the *core* or *kernel*.

(for Li, 0.59) that we are not certain what the *true principal
quantum number* is—that is, whether the ground term for Li
has $n = 1$ or 2.   The numbers in Fig. 24 are not the true
principal quantum numbers of the emission electron.   We
shall find out later what these are.

The common limit of all term series (Fig. 24) corresponds
to the removal of the outer electron (the *emission electron*),
which is moving about the atomic core.   Beyond this
limit, as in the case of hydrogen, extends a *continuous term
spectrum* which corresponds to the removal of the electron
with more or less kinetic energy.   The existence of this continuous term spectrum is proved from observation of continuous spectra extending beyond the limit of the line series
(cf. Figs. 2 and 3).   The height of the limit of the term
series above the ground state $1S$ gives the *energy of ionization
(ionization potential)* of the alkali atom.   From Fig. 24 we
can see directly that this is equal to the wave number of the
limit of the principal series (see also p. 23); for Li, the
ionization potential is 43,486 cm^{-1} or 5.363 volts.

Alkali-like spark spectra.   Just as the spectra of He$^+$,
Li^{++}, and Be^{+++} are similar to that of hydrogen, the spectra
of the alkali-like ions (ions with the same number of electrons) are very similar to the alkali spectra (Paschen,
Fowler, Bowen, Millikan, Edlen, and others).   The spectra
of ions are usually called *spark spectra* and those of neutral
atoms *arc spectra*, since the former are generally produced
in an electric spark (or condensed discharge), and the latter
in arcs.   This corresponds to the fact that the excitation potential of the spectra of ions is much greater than for the
spectra of neutral atoms, on account of the necessity of
producing ionization or multiple ionization of the atom in
the former case.   The spectra of singly, doubly, etc.,
charged ions are called *spark spectra of the first, second, etc.,
order.*   The arc spectrum is indicated by the Roman numeral I placed after the symbol for the element; the first
spark spectrum is indicated by the Roman numeral II; and

so on. The following groups analogous to the alkalis have been investigated:

> Li I, Be II, B III, C IV, N V, O VI, F VII, Na IX
> Na I, Mg II, Al III, Si IV, P V, S VI, Cl VII
> K I, Ca II, Sc III, Ti IV, V V, Cr VI, Mn VII
> Rb I, Sr II, Y III, Zr IV
> Cs I, Ba II, La III, Ce IV, Pr V

In section 2 it was shown that, in the series H I, He II, Li III, the spectra and the corresponding term values differed by a factor Z^2. If the spectra of the above series of atoms and ions were completely similar to H, the wave numbers of the lines or of the term values should similarly differ only by a constant factor $(Z - p)^2$, where $Z - p$ is the effective nuclear charge acting on the outer electron (Z = atomic number or order number of element, and p = number of core electrons).

In each of the above series, $Z - p$ goes through the integral number values 1, 2, 3, $\cdots$. Therefore, if these alkali-like spectra were also hydrogen-like, division of all term values by the factor $(Z - p)^2$ should result in the same values for each member. Actually, though the spectra are completely analogous in all details (the same number and type of terms), the individual term schemes do not coincide exactly after division throughout by $(Z - p)^2$. Fig. 25 shows this for the series from Li I to O VI. As previously explained, this result is due to the fact that the field in which the outer electron moves is not exactly the Coulomb field of a point charge and, therefore, the term values are not simply proportional to $(Z - p)^2$, as in formula (I, 11). However, because of their close similarity to hydrogen, the D and F terms of all members of the above groups and some of the P terms do coincide approximately after division by $(Z - p)^2$ (cf. Fig. 25).

To the right of Fig. 25 is given the position of the H terms with $n = 2, 3, 4, \cdots$, and a hypothetical term with $n = 1.5$. The effective principal quantum numbers of the terms can therefore be read from this scale. For the first P term of the Li series, this number is nearly 2; for the first D term, 3; and so on. Thus 2, 3, $\cdots$ are also the true principal quantum numbers of the terms—that is, they are the principal quantum numbers which the electron would have if the core of the atom were very small so that the terms were identical with Balmer terms.

In contrast to the P, D, and F terms, the S terms are far from being hydrogen-like; for the various members of one of the above series of elements, these terms have a noticeably different position after division by $(Z - p)^2$. (Cf. Fig. 25 for the Li row.) However, even for these S terms the true principal quantum numbers can be determined from Fig. 25 and from similar figures for the other series. With increas-

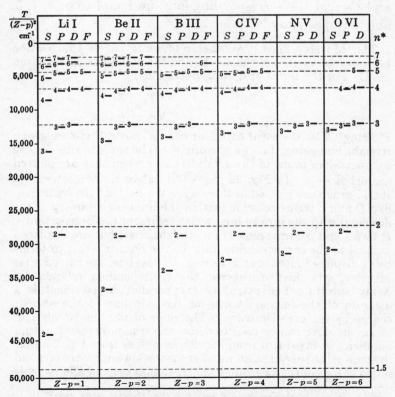

Fig. 25. Energy Level Diagrams of Li and Li-like Ions up to O VI.

ing nuclear charge Z, the core is pulled strongly together and the external field becomes more and more like a Coulomb field with nuclear charge $Z - p$. The terms in the above series must therefore become more and more hydrogen-like with increasing $Z - p$. In Fig. 25 this effect is seen for P terms as well as for S terms; it is particularly marked for the latter. The effective principal quantum number for the $1S$ term is 1.86 for N V and 1.88 for O VI, as compared to 1.6 for Li; that is, it approaches the value 2, which is, therefore, the true principal quantum number for the emission electron of Li in the ground state and also for Be$^+$, etc. In an analogous manner the true principal quantum numbers for the emission electrons in the ground states of Na, K, Rb, and Cs and the corresponding ions are found to be 3, 4, 5, and 6, respectively.[22]

The Moseley lines. Another representation of the relation between the spectra of the alkalis and the alkali-like ions is often used. For the terms of hydrogen-like ions,

$$T = \frac{RZ^2}{n^2} \quad \text{or} \quad \sqrt{\frac{T}{R}} = \frac{Z}{n}$$

Plotting $\sqrt{T/R}$ against the nuclear charge should therefore give a straight line going through the origin. The same is true for the hydrogen-like terms of the alkali-like ions when they are plotted against $Z - p$. In Fig. 26 the $\sqrt{T/R}$ values for some terms in the Li group are plotted in this way. We see that the hydrogen-like D and F terms coincide (within the limits of accuracy of the drawing) with the broken lines which represent the Balmer terms. P terms and S terms also lie on straight lines, but are displaced parallel to the corresponding lines for the Balmer terms (S terms being displaced more than P terms). These lines are named after Moseley, who first discovered the corresponding relation for X-ray spectra. The extent of the parallel displacement is a measure of the incompleteness of the shielding of the nuclear charge by the core electrons. The slope of the line equals $1/n$; hence the slope can be used to derive the true principal quantum number. It is evident from Fig. 26, as well as from Fig. 25, that the true principal quantum number for the lowest S term (ground state) of ions of the Li group is 2. A similar state of affairs holds

---

[22] For more extensive treatment, see: (7), (8), (9), (11), (12), (13).

for the Na, K, Rb, and Cs series, but the Moseley lines become increasingly curved.

In the Moseley diagram, terms of equal principal quantum number (for example, the lowest S and P terms of alkali-like ions, as in Fig. 26) give parallel lines—that is, $\sqrt{T_1/R} - \sqrt{T_2/R}$ is a constant. It is easily seen from this that $T_1 - T_2$ is a linear function of $Z - p$. This is called the *law of irregular doublets or screening doublets*. It is of importance since, when $T_1 - T_2$ is known for two members of a series of ions (such as Li I and Be II), the value $T_1 - T_2$ can be calculated for other members of the series. For $n = 2$, $T_1 - T_2$ is the frequency of the first member of the principal series. Thus, the wave length of this line may be predicted for higher spark spectra of a series—a fact that is, of course, important in the analysis of these spectra. An extended discussion of Moseley diagrams and the irregular doublet law is given in Grotrian (8) and White (12).

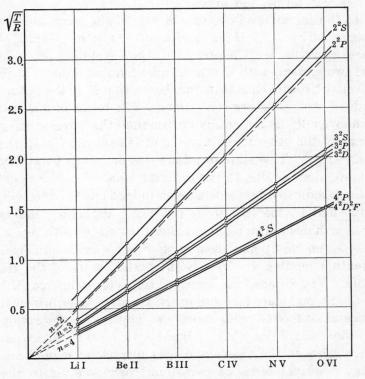

Fig. 26. Moseley Diagram of the Terms of Li-like Ions.

6. Spectrum of Helium and the Alkaline Earths

Helium. The emission spectrum of helium consists of a number of series in the visible region of the spectrum, as well as in the near and far ultraviolet regions. The number of these series is essentially the same as in the spectrogram for Mg given in Fig. 4, which will be further treated at the end of this section. There are twice as many line series as for the alkalis (cf. Fig. 3): two principal series in the visible and near ultraviolet (which have different limits), as well as two diffuse, two sharp, and two fundamental series. These series can again be represented by transitions in an energy level diagram, but the necessary terms are twice as numerous as for the alkalis. There are two series of S terms, two series of P terms, and so on.

In the energy level diagram of Fig. 27 the terms are distinguished by ^1S, ^3S; ^1P, ^3P; and so on. (For the meaning of these symbols, see Chapter II.) Corresponding terms of the two systems with the same order number differ in their effective principal quantum numbers—that is, in the magnitude of their Rydberg corrections. The terms of one system generally lie noticeably deeper than the corresponding terms of the other if the same limit is assumed for all the term series. This state of affairs was described by earlier investigators as due to *two different kinds of helium; parhelium* (indicated by the left upper index 1) and *orthohelium* (indicated by the left upper index 3). Parhelium differs from orthohelium in having, besides the states with $n = 2$, 3, $\cdots$, an additional deep-lying S state with principal quantum number 1. This is the normal state of the He atom. Transitions from higher P terms of parhelium (^1P) to the normal state give rise to the far ultraviolet principal series at 584–504 Å; this series also appears in absorption [Collins and Price (54)]. Besides this principal series, there exists in the visible and near ultraviolet regions another principal series of parhelium corresponding to the transition from higher ^1P terms to the 2 ^1S state (cf. Fig. 27).

Combinations of terms of the para system with those of the ortho system have not been observed.[23]   The term system of He thus splits essentially into *two partial systems, which do not combine with each other* (right and left parts of Fig. 27).   In particular, the lowest state of orthohelium, $2\,^3S$, which lies 19.72 volts above the ground state $1\,^1S$, does not combine with the ground state.   Those terms which cannot go to a lower state with the emission of radiation and, correspondingly, cannot be reached from a lower state by absorption are called *metastable*.   The $2\,^1S$ state is also metastable, since the selection rule $\Delta l = \pm 1$ does not allow any transition to $1\,^1S$.   The metastability of the $2\,^3S$ state

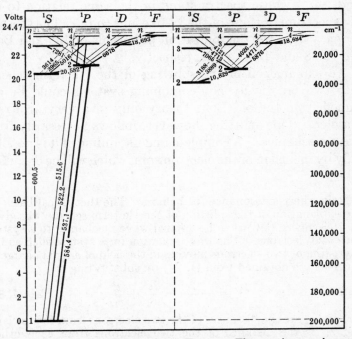

Fig. 27.   **Energy Level Diagram for Helium.**   The running numbers and true principal quantum numbers of the emission electron are here identical. The series in the visible and near ultraviolet regions correspond to the indicated transitions between terms with $n \geqq 2$.

[23] The weak intercombination line reported by Lyman at 591.6 Å is an Ne line according to Dorgelo (55).

is, however, stronger than that of the $2\,^1S$ state, since the transition $2\,^3S \rightarrow 1\,^1S$ would contradict the prohibition of an ortho-para transition as well as $\Delta l = \pm 1$. Transitions with $\Delta l = 0$ can occur in an electric field (for example, $2\,^1S \rightarrow 1\,^1S$), but not ortho-para transitions (cf. Chapter IV).

The *ionization potential of helium* as obtained from the limit of the series $1\,^1S - m\,^1P$ (see Fig. 27) is 24.46 volts. As previously stated, it was in no way possible to derive this value from the Bohr theory, but quantum mechanics gives the spectroscopic value within the limits of accuracy of calculation [Kellner (56); Hylleraas (57)]. The same is true of the ionization potentials of the *helium-like ions*, Li$^+$ and Be^{++}, whose spectra stand in the same relation to the He spectrum as those of the Li-like ions to Li. The spectroscopic values for the ionization potentials of Li$^+$ and Be^{++} are 75.28 and 153.1 volts, respectively.

An explanation of the splitting of the He term scheme into two practically non-combining systems could be obtained from the old Bohr theory only in a very arbitrary manner. This splitting, however, follows necessarily from wave mechanics. A complete understanding of it is possible only by inclusion of the electron spin, which will be discussed later.

Heisenberg's resonance for helium. The theoretical basis for the explanation of the splitting of the He term scheme was given by Heisenberg (58) when he applied wave mechanics to a system with two electrons. The wave equation for a system such as He, consisting of two electrons moving in the field of a fixed charge $2e$ (nucleus), is obtained from (I, 24) by substituting

$$V = -\frac{2e^2}{r_1} - \frac{2e^2}{r_2} + \frac{e^2}{r_{12}} \qquad \textbf{(I, 39)}$$

if r_1 and r_2 are the distances of the two electrons from the nucleus, and r_{12} is the distance of the two electrons from each other. Hence, we obtain:

$$\frac{\partial^2 \psi}{\partial x_1^2} + \frac{\partial^2 \psi}{\partial y_1^2} + \frac{\partial^2 \psi}{\partial z_1^2} + \frac{\partial^2 \psi}{\partial x_2^2} + \frac{\partial^2 \psi}{\partial y_2^2} + \frac{\partial^2 \psi}{\partial z_2^2}$$
$$+ \frac{8\pi^2 m}{h^2}\left(E + \frac{2e^2}{r_1} + \frac{2e^2}{r_2} - \frac{e^2}{r_{12}} \right)\psi = 0 \qquad \textbf{(I, 40)}$$

To zero approximation the repulsion of the electrons e^2/r_{12} may be disregarded. Then, equation (I, 40) is just the sum of two hydrogen wave equations with $Z = 2$. Each electron may therefore take any of the ordinary hydrogen energy values with $Z = 2$, and the eigenfunctions are:

$$\psi(x_1y_1z_1,\ x_2y_2z_2) = \varphi_{n_1}(x_1y_1z_1)\varphi_{n_2}(x_2y_2z_2)$$

where the φ's are ordinary hydrogen eigenfunctions [equation (I, 28)]. This result may easily be verified. n_1 and n_2 are the principal quantum numbers of the two electrons. When electron 1 is in its lowest energy state ($n_1 = 1$) and electron 2 in the state $n_2 = n$, the eigenfunction can be written in an abbreviated form:

$$\psi = \varphi_1(1)\varphi_n(2)$$

where the numbers 1 and 2 in parentheses stand for the coordinates of electrons 1 and 2. Evidently the state in which electron 1 is excited to $n_1 = n$, and electron 2 is in the lowest state, with eigenfunction $\varphi_n(1)\varphi_1(2)$, has exactly the same energy as the state $\varphi_1(1)\varphi_n(2)$. This *resonance degeneracy* is removed if e^2/r_{12}, the electrostatic repulsion of the two electrons in (I, 40), is considered. Because of the coupling between the two electrons, the system will periodically switch over from the state $\varphi_1(1)\varphi_n(2)$ (electron 2 excited) to the state $\varphi_n(1)\varphi_1(2)$ (electron 1 excited), and back again. This is quite similar to the case of two equal coupled pendulums or two equal coupled electric oscillating circuits. If at first only one pendulum (or circuit) is excited, after a time only the other will be excited, and so on.

Mathematically, the eigenfunction of the perturbed system (including the electrostatic repulsion) to a first approximation is $A\varphi_1(1)\varphi_n(2) + B\varphi_n(1)\varphi_1(2)$. Calculation shows that either $A = B$, or $A = -B$; hence we have (omitting the constant factor):

$$\psi_s = \varphi_1(1)\varphi_n(2) + \varphi_n(1)\varphi_1(2) \quad \text{or}$$
$$\psi_a = \varphi_1(1)\varphi_n(2) - \varphi_n(1)\varphi_1(2) \tag{I, 41}$$

These two eigenfunctions correspond to two different eigenvalues, E_s and E_a, into which the originally twofold degenerate level is *split* by introducing the interaction. The first function is *symmetric*—that is, it remains unaltered by an exchange of the electrons (exchange of numbers 1 and 2 in parentheses); whereas the second is *antisymmetric*—that is, it changes sign for this operation.

In the mechanical example, the two eigenfunctions ψ_s and ψ_a correspond to the two stationary vibrations by superposition of which the observed exchange of energy between the two resonating pendulums (circuits) may be represented. These vibrations are: the symmetric vibration, in which the two pendulums (or circuits) are always in phase ($\uparrow\uparrow$); and the antisymmetric vibration in which they are in opposite phases ($\uparrow\downarrow$). The frequencies of the two vibrations are evidently different. Superposition of the two vibrations results in the periodic transfer of all the vibrational energy from one pendulum (circuit) to the other.

Similarly, by superimposing

$$\Psi_s = \psi_s e^{-2\pi i(E_s/h)t} \quad \text{and} \quad \Psi_a = \psi_a e^{-2\pi i(E_a/h)t}$$

we obtain a continuous switching over from $\varphi_1(1)\varphi_n(2)$ to $\varphi_n(1)\varphi_1(2)$. Namely, for $t = 0$,

$$\Psi_s + \Psi_a = \psi_s + \psi_a = 2\varphi_1(1)\varphi_n(2)$$

whereas after a certain interval when $e^{-2\pi i(E_s/h)t} = +1$ and $e^{-2\pi i(E_a/h)t} = -1$ at the same time (which is possible since $E_s \neq E_a$)

$$\Psi_s + \Psi_a = \psi_s - \psi_a = 2\varphi_n(1)\varphi_1(2)$$

After a further equal interval of time, $\Psi_s + \Psi_a$ will again equal $2\varphi_1(1)\varphi_n(2)$; that is, the second electron will be excited once more, and so on.

Actually, however, according to the statistical interpretation of wave mechanics, this superposition of Ψ_s and Ψ_a cannot occur in one and the same atom. *Either* Ψ_s (with energy E_s) *or* Ψ_a (with energy E_a) is excited in the atom. As shown by the functions (I, 41), in each of these stationary states Ψ_s and Ψ_a, both $\varphi_1(1)\varphi_n(2)$ and $\varphi_1(2)\varphi_n(1)$ are contained; or, in other words, in each of these stationary states partly electron 1 is excited and partly electron 2.

The above considerations show that, to every *one* excited state of the hydrogen atom with certain n and l values, there correspond, in the system with two electrons (He), *two* excited states with somewhat different energies, due to Heisenberg's resonance. One of these states is always symmetric; the other, antisymmetric. For the *ground state*, the resonance degeneracy does not exist; the eigenfunction is $\varphi_1(1)\varphi_1(2)$, and there is only one state, which is symmetric. These theoretical results agree exactly with the observed energy level diagram of Fig. 27. The parhelium levels are the symmetric levels; the orthohelium, the antisymmetric. Even quantitatively, the calculated energy levels and particularly the energy differences of the two term systems agree closely with the observed values.

There is, however, one important difficulty which cannot be solved at this stage; namely, it is found theoretically that *the transition probability between symmetric and antisymmetric terms is exactly equal to zero.* This may easily be seen in the following way: For electric dipole radiation, the transition probability (p. 53) is proportional to the square of

$$\sum_k \epsilon_k \int \Psi_n \Psi_m{}^* x_k \, d\tau$$

where x_k is one of the three co-ordinates of the kth particle. In the present case, for two electrons this will be:

$$\epsilon \int \Psi_n \Psi_m{}^*(x_1 + x_2)\, d\tau$$

If we now consider the transition between a symmetric and an antisymmetric state, we have to substitute $\Psi_n = \Psi_s$, and $\Psi_m = \Psi_a$. However, then the integrand and, therefore, the integral change sign when the two electrons are exchanged (exchange of index numbers 1 and 2), because Ψ_a then changes sign (cf. above), whereas Ψ_s and $(x_1 + x_2)$ do not. Since the value of the integral cannot depend upon the designation of the electrons, it follows that the integral must equal zero. This result holds, not only for the transition probability produced by ordinary dipole radiation, but also for any other type of radiation (p. 53), since the term replacing $(x_1 + x_2)$ would also be unaltered by changing the index numbers. Even the transition probability induced by collisions with other particles (electron collision, and so on) will be exactly equal to zero, because the interaction term, necessarily, is always symmetric in the two electrons of He. There is, consequently, no way of bringing about a transition between symmetric and antisymmetric energy levels. If all the atoms are at one time in a state of one system, as is the case for normal He (symmetric state), they should *never* go over to the other system, and hence the latter system should be unobservable. This conclusion flatly contradicts the fact that both systems are actually observed. As will be seen later (cf. Chapter III, section 1), this is due to the presence of electron spin.

The alkaline earths. As in the case of He, the alkaline earths and the other elements in the second column of the periodic system have twice as many series and, correspondingly, twice as many terms as the alkalis. This fact may be clearly seen by comparing the spectrograms of Na (Fig. 3) and Mg (Fig. 4). The Mg spectrogram, it is true, shows mainly diffuse and sharp series and only one line of one principal series. The other lines of this principal series and the other principal series lie in another region of the spectrum.

The alkaline earths thus have two partial systems of terms which practically do not combine with each other and lie at different heights. As for He, only one of them, the para system, has a low-lying state, the ground state ^1S.

The lowest term of the ortho system, however, is a ^3P term —not a ^3S term. (Cf. the Ca energy level diagram, Fig. 32, p. 77.) Just as with He, the two term systems converge to the same limit. From the splitting of the energy level diagram into two partial systems, we may conclude that, as for He, there are only *two electrons outside the atomic core* of the alkaline earths. The same conclusion holds for the alkaline-earth-like ions. The energy level diagram and the difference between the two term systems will be considered in greater detail in Chapter II.

CHAPTER II

Multiplet Structure of Line Spectra and Electron Spin

1. Empirical Facts and their Formal Explanation

Doublet structure of the alkali spectra. As shown in Chapter I, the quantum numbers n and l just suffice to characterize the different term series of the alkalis (Fig. 24, p. 57). However, they no longer are adequate for He and the alkaline earths, since for these there are twice as many term series as for the alkalis—that is, there are two complete term systems, which are distinguished by a left upper index 1 or 3 on the term symbol. The physical meaning of this method of distinction will be made clear in the subsequent discussion. Even if we provide an explanation by assuming that the atom under consideration exists in two different forms (for example, orthohelium and parhelium), the insufficiency of the quantum numbers thus far introduced becomes still more obvious when we examine the alkali spectra with spectral apparatus of greater dispersion. It is then found that each of their lines is double, as is generally known for the D line of Na. The line splitting increases rapidly in the series Li, Na, K, Rb, and Cs. It can be detected for Li only by using spectral apparatus of very high dispersion. However, for the D line of Na, the splitting is 6 Å. Fig. 29(a), page 74, shows this and some other Na doublets. The line splitting can naturally be traced back to a *term splitting*. Either the upper or the lower, or both of the terms involved are double, that is, split into two levels of slightly different energy.

To illustrate, Fig. 28 gives the energy level diagram of potassium. The scale used in the diagram is just sufficient

to show the splitting. The ground state and other S terms
are single; the P terms are split, the splitting decreasing
with increasing order number. The components are drawn
side by side. If the ground state were split and the P states
were single, all the lines in the principal series ($1S - mP$)
would have the same splitting (in cm^{-1}); but this is not the
case. On the other hand, all lines of the sharp series
($2P - mS$) have the same splitting, since the common
lower state $2P$ is split while the upper states mS are not
split. The lines of the diffuse series ($2P - mD$) have the
same splitting, for the same reason. The D terms themselves are split, but the splitting is so much smaller that it
makes scarcely any difference in the case of potassium
(see below).

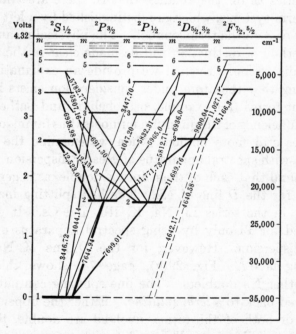

Fig. 28. Energy Level Diagram for Potassium [Grotrian (8)]. Here m is
the empirical order number of the terms (see p. 55). For S terms, the true
principal quantum number of the emission electron (p. 62) is 3 greater than m;
for P terms, it is 2 greater; for D and F terms, it is equal to m.

Quantum number J. Since the quantum numbers thus far introduced do not suffice, we distinguish, at first formally, the components of the doublets by an index number —that is, a new quantum number. We could write: P_1 and P_2. But, instead, we use as indices: for the P terms, $\frac{1}{2}$ and $\frac{3}{2}$; for the D terms, $\frac{3}{2}$ and $\frac{5}{2}$; and so on. The reason for this nomenclature will become apparent later. In Fig. 28 these symbols are written over the corresponding term series. In addition, a left upper index 2 (doublet) is given to all the term symbols (see below). The S terms are given a subscript $\frac{1}{2}$, although they are actually single. This new quantum number (subscript) is designated as J, and was called the *inner quantum number* by Sommerfeld. The different values of J occurring are summarized in Table 3.

TABLE 3

J VALUES FOR DOUBLET TERMS

Term	L	J
S	0	$\frac{1}{2}$
P	1	$\frac{1}{2}$ $\frac{3}{2}$
D	2	$\frac{3}{2}$ $\frac{5}{2}$
F	3	$\frac{5}{2}$ $\frac{7}{2}$
G	4	$\frac{7}{2}$ $\frac{9}{2}$

Each individual term of the alkalis is now characterized by the three quantum numbers n, l, and J. In the future we shall write L instead of l when we wish to characterize the whole atom and not a single electron. The selection rule is the same as for l (Chapter I, section 4):

$$\Delta L = \pm 1$$

Selection rule for J; compound doublets. The splitting of the D terms for potassium is so small that, for most purposes, they can be treated as if they were single. Accordingly, the D terms are not drawn separately in Fig. 28. Thus there will be practically no difference in the splitting of the sharp $(^2P - {}^2S)$ and the diffuse $(^2P - {}^2D)$ series. This also holds for Na, of which a few of the diffuse and the sharp doublets are shown in Fig. 29(a). The splitting of the D terms becomes noticeable for Rb and Cs, as well as for the alkali-like ions Ca^+, Sr^+, and so on. If the individual doublet term components could combine with one another without restriction, four components would be expected for each of the lines of the diffuse series (since each

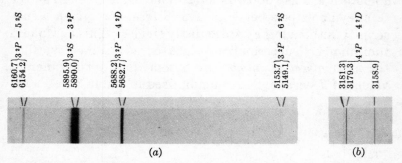

(a)   (b)

Fig. 29. Examples of Line Doublets. (a) Some Na doublets (part of the Na emission spectrum reproduced in Fig. 3, taken with larger dispersion). (b) Compound doublet of Ca^+. True principal quantum numbers are used to designate the terms.

component of the upper D term should combine with each of the two components of the lower P term). Actually, only three components are observed, as is shown in the spectrogram for a $^2P - {}^2D$ transition of Ca^+, in Fig. 29(b). Using the J values given above, we obtain agreement with experiment if we assume for the new quantum number J the selection rule: [1]

$$\Delta J = 0 \quad \text{or} \quad +1 \quad \text{or} \quad -1 \qquad \text{(II, 1)}$$

Fig. 30 shows the energy level diagram (not drawn to scale) corresponding to the Ca^+ doublet reproduced in Fig. 29(b). Transitions allowed by the selection rule are given as solid vertical lines, the horizontal distance between the lines corresponding to their frequency difference. The

---

[1] If we had distinguished the components of the P and D terms simply by the indices 1 and 2, a representation of the observed transitions would not have been possible with such a simple selection rule.

spectrum produced in this way is drawn schematically in the lower part of Fig. 30. For the transition, $^2D_{5/2} - {}^2P_{1/2}$, $\Delta J = 2$. This transition is forbidden by the selection rule, and actually does not appear in Fig. 29(b); however, it is shown by a dotted line in Fig. 30. As already stated, the splitting of the upper D term is relatively small, and thus, using low dispersion, we obtain doublets only, as for the sharp series, since $^2P_{3/2} - {}^2D_{3/2}$ and $^2P_{3/2} - {}^2D_{5/2}$ practically coincide. Using greater dispersion, as in Fig. 29(b), we find that one component of the doublet, and only one, is double. However, this group of lines is called, not a triplet, but a *compound doublet*, since it results from the combination of doublet terms. The lines of the Bergmann series ($^2D - {}^2F$) similarly consist of such compound doublets, which are incompletely resolved still more often than those of the diffuse series. Allowed combinations for the different series are also indicated in Table 3.

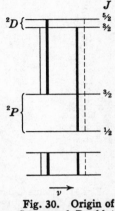

Fig. 30. Origin of a Compound Doublet $^2P - {}^2D$. [Cf. Fig. 29 (b).] Intensities are indicated by the thickness of the lines.

Triplets and singlets of the alkaline earths and helium. A more accurate investigation of the two systems of lines of the alkaline earths, using high dispersion, shows that the *para system* consists of single lines (*singlets*), whereas the *ortho system* consists of threefold lines (*triplets*). The splitting of the latter increases rapidly with increasing atomic number of the element in the second column of the periodic system. For Hg, the splitting is so great that different lines of one and the same multiplet lie in different regions of the spectrum.

Similar to the spectrum of the alkaline earths, even under large dispersion, the lines of the para system of He appear single, whereas those of the ortho system appear as very close triplets.[2] The symbols already used for He and the alkaline earths (left upper indices 1 and 3) are now understandable (see Fig. 27, p. 65). Fig. 31 shows spectrograms of some of the calcium triplets. As in the case of the alkalis,

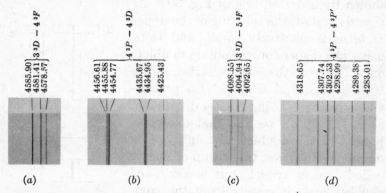

Fig. 31. Some Calcium Triplets (Ca I). (a), (b), and (c) Normal triplets. (d) Anomalous triplet (see p. 165). These photographs were taken with fairly large dispersion (2 Å/mm.).

the line splitting can be traced back to a splitting of the terms—this time into three components. Fig. 32 shows the energy level diagram for calcium, with this splitting taken into consideration.

As in the case of doublet terms, the components of the triplet terms can be distinguished by indices J, which must now be assumed to be integers and to have the values given in Table 4 (p. 78). The reason for this choice will be made clear later. For the alkalis, we found that the S terms of the doublet system are single. Similarly, here the S terms of the triplet system are single. In spite of that fact, they are given a J index which, in this case, is equal to 1. These S terms must be clearly distinguished from the S terms of the singlet system (^1S) of the same element, which lie somewhat higher (cf. Fig. 32). The former combine only with triplet terms, although they themselves are single; the latter, only with singlet terms.

---

[2] For He, two of the components lie so close together that for a long time the lines were thought to be doublets.

Use of the J selection rule (II, 1) gives the possible combinations indicated in Table 4. For small resolution, all the resulting lines of the triplet system are threefold, since then only the splitting of the lower term (which is the greater) is effective. Even under greatest resolution the lines of the principal series ($^3S - {}^3P$) and of the sharp series ($^3P - {}^3S$) are only threefold, since the ^3S terms are single. However, each line of the diffuse series ($^3P - {}^3D$) and of the Bergmann series ($^3D - {}^3F$)

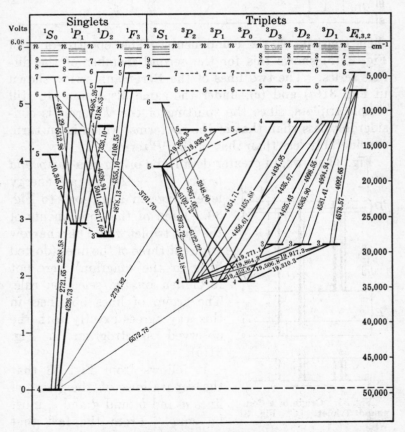

Fig. 32. Energy Level Diagram of Ca I [Grotrian (8)]. The diagram shows only the normal terms. (For the anomalous terms, see p. 164.) The n values are true principal quantum numbers. The transitions corresponding to spectrograms (a) to (c) in Fig. 31 are included, among others, in this figure.

TABLE 4

J VALUES FOR TRIPLET TERMS

Term	L	J
S	0	1
P	1	0 1 2
D	2	1 2 3
F	3	2 3 4
G	4	3 4 5

then consists of six components. The spectrogram of Fig. 31(b) shows this for the second member of the diffuse series. The two lines of the Bergmann series, shown in Fig. 31(a) and (c), under the same dispersion are still simple triplets, since the splitting of the ^3F terms is considerably less than that of the ^3D terms, which is, in turn, considerably less than that of the ^3P terms.

Fig. 33 shows, in greater detail, the origin of a *compound triplet* ($^3P - {}^3D$) in an energy level diagram analogous to Fig. 30. Each of the components of the line triplet would be a narrow triplet if three of the lines (dotted lines in the diagram) were not forbidden by the selection rule. The group of lines obtained in this way agrees exactly with the observed spectrogram in Fig. 31(b).

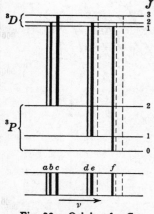

Fig. 33. Origin of a Compound Triplet. [Cf. Fig. 31 (b).]

It follows from Fig. 33 that the separations of the pairs of lines a and b, and d and e, must be equal. From the fact that this relation is satisfied by an observed group of six lines in an unknown spectrum, we can conclude, conversely, that the lines actually belong together and form such a compound triplet. Apart from this there are other checks (intensity and interval rules, Chapter IV, section 4).

Prohibition of intercombinations; intercombination lines. As already stated, terms of the triplet system of He practically do not combine with the terms of the singlet system, and conversely. That is, a prohibition of intercombinations is observed. This also holds for the alkaline earths. However, for them, some intercombination lines (combinations between singlet and triplet terms) actually do appear, although they are very weak compared to the allowed transitions. The number and intensity of forbidden lines which do appear increase with increasing atomic number. Some of these intercombination lines are included in the energy level diagram for Ca I (Fig. 32). The best-known example of such an intercombination line is the Hg resonance line $\lambda 2537$, corresponding to the transition $^3P_1 \rightarrow {}^1S_0$ (Fig. 74, p. 202). (The Ca line $\lambda 6573$ is analogous.) This is one of the strongest Hg lines, but it is considerably weaker than the corresponding non-intercombination line $^1P_1 \rightarrow {}^1S_0$ at $\lambda 1849$. It should be noted that the selection rule $\Delta J = 0$ or ± 1 holds also for these intercombination lines, with the additional restriction that

$$J = 0 \text{ does } not \text{ combine with } J = 0 \qquad \text{(II, 2)}$$

Thus, for Ca or Hg, the lines $^3P_0 \rightarrow {}^1S_0$ and $^3P_2 \rightarrow {}^1S_0$ either do not appear at all or appear extremely weakly.[3]

Higher multiplicities; term symbols. For many elements other than those dealt with thus far, not only singlet, doublet, or triplet terms, but also terms of higher multiplicity occur; and, correspondingly, higher multiplets of lines are observed—such as, quartets, quintets, and so on. Also for the higher multiplicities, it is found experimentally that terms of different multiplet systems usually do not

---

[3] The selection rules do not hold quite rigorously. See also Chapter IV.

combine with one another or combine only very weakly (*prohibition of intercombinations*).

In accordance with the suggestion of Russell and Saunders, terms are now generally distinguished by using the multiplicity as the left upper index of the letter giving the L value (S, P, D, $\cdots$); this practice is analogous to the method already used for singlets and triplets. The J value is given as the right lower index. Thus each individual component of a multiplet term can be characterized. For even multiplicities, J takes half-integral values; for odd multiplicities, integral values. (The reason for this difference will be explained later.) Hence we have symbols such as $^2P_{1/2}$ (read "doublet P one half"), $^3D_2$, $^3S_1$, $^4F_{5/2}$, and so on. These symbols are also used for singlet terms where the J value is equal to the L value; for example, $^1S_0$, $^1P_1$, and so on. Sometimes the principal quantum number, or even the whole electron configuration, precedes this symbol, as we shall see later.

If higher multiplicities occur, the spectra appear more and more complex. In principle, however, there are the same regularities as described earlier in this chapter—similar series of line multiplets (principal series, and so on), and the same selection rules; hence we need not go into further detail here (see Chapter IV).

As an illustration of a somewhat more complicated multiplet, a $^4P - {}^4D$ transition of the C^+ spectrum is given in

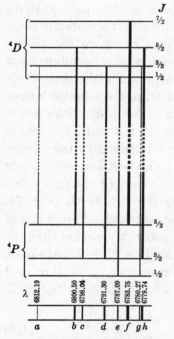

Fig. 34. $^4P - {}^4D$ Transition for C^+ at 6800 Å. The relative separations of term and line components are drawn to scale from data given by Fowler and Selwyn (59).

Fig. 34, similar to the compound triplet of Fig. 33. It should be noted that a ^4P term has only three components. This fact and the given values of J are explained in the following section.

Alternation of multiplicities. The atoms of the elements B, Al, and the other earths, which follow the alkaline-earth column in the periodic system, have doublet terms like the alkalis, as their spectra show (see the energy level diagram of Fig. 73, p. 198). However, quartet terms also have been observed for them, and consequently their energy level diagram splits into two partial systems (doublets and quartets), just as in the case of the alkaline earths (singlets and triplets).

All the elements of the *carbon* group have singlets and triplets, and sometimes quintets; those of the *nitrogen* group have doublets and quartets, and sometimes sextets; those of the *oxygen* group have singlets, triplets, and quintets; the *halogens* have doublets and quartets; and the *inert gases* have singlets and triplets, as we have already seen for He. *Even and odd multiplicities, therefore, alternate in successive columns in the periodic system.*

Quite analogous to the alkalis and alkaline earths, there are, for the other elements, series of arc and spark spectra; for example, C I, N II, O III, whose spectra, apart from a shift to the ultraviolet, are completely similar to one another. The *Sommerfeld-Kossel displacement law* thus holds: *The first spark spectrum of an element is similar in all details to the arc spectrum of the element preceding it in the periodic system; similarly, the second spark spectrum is similar to the first spark spectrum of the element preceding it, or to the arc spectrum of the element with atomic number two less, and so forth.* On the other hand, arc and spark spectra of the same element are fundamentally different. The multiplicity and type of the terms of an atom or ion are thus determined solely by the number of electrons. The nuclear charge affects only the position of the spectrum. The alternation of multiplicities may therefore be expressed in the following generalized form:

The terms of atoms or ions with an even number of electrons have odd multiplicities; the terms of atoms or ions with an odd number of electrons have even multiplicities. This rule holds also for elements not fitting into one of the eight columns of the periodic system; for example, the rare earths.

2. Physical Interpretation of the Quantum Numbers

Meaning of L for several emission electrons. For the H atom and the alkalis (which have one emission electron), L is the same as l, which is itself proportional to the orbital angular momentum of the electron. For elements with a larger number of emission electrons, such as the earths or the elements of the oxygen group, the quantum number L was at first introduced purely empirically to distinguish the different term series (S, P, D, $\cdots$) of a term system. Its numerical value and, from this, the symbol for the corresponding term were obtained from the combination properties, the same selection rule being assumed for L as for l, that is, $\Delta L = \pm 1$. Further information was obtained from the investigation of multiplet structure and of the Zeeman effect. In more general cases, transitions with $\Delta L = 0$ are also observed (see Chapter IV). The question is: In the more general cases what meaning does L have in our model of the atom?

If we recall that a definite, constant orbital angular momentum l is ascribed to the emission electron of the H atom or of the alkali atoms, it appears very plausible, even in a complicated atom, to ascribe *to each individual electron a definite, constant orbital angular momentum l_i*, where l_i is a vector of magnitude 0, 1, 2, $\cdots$ in units $h/2\pi$.

That this assumption is true to a first approximation follows from the consideration that in complicated atoms each electron may be thought of as moving in the smeared-out field of the other electrons. This smeared-out field is approximately spherically symmetrical, and an electron moving in a spherically symmetric field has, according to wave mechanics, quantum numbers n and l, where l is proportional to the angular momentum (see p. 46 f.).

The individual angular momenta produce, when added vectorially, a resultant which depends on the number, magnitude, and direction of the respective vectors. Classically, since these can take all possible directions, the resultant momentum can, in general, take all values up to $\sum |l_i|$, the last when all l_i are in the same direction.[4] Quantum mechanics, however, shows that for atomic systems the resultant orbital angular momentum, as well as the individual angular momenta l_i, can be only an integral multiple of $h/2\pi$.[5] The resultant orbital angular momentum is thus $L'(h/2\pi)$, or more accurately $\sqrt{L'(L' + 1)}\, h/2\pi$ where L' is taken temporarily as the corresponding quantum number. The individual l_i can therefore be oriented *only in certain discrete directions to one another*. For the case of two electrons with orbital angular momenta l_1 and l_2, the possible resultant L' values are given by:

$$L' = (l_1 + l_2),\quad (l_1 + l_2 - 1),\quad (l_1 + l_2 - 2),\quad \cdots,\quad |l_1 - l_2|$$

Fig. 35 (p. 84) shows the possible resultants for $l_1 = 2$, $l_2 = 1$. Thus we obtain as many different states of the atom as there are different L' values. They are distinguished by the orientation of the orbital planes to one another (to use the old Bohr mode of expression).

However, the individual electrons do not move even approximately independent of one another, as do, for example, the planets in the solar system; rather, they exert strong forces on one another (*interactions*), due partly to their electric repulsion and partly to the magnetic moments resulting from their angular momenta (see section 3). These interactions have magnitudes which depend on the particular circumstances. For example, if the two electrons

---

[4] In general, the smallest possible value for the resultant is 0. But it will be greater than 0 if one l_i is larger than the sum of the magnitudes of all the others.

[5] The basis for this conclusion is quite analogous to the basis for the integral value of l, given on page 41.

have very different principal quantum numbers, the interactions are relatively small on account of the large mean separation; whereas they will, in general, be rather large when the principal quantum numbers are equal.

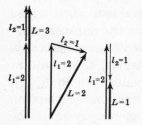

Fig. 35. Addition of l_1 and l_2 to Give a Resultant Orbital Angular Momentum L for $l_1 = 2$, $l_2 = 1$, and $L = 3, 2, 1$.

This interaction now has the effect that the direction of the individual angular momenta is no longer constant with time (as in the case of the one-electron problem) but carries out a *precessional movement* (just as the direction of the earth's axis carries out a very slow precession due to the interaction with the gravitational field of the sun, which seeks, on account of the flattening of the earth at the poles, to set the earth's axis perpendicular to the orbital plane). In classical as well as in wave mechanics, the resultant angular momentum L' remains, however, constant in magnitude and direction during this precession of the individual momenta. The precession for the case of two electrons is shown in Fig. 36. The greater the interaction, the greater will be the velocity of precession.[6] If this velocity is of the same order as the angular velocity corresponding to the individual angular momenta themselves, the latter lose their meaning completely, since then the electron does not describe, even to a first approximation, a

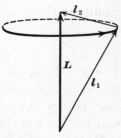

Fig. 36. Precession of l_1 and l_2 about the Resultant L. Replacing l_1, l_2, and L by L, S, and J gives a picture of the precession of L and S about J. (See p. 90.)

rotational motion about the individual angular momentum vector as axis, but rather a much more complicated motion. For very strong coupling (very high velocity of precession), this motion reduces, in a first approximation, to a simple

---

[6] In the case of the precession of the earth's axis, the interaction is so small that the period of precession is 25,000 years.

rotation about the precessional axis (the axis of the resultant angular momentum). In this case only the resultant L' has an exactly defined meaning.

If the selection rules for the quantum number L' of the resultant orbital angular momentum are derived in the way outlined in Chapter I, section 4, it is found that the selection rule $\Delta L' = \pm 1$ usually holds, although $\Delta L' = 0$ can also occur. L' therefore has just the properties observed for the empirically introduced L. Therefore L' must be identified with L. Thus *the different term series S, P, D, $\cdots$ of an atom with more than one emission electron are distinguished by different values* $(0, 1, 2, \cdots)$ *for the resultant orbital angular momentum L of the electrons.* Hence the selection rule

$$\Delta L = 0, \quad \pm 1 \qquad \qquad \textbf{(II, 3)}$$

holds. In addition, there is the rule that, so long as the interaction of the electrons is not very large, only those quantum transitions take place for which only one of the emission electrons makes a jump—that is, only one alters its l value, the alteration being in accordance with the selection rule (I, 29): $\Delta l = \pm 1$. For example, a state of an atom with two emission electrons with $L = 1$, $l_1 = 1$, $l_2 = 0$ cannot combine with a state $L = 2$, $l_1 = 3$, $l_2 = 3$, although this combination would be allowed according to (II, 3) alone.

For strong coupling of the angular momentum vectors, the energy of the entire system will obviously differ according to the orientation of the individual angular momenta to one another. Thus in the case of two electrons (considered above), the energies of the states

$$L = (l_1 + l_2), \quad (l_1 + l_2 - 1), \quad (l_1 + l_2 - 2),$$
$$\cdots, \quad |l_1 - l_2| \qquad \textbf{(II, 4)}$$

differ—the difference being greater, the stronger the coupling (interaction). The observed magnitude of the energy difference is a direct measure of the strength of the coupling.

As we have shown above, when there is strong interaction in an atom, the individual angular momenta l_i no longer have any exact meaning as angular momenta; only their resultant L has an exact meaning. The momenta l_i are, however, still of importance in determining the number and type of the terms. Both in the Bohr theory and in quantum mechanics, *Ehrenfest's adiabatic law* holds: *For a virtual, infinitely slow alteration of the coupling conditions, the quantum numbers of the system do not change* [7] and, in particular, the number of terms does not vary. Hence, if we "uncouple" the individual orbital angular momenta by assuming their interactions removed, we come, in the limiting case, to the state in which each individual l_i actually has the meaning of an angular momentum and in which we can carry out the above vector addition. Thus we obtain the correct number and type of the resulting terms.

Consequently, for the case of a number of electrons in an atom, we ascribe to each electron an l value that would correspond to the angular momentum of this electron for infinitely small or vanishing coupling. Electrons with $l = 0$ are called *s-electrons;* those with $l = 1$, *p-electrons;* those with $l = 2$, *d-electrons;* and so on (small letters being used in contrast to capital letters, which represent terms of a complete atom or ion). The principal quantum number of the electron is added to this, and we have such symbols as $1s$, $2p$, $4d$, and so on. At all events, even in the actual atom, the quantum numbers l_i still retain their importance for deriving the number and type of terms, but do not always correspond to angular momenta—at least not in the strict sense of the word.

Table 5 shows the term types given by various electron configurations (cf. Table 10, p. 132).

If all but one of the l_i are zero, the resulting L value will naturally be that of the single l_i. This single l then retains literally its physical meaning of an angular momentum.

---

[7] The converse of this law is: Only such magnitudes can be quantized as remain constant (invariant) for adiabatic changes. According to Ehrenfest, this converse may be considered the fundamental law of the old quantum theory.

Such, for example, is the case for most (normal) terms of the alkaline earths and He. The term type S, P, D, $\cdots$ then depends only upon the l value of this one emission electron, just as for the alkalis. However, even for the alkaline earths there are terms—the so-called *anomalous terms* (see Chapter IV, section 2)—for which two electrons have $l \neq 0$. For elements of the carbon group and beyond, the occurrence of such terms with more than one electron having $l \neq 0$ is quite general.

TABLE 5

L VALUES AND TERM SYMBOLS FOR TERMS WITH
DIFFERENT ELECTRON CONFIGURATIONS

Electron Configuration	L							Term Symbol						
$s\,p$				1							P			
$p\,p$			0	1	2					S	P	D		
$p\,d$			1	2	3						P	D	F	
$d\,d$		0	1	2	3	4				S	P	D	F	G
$p\,p\,p$	0	1	1	1	2	2	3		S	P	P	P	D	D	F

When there are three electrons for which $l \neq 0$, the vector addition may be carried out simply by combining the l values of two electrons and then combining each of the resulting L values with the l of the third electron.

Physical interpretation of J: cause of multiplet splitting. On the basis of the foregoing, a term with a given L is single. How can we then explain the observed splitting into multiplets of the terms with a given value of L? As we shall anticipate here (cf. the following section), investigations of the anomalous Zeeman effect have shown that the individual components of a multiplet are distinguished from one another by the *total angular momentum of the atom*. In fact, using the above nomenclature for distinguishing the sub-levels (empirical quantum number J), the total angular momentum is found to be equal to $J \times h/2\pi$, where, as will be remembered, J is the quantum number at first introduced purely formally in order to distinguish the sub-levels. According to quantum mechanics, the exact value of the total angular momentum is, not $J(h/2\pi)$, but $\sqrt{J(J+1)}$ $\times h/2\pi$, as in the case of l. As before, the difference can in many cases be disregarded.

The total angular momentum of the atom is thus *not* equal to the resultant (integral) *orbital* angular momentum L, which is the same for all components of a multiplet term, but can take as many different values as the multiplicity of the term. Thus, to obtain the total angular momentum J, one has to add vectorially to L an *additional integral or half-integral angular momentum vector* S, whose exact meaning we shall leave undefined for the moment. According to the quantum theory, L and S cannot be oriented to each other in any arbitrary direction but only in certain directions (similar to the case of the individual l_i), and therefore only certain discrete values of the resultant J are possible. The largest and the smallest values of J for a given pair of values L and S are obtained by a simple addition and subtraction of the corresponding quantum numbers L and S.[8] In this calculation only the magnitude of the resultant vector is of importance, since J, naturally, can only be positive. Intermediate values of J are also possible, and these differ from the extreme values (sum and difference) by integral amounts, just as in the addition of the l_i to form a resultant L. In this case we have therefore:

$$J = (L + S), \quad (L + S - 1), \quad (L + S - 2),$$
$$\cdots, \quad |L - S| \quad \textbf{(II, 5)}$$

In other words, the rule is: the vector addition of L and S is such that the different possible values of their vector sum have integral differences. Fig. 37 illustrates this rule for the cases $L = 1$, $S = \frac{1}{2}$; $L = 1$, $S = 1$; $L = 2$, $S = 1$; $L = 1$, $S = \frac{3}{2}$; $L = 2$, $S = \frac{3}{2}$. When $L > S$, it is easily

---

[8] This S, naturally, has nothing to do with the S of the S terms. The former is a quantum number; the latter, a symbol for $L = 0$. This nomenclature is internationally used and must therefore be used here, although it may lead to confusion.

seen from (II, 5) that the number of possible J values for a given value of L is

$$2S + 1$$

On the other hand, if $L < S$, the number of possible J values for a given value of L is

$$2L + 1$$

In particular, for S terms ($L = 0$, $2L + 1 = 1$) there is only one value of J; namely, $J = S$.

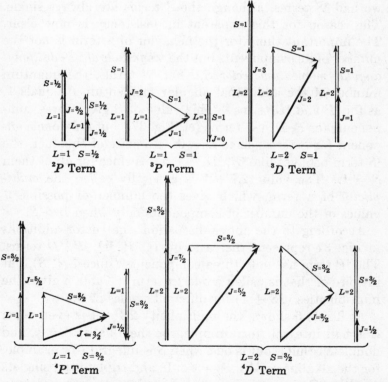

Fig. 37. Vector Addition of L and S to Give a Resultant J for Different Examples. For a given combination of L and S, all the possible orientations of L and S with respect to one another and the corresponding total angular momenta are illustrated. The vector J is indicated by a heavy line. Its direction is fixed in space. The magnitude of the vector J (and, correspon lingly, of L and S) is taken as $J(h/2\pi)$, and not $\sqrt{J(J + 1)}\, h/2\pi$, as it should be strictly speaking.

Note that, in drawing such figures, the direction of the first vector is quite arbitrary. It is only for simplicity that all these have been drawn vertically.

The number of possible J values—that is, possible values of the total angular momentum—is equal to the number of components into which a term of given L is split. Evidently when the angular momentum is different for two states, the energy will, in general, also be different, as we have already seen when dealing with the vector addition of the l_i. Now, we had previously associated some terms with a system of higher multiplicity, though they themselves actually had a smaller number of components; for example, we had ^3S terms, although the S terms are always single. The reason for this apparent inconsistency is now clear. The important thing for the behavior of a term is not the number of its components but the *magnitude of its additional angular momentum vector* S. For ^3S terms, the quantum number of the additional angular momentum S equals 1, as for ^3P and ^3D terms. This value of S gives three components for P, D, $\cdots$ terms (cf. Fig. 37), but only one component for S terms since $L = 0$. In spite of this fact, the ^3S term behaves like ^3P, ^3D, $\cdots$ terms since for all of them $S = 1$. The value $2S + 1$ is generally called the *multiplicity* of a term, which gives the number of possible J values or the number of components only when $L > S$.

According to the above discussion, the vector additions in Fig. 37 represent the cases of ^2P, ^3P, ^3D, ^4P, ^4D terms. The ^4P term has only three components (since $L < S$), but in spite of that is called a *quartet* term. Table 6 gives the multiplicities ($2S + 1$) for different values of S.

As Table 6 shows, the multiplicity $2S + 1$ is even when S is half integral (for example, for the alkalis, $S = \frac{1}{2}$, and doublets result), but is odd when S is integral (for example, for the alkaline earths, $S = 1$ or 0, and triplets and singlets result). Conversely, in order to explain an observed even number of components (for example, doublets), we must necessarily assume that S is half integral; whereas, for an odd number of components, S must be integral.

Just as in the combination of the l_i to give L, a precession of the components L and S takes place about the resultant J

TABLE 6

MULTIPLICITIES FOR DIFFERENT VALUES OF S

S	Multiplicity of the Terms
0	Singlets
½	Doublets
1	Triplets
3/2	Quartets
2	Quintets
5/2	Sextets
...	...

(cf. Fig. 36, p. 84). The greater the interaction of L and S, the faster will be the precession and the greater will be the difference in energies of the states with different J; that is, the greater will be the multiplet splitting. Furthermore, according to Dirac's wave mechanical theory of the electron spin, Sommerfeld's fine structure formula (I, 12) still holds if k is replaced by $j + \frac{1}{2}$, where j corresponds to J for the case of one electron. It thus follows from (I, 12) that, for the case of one emission electron, the doublet splitting is proportional to Z^4. Strictly speaking, this conclusion should hold only for hydrogen-like ions, but qualitatively this rapid increase in multiplet splitting with increasing Z will also hold for all other cases. This result is in agreement with experiment. For example, for Li ($Z = 3$), the splitting of the lowest ^2P level is 0.34 cm⁻¹, for Cs ($Z = 55$), it is 5540 cm⁻¹; for Be ($Z = 4$), the total splitting of the first ^3P level is 3.03 cm⁻¹, for Hg ($Z = 80$), 6397.9 cm⁻¹. On the other hand, according to (I, 12), the splitting should decrease with increasing n and L. This effect is also observed. For a not too high atomic number, the multiplet splitting is, in general, relatively small; that is, the velocity of the precession of L and S about J is small. L and S therefore retain, to a good approximation, their meaning as angular momenta, even when the interaction is allowed for. However, for heavy elements, sometimes only

J retains its meaning as an angular momentum (see Chapter IV, section 3).

If the components in a multiplet term lie energetically in the same order as their J values (smallest J value lowest) the term is called *regular* or *normal* and, in the converse case, *inverted*. For example, most of the P and D terms of the alkalis and the alkaline earths are regular doublets or triplets (Figs. 30 and 33). Similarly, the quartet terms of C^+ in Fig. 34 (p. 80) are also regular. Fig. 38 gives a ^4D term as an example of an inverted term. The reason for the appearance of the inverted order of the terms will not be discussed here [cf. White (12) and Condon and Shortley (13)].

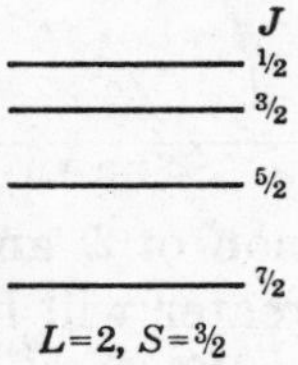

$$
\begin{array}{ll}
& J \\
\hline & \frac{1}{2} \\
\hline & \frac{3}{2} \\
\hline & \frac{5}{2} \\
\hline & \frac{7}{2} \\
\end{array}
$$

$L=2,\ S=\frac{3}{2}$

Fig. 38. Example of an Inverted Term ^4D. Corresponding to the interval rule (see p. 178), the separation of the components increases from top to bottom, contrary to a normal term.

Selection rule for J. Wave mechanical calculation of the transition probability (cf. Chapter I, section 4) shows that the selection rule $\Delta J = 0, \pm 1$ holds for the quantum number J of the total angular momentum of an atomic system. In addition, it is found that a level with $J = 0$ does not combine with another level with $J = 0$. These results agree exactly with the selection rules (II, 1) and (II, 2), which were derived purely empirically from spectroscopic observations (see p. 74 and p. 79).

Physical interpretation of S. What meaning can we now give to the additional angular momentum S in our atomic model? Historically, the first assumption held that this angular momentum was the angular momentum of the atomic core. The assumption has proved untenable, since for the alkalis, for example, the atomic core is formed by the ground state of the corresponding alkali ion and, according to the spark spectrum, this is a $^1S_0$ state (just as for the inert gases, according to the Sommerfeld-Kossel displacement law) and thus has $J = 0$, $L = 0$, and $S = 0$. That is to say, an angular momentum of the atomic core cannot be present in the case of a neutral alkali atom. Apart from this, it is difficult to see why the angular momentum of the atomic core should be half integral. But that J and therefore the additional angular momentum S really must be half integral for even multiplicities is also confirmed definitely by the investigation of the anomalous Zeeman effect, as will be seen later. Goudsmit and Uhlenbeck were thus led to the assumption that the additional angular momentum S is due to the electron or electrons themselves. According to this assumption, *each electron performs a rotation about its own axis* as well as a motion about the nucleus. This rotation is such that the angular momentum s has the same magnitude for each electron, $\frac{1}{2}(h/2\pi)$; the rotation is usually called the *spin*, or the *electron spin*.[9] The assumption of electron spin has been verified by an extraordinarily large amount of experimental material and must be regarded today as entirely correct.[10]

When several electrons are present, the individual spin vectors s_i combine with one another just as in the case of the l_i previously discussed. It is the *resultant spin vector* which, according to Goudsmit and Uhlenbeck, is identical with the above empirically derived, additional angular momentum vector S. Analogous to L, the resultant spin vector S can take only certain discrete values according to the quantum theory, the maximum value being obtained when all the s_i are parallel. In that case, if N is the number of electrons, the corresponding quantum number S is equal to $N/2$, since each electron contributes $\frac{1}{2}$. For other orientations of the s_i, the following S values are possible:

$$\frac{N}{2} - 1, \quad \frac{N}{2} - 2, \quad \cdots, \quad \frac{1}{2} \text{ or } 0$$

The smallest value is $\frac{1}{2}$ or 0 according as $N/2$ is half integral

---

[9] The rigorous quantum mechanical formula for the magnitude of the vector s would be $\sqrt{s(s+1)}\, h/2\pi$; that is, with $s = \frac{1}{2}$; $\frac{1}{2}\sqrt{3}\, h/2\pi$.

[10] The assumption appears as a necessary result of Dirac's relativistic wave mechanics. However, this theory has thus far been completely worked out only for the one-electron problem.

or integral. It follows that S is *half integral or integral according as the number of electrons is odd or even.* The empirically obtained alternation law of multiplicities follows directly from this result, since the multiplicity is equal to $2S + 1$ and will therefore be even or odd, according as the number of electrons is odd or even (see p. 81).

The same conclusions that we have derived for the spin from analogy and consideration of the old quantum theory may also be reached by an accurate wave mechanical treatment [Condon and Shortley (13)]. Also, we can obtain these conclusions rather more simply and schematically (but less rigorously) by assuming that the spins of the individual electrons in an atom will be either parallel or antiparallel to one another. It is then obvious that the resultant will be half integral or integral according to whether the number of electrons is odd or even.

The exact theoretical derivation shows that, to a first approximation, states with different S (different multiplicities) do not combine with one another. This prohibition of intercombinations has also been observed empirically (p. 79). We therefore have the selection rule for S:

$$\Delta S = 0 \qquad \text{(II, 6)}$$

Both theory and experiment show that this selection rule is adhered to less and less strictly as the atomic number increases.

The alkalis have one electron outside the atomic core (see Chapter III). Consequently $S = \frac{1}{2}$, and doublet terms result, in agreement with experiment.

The alkaline earths and He have two electrons outside the atomic core. Their spins can be either parallel ↑↑ or antiparallel ↑↓ to one another; that is, $S = 1$ or 0, and there result triplet as well as singlet states. Each state with a given L can, in general, occur as a triplet state as well as a singlet state. The ground state, which occurs only as a singlet state, forms an exception (cf. the energy level diagrams of Figs. 27 and 32), which will be explained in the next chapter.

With three electrons outside the core, S can have the values $\frac{3}{2}$ and $\frac{1}{2}$, corresponding to ↑↑↑ and ↓↑↑. This gives quartets and doublets.

Table 7 lists the possible term multiplicities for various numbers of electrons.

TABLE 7

POSSIBLE MULTIPLICITIES FOR VARIOUS NUMBERS
OF ELECTRONS

Number of Electrons	Possible Multiplicities
1	Doublets
2	Singlets, triplets
3	Doublets, quartets
4	Singlets, triplets, quintets
5	Doublets, quartets, sextets
6	Singlets, triplets, quintets, septets
7	Doublets, quartets, sextets, octets
8	Singlets, triplets, quintets, septets, nonets

According to the preceding discussion, the spectrum of the H atom should also be a doublet spectrum. Actually, it has been shown that the hydrogen fine structure can only be explained quantitatively by taking account of this fact. The relations are, however, complicated in this case by the fact that the separation of terms with different l (and equal n) is of the same order as the doublet splitting. We shall not go into these complications [see White (12)] but merely note that, according to this interpretation, the lines of the Lyman series are not single, as assumed in Fig. 13, but consist of two components like the lines of the principal series of the alkalis. (The experimental investigation of the fine structure of the Lyman lines offers many difficulties because the lines lie in the vacuum region, and has therefore not yet been carried out.)

The fact that multiplet splitting does occur shows that an interaction between L and S exists. It is, in general, small for a not too great atomic number. This interaction is due to the fact that a *magnetic moment* is associated with the electron spin, just as with any rotation of charges. The magnetic moment of the spin is influenced by the magnetic moment associated with the orbital angular momentum L, the magnitude of this interaction depending upon their orientation to each other.   Therefore, as already mentioned, a precession of L and S about the direction of the total angular momentum J takes place (cf. Fig. 36, p. 84).

For the *magnitude* of the magnetic moment of the electron, Goudsmit and Uhlenbeck made the assumption that it is *twice* as great as follows from the *classical* connection between magnetic moment and angular momentum.   The meaning of this assumption will be amplified in section 3 of this chapter.

As already noted, states with different S (different multiplicities but with other quantum numbers the same) have appreciably different energies (cf. Figs. 27 and 32).   For a not too high atomic number, the energy difference is appreciably greater than the energy difference between the individual components of a multiplet.   Although it might appear that this energy difference of terms with different multiplicities is due to the different interactions of the spins resulting from their different orientations, the interaction of the spin vectors s_i due to their magnetic moments cannot possibly be very much greater than that of L and S.   In fact, theoretically it should be appreciably smaller.   The energy difference of the various multiplet systems must, therefore, have another origin, which will be dealt with in Chapter III.

3. Space Quantization: Zeeman Effect and Stark Effect

General remarks on Zeeman effect and space quantization.   The necessity for the assumption of an angular momentum or spin of the electron itself and, in particular, its double magnetism is made especially clear in the explanation of the Zeeman effect of spectral lines.   This effect may be described as follows.   When a light source is brought into a magnetic field, each emitted spectral line is split into a number of components.   To a first approximation, the splitting is proportional to the strength of the magnetic field.   Fig. 39 shows three examples of such splitting.

The splitting of the lines is evidently due to a splitting of the terms in the magnetic field.   The influence of a magnetic field on energy levels is, perhaps, most clearly understood by considering how a magnetic needle behaves in a magnetic field. The potential energy of the magnetic needle depends upon its direction with respect to the magnetic field. Therefore, if the needle is displaced from the

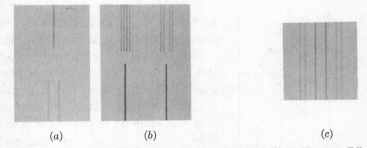

(a)   (b)   (c)

Fig. 39.   Examples of Line Splitting in a Magnetic Field (Zeeman Effect) [after Back and Landé (6)].
(a) *Normal* Zeeman triplet of the Cd line 6438.47 Å ($^1P - {}^1D$ transition). Above, the exposure was so made that only light polarized parallel to the field direction could reach the plate (single component at the position of the original line). Below, the components were polarized perpendicular to the field; they lie symmetrical to the original line.
(b) *Anomalous* Zeeman splitting of the two D lines of Na, 5889.96 Å and 5895.93 Å ($^2S - {}^2P$ transition). Above, with magnetic field. Below, without magnetic field.
(c) *Anomalous* splitting of the Zn line 4722.16 Å ($^3P_1 - {}^3S_1$ transition).

direction of the field and then released, it will vibrate back and forth about its equilibrium position (the position of minimum potential energy—that is, when the needle is in the direction of the field) and can be brought to rest only by the dissipation of its energy.   Like the magnetic needle, the atom generally has a magnetic moment **μ**.   The rotation of electric charges which, even according to wave mechanics, takes place in the atom always leads to the production of a magnetic moment in the direction of the axis of rotation. This effect follows the same laws that operate when a current flows through a wire ring (circular electric current). The greater the angular momentum of the atom, the greater will be the magnetic moment **μ**. Because of the inherent connection between magnetic moment and angular momentum, we have to take into account the gyroscopic forces when we discuss the behavior of an atom in a magnetic field.

The effect of these gyroscopic forces is that the rotational axis of the atom (direction of $\mathbf{\mu}$) does not vibrate back and forth about the position of minimum energy, but executes a *precessional motion* with uniform velocity about the direction of the field (so-called *Larmor precession*). This precession is shown diagrammatically in Fig. 40.

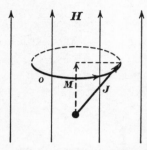

Fig. 40. Precession of the Total Angular Momentum *J* in a Magnetic Field *H* about the Field Direction as Axis.

Just as for the combination of the l_i vectors, the velocity of precession depends upon the strength of the coupling; that is, in this case the velocity depends upon the field strength *H* of the magnetic field. It is directly proportional to the latter. (This holds also for the vibration frequency of a magnet.) So long as no energy is dissipated, the precession continues at a constant angle to the field direction; that is, *J* has a constant component *M* in the direction of the field. The energy in a magnetic field (as for the magnetic needle) is:

$$W = W_0 - H\mathbf{\mu}_H \qquad\qquad \text{(II, 7)}$$

where $\mathbf{\mu}_H$ is the component of the magnetic moment in the field direction and W_0 is the energy in the field-free case. When $\mathbf{\mu}$ or *J* is perpendicular to the field direction, $W = W_0$.

Just as two angular momentum vectors in an atomic system cannot, according to quantum mechanics, take any arbitrary direction with respect to one another but only certain discrete directions, so an angular momentum vector can take *only certain discrete directions* in a magnetic field. This means that *J* (and therefore $\mathbf{\mu}$) is *space quantized* in a magnetic field. Just as the resultant in the afore-mentioned case of two angular momentum vectors can take only integral or half-integral values, so in this case *the component M of the angular momentum J in the direction of the field can be only an integral or half-integral multiple of $h/2\pi$*. It will be integral when J is integral, or half integral when J is half integral.   Thus the following relation holds:

$$M = J, \quad J - 1, \quad J - 2, \quad \cdots, \quad \cdot - J \qquad \textbf{(II, 8)}$$

This gives $2J + 1$ different values.

The left half of Fig. 41 illustrates the possible orientations of J to the direction of the magnetic field H for $J = 2$ and $J = \frac{5}{2}$.   The precession which J carries out about the field direction, as in Fig. 40, can take place only at one of the given angles to the field direction.   For $J = \frac{1}{2}$, only the directions parallel or antiparallel to the field are possible.

Corresponding to this space quantization, the energy of the system in a magnetic field cannot take *any* value

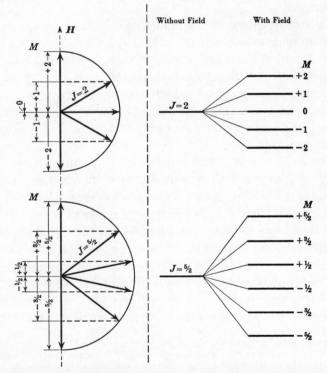

Fig. 41.   Space Quantization of the Total Angular Momentum J in a Magnetic Field H for $J = 2$ and $J = \frac{5}{2}$.   To the left are the possible orientations to the magnetic field.   To the right, in an energy level diagram, the corresponding energy values are indicated.

between $W_0 + H|\mathfrak{y}|$ and $W_0 - H|\mathfrak{y}|$; but it can take only $2J + 1$ discrete values. The right half of Fig. 41 shows this term splitting in a magnetic field. According to (II, 7), the splitting is proportional to the field strength. It is, in first approximation, symmetrical about the undisplaced term. All the energy differences between the individual components are the same, since $H\mathfrak{y}_H$ is proportional to M (cf. below) and the possible M values have whole-number differences.

The space quantization itself is independent of the field strength. It remains even when the field strength decreases to zero, although then all the $2J + 1$ different states, differing in orientation, have equal energy: they are degenerate.

This degeneracy in the field-free case is the same as that already mentioned for the H atom (p. 47). There we had a $2l + 1$ fold space degeneracy. Now, in the general case, J replaces l. Without field, there are consequently $2J + 1$ different eigenfunctions which belong to the same eigenvalue; with field, there are $2J + 1$ slightly different eigenvalues or energy values belonging to these $2J + 1$ different eigenfunctions.[11]

The existence of space quantization is shown most strikingly by the *Stern-Gerlach experiment* in which a beam of atoms is sent through an *inhomogeneous* magnetic field. In such a field, a body with a magnetic moment is subject, not only to a force moment tending to turn the direction of the magnetic moment into the field direction, but also to a deflecting force due to the difference in field strength at the two poles of the body. Depending on its orientation, the body will therefore be driven in the direction of increasing or decreasing field strength. Suppose we now send through

---

[11] In the field-free case, *any* linear combination of the $2J + 1$ eigenfunctions is an eigenfunction of the same energy value. The eigenfunctions *with* field will be approximately equal to those without field only when one has chosen the "correct" linear combinations of the field-free eigenfunctions that are appropriate for the problem; that is, when one has placed the z-axis of formula (I, 28) in the direction of the field.

such an inhomogeneous field atoms possessing a magnetic moment (Fig. 42). If atoms with all possible orientations to the field are present, a sharp beam should be drawn out into a band. Actually, a splitting of the beam into $2J + 1$ different beams takes place. In Fig. 42, J is assumed to be $\frac{1}{2}$ and a splitting into two beams results. This experiment shows unambiguously that in a magnetic field not all orientations to the field, but only $2J + 1$ discrete directions, are possible.

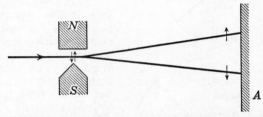

Fig. 42. Schematic Representation of the Stern-Gerlach Experiment. A beam of atoms possessing a magnetic moment ($J = \frac{1}{2}$) comes from the left, passes through an inhomogeneous magnetic field between the poles N and S, and falls on the receiving plate A. The directions of the angular momenta of the atoms are indicated by the small arrows.

It must be noted that, whereas the rigorous quantum theoretical value for the magnitude of J is $\sqrt{J(J + 1)}\, h/2\pi$ (cf. p. 88), the rigorous value for the component M of J is $M(h/2\pi)$, not $\sqrt{M(M + 1)}\, h/2\pi$. Therefore the maximum component of the vector J in the direction of the field is $J(h/2\pi)$ and not $\sqrt{J(J + 1)} \times h/2\pi$. This may at first seem rather puzzling because in classical mechanics the maximum component of a vector in a given direction is equal to the magnitude of the vector. In fact the magnitude of a vector in classical mechanics may be defined either (a) by the usual square root of the sum of the squares of the three components, or (b) as the largest value its component can have on some fixed axis. In classical mechanics, the two definitions are equivalent and hence the distinction between (a) and (b) is never made explicit. In quantum mechanics, the two are not equivalent—the magnitude being $\sqrt{J(J + 1)}\, h/2\pi$ in the sense of (a), and $J(h/2\pi)$ in the sense of (b), as stated above.

Thus in quantum mechanics the component of J is always smaller than its magnitude, which means that *the angular momentum vector cannot point exactly in the direction of the field* (fixed axis). This is illustrated on the right in Fig. 43 for $J = \frac{1}{2}$ and

$J = 1$, whereas on the left the more naive representation of Fig. 41 is given. For larger values of J the difference between the two ways of representation—that is, between definitions (a) and (b)—becomes smaller and smaller in accordance with the correspondence principle (see p. 28). For the cases where only the components of the angular momenta matter, definition (b) is sufficient even in quantum mechanics. For some calculations, however, it is necessary to use definition (a). (See below.)

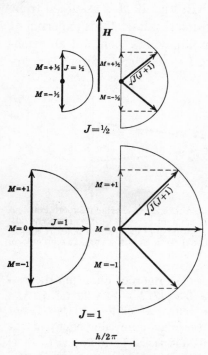

The difference between (a) and (b) in quantum mechanics is intimately connected with Heisenberg's uncertainty relation. If the angular momentum could point exactly in the direction of the field, it would of course mean that the other two components were equal to zero. As then all the three components of the angular momentum would have exact values, it follows from Heisenberg's uncertainty relation that the three corresponding co-ordinates (the angles about the x-, y-, and z-axes) are completely undetermined. This is only possible if the probability distribution is spherically symmetrical—that is, if the angular momentum is zero (^1S state; cf. p. 135). As soon as the angular momentum J is different from zero, only one of the three components p_x, p_y, p_z can have an exact value, $p_z = M(h/2\pi)$; whereas, for the other two, only the sum of the squares is known, $p_x^2 + p_y^2 = J^2 - p_z^2 = J(J + 1)(h/2\pi)^2 - M^2(h/2\pi)^2$, which can never be equal to zero.

Fig. 43. Space Quantization for $J = \frac{1}{2}$ and $J = 1$. To the left is the naive representation (see Fig. 41) taking the magnitude of the total angular momentum equal to $J(h/2\pi)$. To the right is the exact representation taking the magnitude equal to $\sqrt{J(J + 1)}\, h/2\pi$.

With increasing magnetic field strength and therefore increasing velocity of precession, J loses its meaning of angular momentum. This is similar to the previously considered case of the vectors l_i. For strong fields, only M retains a strict physical meaning, since there results what is essentially a rotation of the system about the direction of the field.

Normal Zeeman effect. The magnetic moment resulting from the revolution of a negative electric point charge is given classically by:

$$\mathbf{\mu} = -\frac{e}{2mc}\mathbf{p} \qquad (II, 9)$$

where p = angular momentum and m = mass of the charged particle. Because of the negative sign of the charge, the magnetic moment has the opposite direction to the angular momentum. For atoms, the angular momentum is $J(h/2\pi)$ [or more accurately, $\sqrt{J(J + 1)}\, h/2\pi$]. The magnitude of the magnetic moment is thus:

$$\mu = -\frac{e}{2mc}\frac{h}{2\pi}J \left[\text{or more exactly,} -\frac{e}{2mc}\frac{h}{2\pi}\sqrt{J(J + 1)} \right]$$

For $J = 1$, the magnetic moment is accordingly:

$$\mu_0 = \frac{e}{2mc}\frac{h}{2\pi}$$

which is known as the *Bohr magneton* and has the value 0.9273×10^{-20} erg oersted. The component of $\mathbf{\mu}$ in the field direction is:

$$\mathbf{\mu}_H = -\frac{e}{2mc}\frac{h}{2\pi}M \qquad (II, 10)$$

Substituting this value of $\mathbf{\mu}_H$ in (II, 7), we find that the energy in a magnetic field is:

$$W = W_0 + hoM, \quad \text{where } o = \frac{1}{2\pi}\frac{eH}{2mc} \qquad (II, 11)$$

Here o is the so-called *Larmor frequency*, which may be shown to be the frequency of precession. From (II, 11) we see that the state with smallest energy has its angular momentum antiparallel to the field direction ($M < 0$). Because of the negative sign in (II, 9), the magnetic moment is then in the field direction.

From (II, 11) it follows that terms with different J values will have different numbers of components ($2J + 1$) in a magnetic field, but that the separation of consecutive components must be the same for all terms of an atom for a given field strength. This separation is ho. If two terms combine, it may be shown theoretically (cf. below) that the selection rule for M is:

$$\Delta M = 0, \quad \pm 1 \tag{II, 12}$$

with the addition that the combination

$$M = 0 \rightarrow M = 0 \text{ is forbidden for } \Delta J = 0 \tag{II, 13}$$

Because there is equal splitting for all terms, the number of line components is always 3 since all lines with equal ΔM coincide (see Fig. 44). Lines with $\Delta M = 0$ fall in the position of the original field-free line; lines with $\Delta M = \pm 1$ lie to the right and left at a distance

$$\Delta\nu_{\text{norm}} = \frac{o}{c} = 4.6699 \times 10^{-5} \times H$$

This kind of splitting is called the *normal Zeeman effect*. It is observed *only for singlet lines* ($S = 0$). [Cf. Fig. 39(a), p. 97.]

It should perhaps be added that, for observations made in a direction perpendicular to the field, the lines with $\Delta M = 0$ are polarized parallel to the field (π-components); the lines with $\Delta M = \pm 1$, perpendicular to the field

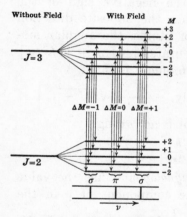

Fig. 44. Normal Zeeman Effect for a Combination $J = 3 \rightarrow J = 2$. The arrows representing the transitions form three groups (indicated by brackets). The arrows in each group have equal length and give rise, therefore, to one and the same line in the splitting pattern (lower part of figure).

(σ-components). [Cf. Fig. 39(a).] These results are in agreement with more detailed calculations, as given below.

The *selection rule for the magnetic quantum number M* will now be briefly derived, according to the methods previously mentioned (p. 51 f.), as a simple example of the wave mechanical derivation of selection rules. Let $\psi' = \chi' e^{iM'\varphi}$ and $\psi'' = \chi'' e^{iM''\varphi}$ be the eigenfunctions of the upper and lower states, respectively.

With the field direction taken as the z-axis, the dependence of the eigenfunction on the azimuthal angle φ is completely allowed for in the factor $e^{iM\varphi}$. [The form of the dependence on φ given previously for the H atom is generally true (p. 39).] Thus φ does not occur in χ. The matrix element R, associated with the transition, has components

$$\int \psi' \psi^{*''} x \, d\tau = \int \chi' \chi^{*''} e^{i(M'-M'')\varphi} x \, d\tau$$

and similarly for y and z.

We introduce co-ordinates z, ρ (distance from z-axis), and φ. Then $d\tau = \rho \, d\varphi \, dz \, d\rho$; $x = \rho \cos \varphi$; $y = \rho \sin \varphi$. Considering first the z component of the matrix element, it is:

$$\int \psi' \psi^{*''} z \, d\tau = \int\int\int \chi' \chi^{*''} e^{i(M'-M'')\varphi} z \rho \, d\varphi \, dz \, d\rho$$

$$= \int\int \chi' \chi^{*''} z \rho \, dz \, d\rho \int e^{i(M'-M'')\varphi} \, d\varphi$$

This integral is different from zero only when

$$\int_0^{2\pi} e^{i(M'-M'')\varphi} \, d\varphi$$

does not vanish. Such is the case only when $M' = M''$. Thus the z component of the transition moment will always vanish unless $M' = M''$ or, in other words, light polarized in the z direction (direction of the field) will be emitted only when the selection rule $\Delta M = M' - M'' = 0$ is obeyed.

The x component of the matrix element becomes:

$$\int \psi' \psi^{*''} x \, d\tau = \int\int\int \chi' \chi^{*''} e^{i(M'-M'')\varphi} \rho \cos \varphi \rho \, d\varphi \, dz \, d\rho$$

$$= \int\int \chi' \chi^{*''} \rho^2 \, dz \, d\rho \int e^{i(M'-M'')\varphi} \cos \varphi \, d\varphi$$

which is different from zero only if the second integral does not vanish. By using $\cos \varphi = \frac{1}{2}(e^{i\varphi} + e^{-i\varphi})$, the second integral becomes:

$$\frac{1}{2} \int e^{i(M'-M''+1)\varphi} \, d\varphi + \frac{1}{2} \int e^{i(M'-M''-1)\varphi} \, d\varphi$$

This vanishes unless the exponent in at least one of the two integrals $= 0$; that is, we have the selection rule $\Delta M = +1$ or -1. The same result is obtained for the y component. For both components of the transition moment perpendicular to the field direction, we therefore have the selection rule $\Delta M = \pm 1$. In this way we obtain not only the selection rules but also the polarization rules. The components of the splitting pattern with

$\Delta M = 0$ are polarized parallel to the field direction; those with $\Delta M = \pm 1$, perpendicular to the field direction. These results are in agreement with experiment. [Cf. Fig. 39(a).] A more detailed treatment, which we shall not discuss here, leads to the additional rule that the transition $M = 0 \rightarrow M = 0$ is forbidden for transitions with $\Delta J = 0$.

Anomalous Zeeman effect. For all lines that are not singlets, the so-called *anomalous Zeeman effect* is observed. [See Fig. 39(b) and (c), p. 97.] It consists of a splitting into many more than three components with separations that are rational multiples of the normal splitting $\Delta \nu_n$ (Runge's rule). This effect can be explained only by assuming that the magnitude of the term splittings for a given field strength is not the same for all terms but differs according to the values of L and J. We may account for this formally by replacing equation (II, 11) by:

$$W = W_0 + hoMg \qquad (\textbf{II, 14})$$

where g, which is called *Landé's g-factor*, is a rational number which depends upon J and L. It is quite obvious that, even if we retain the above selection rule $\Delta M = 0, \pm 1$, the number of line components obtained in a magnetic field will now depend upon the number of term components ($2J + 1$).

Consider, for example, the D lines of sodium, which correspond to the transitions $^2P_{1/2} \rightarrow {}^2S_{1/2}$ and $^2P_{3/2} \rightarrow {}^2S_{1/2}$. Since M has only two values for each of the terms $^2P_{1/2}$ and $^2S_{1/2}$, and has four values for $^2P_{3/2}$, it is clear that with a different g value for each of the three terms the number of components of the splitting pattern for one D line of Na will be different from that for the other. As Fig. 45 shows, we obtain four and six components, respectively, in agreement with experiment. [Cf. Fig. 39(b).] Conversely, the observed difference in the splitting patterns of D_1 and D_2 shows that the two P levels, $^2P_{1/2}$ and $^2P_{3/2}$, differ from each other in the magnitude of their total angular momentum (the orbital momentum being the same), since it is this which is space quantized. Thus J is actually to be identified with the total angular momentum, as we have already assumed in the foregoing discussion. Finally, the fact that $^2P_{1/2} \rightarrow {}^2S_{1/2}$ gives exactly four components shows that,

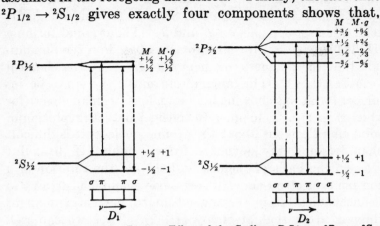

Fig. 45. **Anomalous Zeeman Effect of the Sodium D Lines, $^2P_{1/2} \rightarrow {}^2S_{1/2}$ and $^2P_{3/2} \rightarrow {}^2S_{1/2}$.** [Cf. Fig. 39 (b), p. 97.] The components designated by σ have $\Delta M = \pm 1$; those designated by π have $\Delta M = 0$. It should be noted that, contrary to Fig. 44, arrows indicating transitions with equal ΔM no longer have the same length, because of the difference in the splitting in the upper and lower states.

actually, J must be taken equal to $\frac{1}{2}$ in both cases. With no other choice of J values is it possible to obtain a splitting of each of the terms into two components. For example, if J were equal to 1 for both terms, the terms would split into three components each, and the line into six components (cf. Fig. 46). In a similar manner, the correctness of the other J values in Tables 3 and 4 can be shown (p. 73 and p. 78). Fig. 46 gives the explanation of the splitting for a $^3S_1 \rightarrow {}^3P_1$ transition, a spectrogram of which is reproduced in Fig. 39(c).

We saw above (II, 14) that the anomalous Zeeman effect

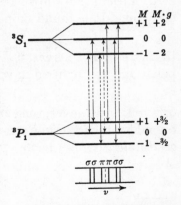

Fig. 46. **Anomalous Zeeman Splitting of a $^3S_1 \rightarrow {}^3P_1$ Transition.** [Cf. Fig. 39 (c), p. 97.] According to the selection rule (II, 13), the transition $M = 0 \rightarrow M = 0$ is forbidden, since at the same time $\Delta J = 0$. This transition is indicated by a dotted line.

can be explained formally by introducing the factor $g \neq 1$ into formula (II, 11) for the splitting of a term in a magnetic field, where g depends on L and J. The original formula (II, 11) with $g = 1$ for all terms was based on the assumption that the magnetic moment was given by the classical formula (II, 9). This assumption must, therefore, be incorrect for atoms showing an anomalous Zeeman effect (for which $g \neq 1$). So long as we consider only a revolution of point-like electrons about the atomic nucleus, it is difficult to understand any deviation from formula (II, 9). But even on the basis of the classical theory, the rotation of a non-point electron about its own axis would lead to a ratio of mechanical angular momentum to magnetic moment different from that given by (II, 9). Thus we can well imagine that the magnetic behavior of the spin of the electron is not the same as that arising from orbital motion.

The extent of the departure from the normal orbital type can be obtained, for example, when the behavior of the ground state ^2S of the alkalis in a magnetic field is considered, since in this state J results wholly from the spin of one electron. It is found empirically that, for this ^2S state,

$$\Delta W = \pm ho1$$

that is, $g = 2$; whereas, if $J = s = \frac{1}{2}$ had a normal magnetic behavior, we ought to have:

$$\Delta W = \pm ho\tfrac{1}{2}$$

or $g = 1$. However, the empirical splitting $\Delta W = ho1$ is obtained for the ^2S term if we assume that *the magnetic moment of the electron due to its spin is one whole Bohr magneton,*

$$-\frac{e}{2mc}\frac{h}{2\pi}1$$

and not

$$-\frac{e}{2mc}\frac{h}{2\pi}\frac{1}{2}$$

as would be the case if the electron behaved normally. The assumption that the electron has a magnetic moment of one whole Bohr magneton (whose direction is opposite to that of the spin), in spite of the fact that its spin is only $\frac{1}{2}h/2\pi$, was first put forward by Goudsmit and Uhlenbeck, simultaneously with the hypothesis of electron spin, and leads to a complete explanation of the splitting in all other cases as well as in the special case considered above.   It is clear that in the general case g depends on the values of L, S, and J, and will differ from the limiting values $g = 1$ for $S = 0$, and $g = 2$ for $L = 0$.   Theoretically it is found (cf. below) that the following formula holds (Landé):

$$g = 1 + \frac{J(J + 1) + S(S + 1) - L(L + 1)}{2J(J + 1)} \qquad \text{(II, 15)}$$

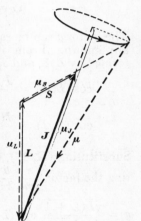

Suppose an atom has the values of L, S, and J given in Fig. 47.   The length of these vectors is proportional to $\sqrt{L(L + 1)}$, $\sqrt{S(S + 1)}$, and $\sqrt{J(J + 1)}$, respectively, if we take the rigorous formula.   The magnetic moments $\mathbf{\mu}_L$ and $\mathbf{\mu}_S$ associated with L and S are included in the same figure.   The resulting magnetic moment would lie in the direction of J if the magnetic moment $\mathbf{\mu}_S$ connected with the spin were normal, since then $\mathbf{\mu}_S/S$ would equal $\mathbf{\mu}_L/L$. Actually, the magnetic moment of the spin is twice as large as if it were normal; that is,

$$\frac{\mathbf{\mu}_S}{S} = \frac{2\mathbf{\mu}_L}{L}$$

The resultant $\mathbf{\mu}$ therefore falls, not in the direction of J, but in the direction shown, which is different from J and precesses with L and S about the direction of the total angular momentum.   Since this precession is, in general, much faster than the Larmor precession, usually only the component of $\mathbf{\mu}$ in the J direction, $\mathbf{\mu}_J$, need be considered in calculating the magnetic effect.   This is (see Fig. 47):

Fig. 47. Addition of Magnetic Moments in an Atom (in Explanation of the Landé g-formula). The length of the vector $\mathbf{\mu}_L$ is taken equal to L. Therefore $\mathbf{\mu}_S$ is double the length of S. It should be noted that the direction of the angular momentum vectors is opposite to that of the corresponding magnetic moments.

$$\mathbf{\mu}_J = \mathbf{\mu}_L \cos(L, J) + \mathbf{\mu}_S \cos(S, J) \qquad \text{(II, 16)}$$

In this,

$$\mathbf{\mu}_L = -\frac{e}{2mc} \frac{h}{2\pi} \sqrt{L(L + 1)} \qquad \text{and}$$

$$\mathbf{\mu}_S = -\frac{2e}{2mc} \frac{h}{2\pi} \sqrt{S(S + 1)} \qquad \text{(II, 17)}$$

Here the minus sign indicates, as before, that the magnetic moment has the opposite direction to the corresponding angular momentum vector.

In the calculation of the magnetic splitting, it is $\boldsymbol{\mu}_H$, the component of $\boldsymbol{\mu}_J$ in the direction of the field, which matters. In order to obtain (II, 14) instead of (II, 11) for the energy in a magnetic field, we have to replace formula (II, 10) for $\boldsymbol{\mu}_H$ formally by

$$\boldsymbol{\mu}_H = - \frac{e}{2mc} \frac{h}{2\pi} M g$$

This substitution means we have to take as definition for g

$$\boldsymbol{\mu}_J = - \frac{e}{2mc} \frac{h}{2\pi} \sqrt{J(J+1)} \, g \qquad \textbf{(II, 18)}$$

The factor g can be calculated from (II, 16) when both cos terms are known. From Fig. 47, using the obtuse-angled triangle formed by L, S, and J, we obtain, with the help of the cosine law:

$$\cos (L, J) = \frac{J(J+1) + L(L+1) - S(S+1)}{2\sqrt{J(J+1)} \sqrt{L(L+1)}}$$

$$\cos (S, J) = \frac{J(J+1) + S(S+1) - L(L+1)}{2\sqrt{J(J+1)} \sqrt{S(S+1)}} \qquad \textbf{(II, 19)}$$

Substituting (II, 17), (II, 18), and (II, 19) in (II, 16), and omitting the factor $\frac{e}{2mc} \frac{h}{2\pi}$, we find:

$$\begin{aligned}
g &= \frac{\sqrt{L(L+1)}}{\sqrt{J(J+1)}} \cos (L, J) + \frac{2\sqrt{S(S+1)}}{\sqrt{J(J+1)}} \cos (S, J) \\
&= \frac{J(J+1) + L(L+1) - S(S+1)}{2J(J+1)} \\
&\quad + \frac{2[J(J+1) + S(S+1) - L(L+1)]}{2J(J+1)} \qquad \textbf{(II, 20)}
\end{aligned}$$

This last expression shows clearly the meaning of the factor 2 in the second term. If the factor 2 were not present, that is, if the electron spin were magnetically normal, g would obviously equal 1. But, by including the factor 2, we obtain from (II, 20) the Landé formula already given in (II, 15). Thus g is a rational number which is generally different from 1, in agreement with experiment. For $J = S$ and $L = 0$, $g = 2$, a value that we have already used.

If, in the derivation of the g-formula, we had used simply $J(h/2\pi)$, $L(h/2\pi)$, $S(h/2\pi)$ for the magnitudes of the vectors, instead of the accurate quantum mechanical values, obviously a different formula would have been obtained. The fact that the Landé g-formula gives extraordinarily close agreement with experiment is further evidence of the correctness of the quantum mechanical formula for the magnitudes of the angular momentum vectors.

From (II, 15) the g values for $^2P_{1/2}$ and $^2P_{3/2}$ are $\frac{2}{3}$ and $\frac{4}{3}$. Using these values, the energy level diagram for the Zeeman splitting of the sodium D lines has been drawn in Fig. 45, and is in quantitative agreement with experiment. [Cf. Fig. 39(b).]

It might at first appear remarkable that the term $^2P_{1/2}$ shows any splitting at all. According to our earlier discussion, for $^2P_{1/2}$ the vectors L and S are in opposite directions [cf. Fig. 37, p. 89] and, since $L = 1$ and $S = \frac{1}{2}$, we would expect zero magnetic moment because of the double magnetism of S; correspondingly, no splitting should result. The above formula gives, however, $g \neq 0$. A magnetic moment will therefore be present.

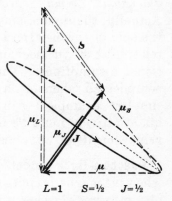

When the accurate wave mechanical values for the angular momentum vectors are taken, J, L, and S for $^2P_{1/2}$ do not fall in a straight line but produce the diagram shown in Fig. 48. It is seen that the two magnetic moments of $L = 1$ and $S = \frac{1}{2}$ do not compensate each other. When the length of L represents at the same time the magnitude of μ_L, μ_S is twice as long as S, and μ has the indicated direction and magnitude. The whole system of vectors precesses about J. The magnetic behavior depends only upon μ_J, the component of μ in the direction of J. We can easily see from Fig. 48 that μ_J is *not* zero and, correspondingly, the splitting differs from zero. The difference

$L=1 \qquad S=\frac{1}{2} \qquad J=\frac{1}{2}$

Fig. 48. Origin of the Magnetic Moment for a $^2P_{1/2}$ State. (Cf. Fig. 47.)

between the old quantum theory and the new quantum mechanics is particularly striking in this case.

The foregoing considerations have shown that when L and S in a stationary state differ from zero, the magnetic moment μ is not constant, but continually changes its direction (precesses about J). The possibility of *magnetic dipole* radiation, mentioned previously, depends on this fact.

In addition to the term splitting, the relative intensities of the individual components in the transitions can also be predicted theoretically. [Cf. Hund (7); Condon and Shortley (13).]

The line splitting will vary according to the values of J, L, and S in the upper and lower states—that is, according to the term type in the upper and lower states. Conversely, the investigation of the Zeeman effect forms a very effective means of establishing the type of term taking part in a transition. This is particularly useful for complicated line spectra. For example, it enables us to find which lines belong to a Rydberg series since they must all show the same Zeeman effect. [Further details may be found in Back and Landé (6).]

From the above discussion it is clear that the *double magnetism of the electron is fundamental to the explanation of the anomalous Zeeman effect* and phenomena related to it. Actually, the double magnetism of the electron, as well as the spin of the electron itself, may be derived from Dirac's relativistic wave mechanics without the use of any additional assumptions. The fact that such a large body of complicated phenomena (Fig. 39, p. 97, shows only the simplest examples) can be dealt with completely and quantitatively must be regarded as one of the remarkable achievements of wave mechanics.

Paschen-Back effect. With increasing field strength, when the magnetic splitting becomes greater than the multiplet splitting, Paschen and Back found that the *anomalous Zeeman effect changes over to the normal*. This has the following reason: When the magnetic splitting becomes greater than the multiplet splitting, the precessional velocity o of J in the magnetic field about the field direction becomes greater than the precessional velocity of S and L about J (see above). The resultant motion is, therefore, better described as an independent precession of S about the field direction and a similar precession of L about the field direction, the motion being somewhat disturbed by the coupling of L and S. Hence we say that L and S are *uncoupled* by the magnetic field. To a first approximation, each of these vectors is therefore space quantized in the magnetic field independently of the other with components M_L and M_S, respectively. For each value of $M_L = L,\ L-1,\ L-2,$ $\cdots,\ -L,\ M_S$ can take each of the values $S,\ S-1,\ \cdots,$ $-S$. The magnitude of the term splitting is then, to a first approximation:

$$\Delta W = ho M_L + 2ho M_S \qquad \text{(II, 21)}$$

(S has double magnetism) and is, therefore, again an integral multiple of the *normal* splitting, as in (II, 11).

For M_L, we have the same selection rules as for M, and for the same reasons as those given earlier:

$$\Delta M_L = 0,\quad \pm 1 \quad \text{(II, 22)}$$

For M_S, the following selection rule is obtained from theory:

$$\Delta M_S = 0 \qquad \text{(II, 23)}$$

Taking into account these selection rules and using (II, 21), a normal Zeeman triplet is obtained for a transition between two multiplet terms in a strong magnetic field. Fig. 49 shows this for a $^2P \rightarrow\ ^2S$ transition (for example, the D lines of Na). It should be compared with Fig. 45 (p. 107), which applies to the same transition in a weak field. In a more rigorous treatment a correction term of the form $ah M_S M_L$ must be added to ΔW in (II, 21), because of the inter-

Fig. 49. Paschen-Back Effect for a $^2P \rightarrow\ ^2S$ Transition. Here transitions with equal ΔM or ΔM_L *nearly* coincide, whereas in the normal Zeeman effect they *exactly* coincide. [Cf. Fig. 44, p. 104.] Thus, in the figure shown here, each component of the "normal" triplet has two components.

action of L and S which is naturally still present. As a result of this, each component of the normal line triplet will generally give a narrow doublet, triplet, etc., according as the original field-free transition was a doublet, triplet, etc., transition. The reason for this line splitting is apparent from Fig. 49 for the case of a doublet transition.[11a]   More com-

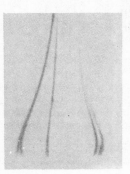

plicated splitting patterns are obtained by using intermediate fields.   [Incomplete Paschen-Back effect.   See Back and Landé (6); White (12).]

It is readily seen that the total number of term components is the same in both strong and weak fields: $(2L + 1) \times (2S + 1)$, in agreement with the Ehrenfest adiabatic law (mentioned previously).

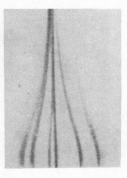

Stark effect. As Stark first discovered, *a splitting of the spectral lines* also takes place *in an electric field.* Fig. 50 illustrates the splitting of the He line λ4388 in the two directions of polarization (parallel and perpendicular to the field).   In each pattern the strength of the field increases from top to bottom.   [For experimental details, see Foster (132).]   As will be seen, the patterns are not symmetrical about the original line, in contrast to the Zeeman patterns.   The splitting of the lines in an electric field can naturally be traced to a splitting of the terms.   The relationships are, however, not quite so simple as for the Zeeman effect, and therefore the Stark effect is of no particular value as a help in the analysis of a spectrum.

Fig. 50. Stark Effect Splitting of the Helium Line λ4388 [after Foster (132)]. Above, the exposure was so made that only light polarized parallel to the field direction could reach the plate. Below, only light polarized perpendicular to the field could reach the plate. In each pattern the field increases from top to bottom.

On the other hand, apart from its intrinsic interest and as an application of quantum theory the Stark effect plays a very important part in the theories of molecule formation from atoms, of the broadening of spectral lines, and of dielectric constants.

[11a] The two components of the central "line" in this case coincide almost exactly since ahM_SM_L is zero for both upper states; but in higher approximation they would not coincide.

The components of the angular momentum J can take only the values $+ J, J - 1, J - 2, \cdots, - J$ with respect to any preferred direction. This rule holds also for the direction of an electric field. Thus *space quantization takes place also in an electric field.* If, and how, the states with different M differ from one another energetically depends upon the kind of field acting.

An electric field does not act on the magnetic moment associated with J. The result of the action of an electric field is, rather, that the atom becomes electrically polarized, as shown schematically in Fig. 51. The positively charged nucleus K becomes separated from the center of gravity S of the negative charges by an electric field E. There results an *electric dipole moment,* proportional to the field, whose magnitude depends upon the orientation of the orbit, that is, of the angular momentum J, to the field. The atom seeks to set itself in the direction of smallest energy, just as in the case of a magnetic field. Because of the gyroscopic forces, this produces a precession of J about the field direction such that the component M of J is constant (see Fig. 51). The stronger the field, the more rapid will be the velocity of precession. The energy shift is given by the product of the field strength and the dipole moment—a result analogous to that of the magnetic case.

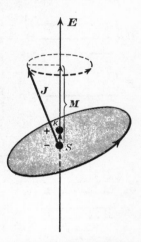

Fig. 51. Production of an Electric Dipole Moment in an Electric Field (Stark Effect) and Precession of J about the Field Direction. The shaded surface represents the orbital plane of the atom. The angular momentum vector is perpendicular to that plane.

However, since the dipole moment is itself proportional to the field strength, the term shift in the Stark effect is proportional to the *square* of the field strength. Closely connected with this relation is the fact that, in an electric field, the term components, which differ only in the sign of M, have the same energy. Obviously the dipole moment produced by the field will not be altered by reversing the direction of rotation (change from $+ M$ to $- M$), and consequently *the energy shift for $+ M$ and $- M$ is the same.* Thus there is qualitatively an essential difference between the Stark effect and the Zeeman effect. The number of term components in an electric field is therefore $J + \frac{1}{2}$ or $J + 1$, according as J is half integral or integral.

If the behavior of an atom (other than hydrogen) in an electric field is calculated according to quantum mechanics,

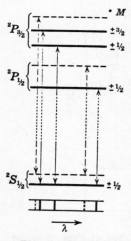

as first done by Foster (61) for the case of helium, it is found that the magnitude of the shift of the terms by an electric field depends, in a rather complicated manner, on the quantum numbers of the given atomic state and its distance from neighboring terms. In general, the component with smallest $|M|$ lies lowest (that is, $M = 0$, or $M = \pm \frac{1}{2}$).

Fig. 52 illustrates the Stark effect of the D lines of Na. This case has been thoroughly investigated experimentally and agrees closely with the accurate theoretical formulae [see Condon and Shortley (13); Ladenburg (60)]. From the illustration it may be seen that the splitting of the lines and terms is, in contrast to the Zeeman effect,

Fig. 52. Stark Effect of the D Lines of Na. Field-free terms and transitions are indicated by broken lines.

not symmetrical about the field-free positions. In the case of the D lines of Na, a shift to longer wave lengths takes place. In the case of He (cf. Fig. 50), some components are shifted to longer and some to shorter wave lengths.[12]

If the field becomes so great that the velocity of precession

---

[12] That the shift in this case is in both directions (though in general it is in only one direction) is due to the fact that, for He, a number of terms are fairly close to one another (cf. below).

about the field direction is greater than the velocity of precession of L and S about J, an *uncoupling* takes place, as in the Paschen-Back effect. L and S are then independently space quantized with respect to the field direction in such a way that the components are M_L and M_S. States with $|M_L| = L, L - 1, \cdots, 0$ have noticeably different energies. For each of these states, M_S can take the values $+ S, S - 1,$ $\cdots, - S$. When $M_L = 0$, states with different M_S do not have different energies, since no electric dipole moment can be induced in the electron itself. When $M_L \neq 0$, on the average a magnetic field in the direction of the electric field results from the precession, because of the magnetic moment associated with L. This produces, as a secondary effect, an energy difference for the states with different M_S. Fig. 53 shows these relations for a ^3D term in an energy level diagram; they are especially important in the theory of the electron structure of molecules.

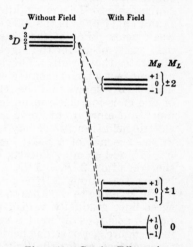

Fig. 53. Stark Effect in a Strong Electric Field for a ^3D Term (Analogous to the Paschen-Back Effect).

Although the Stark effect was first discovered for hydrogen and although it is particularly large in this case, theoretically it is more complicated because of the fact that states with different L and equal n are degenerate with one another, except for relativity and spin effects. Disregarding this last influence, Bohr's theory had already given the observed splittings both qualitatively and quantitatively. In fact, this application was one of the striking successes of Bohr's theory. Wave mechanics gives exactly the same formulae. Both theories show that a level with given n splits, in an electric field, into $2n - 1$ equidistant levels. This splitting increases linearly with field strength (*linear Stark effect*) and takes place symmetrically with respect to the field-free position of the terms. For the upper state of H_α, the total splitting amounts to 7.8 cm^{-1} for a field of 10,000 volt/cm. In the case of non-hydrogen-like atoms, the splitting is in general very much smaller.

In order to obtain theoretically the Stark effect splitting of H and H-like ions for *low* field strengths, relativity and spin effects have to be considered, and these then give an unsymmetrical splitting of the individual fine structure components.

For hydrogen, at very high field strengths a quadratic effect is superimposed on the linear effect, and results essentially in a one-sided shift of the whole splitting pattern. The experimentally observed magnitude of this effect is in agreement with wave mechanical calculations but not with the old Bohr theory [Rausch von Traubenberg (133)].

For atoms with several electrons, the *linear* Stark effect becomes important if the splitting due to the quadratic effect is comparable to the energy difference between states with different L and equal n, as is the case for H and H-like ions even for very weak fields. For atoms other than hydrogen, the linear effect may easily occur for the higher series numbers. In fact, Fig. 50 illustrates that result. This spectrogram also shows another important fact which is connected with the above. With increasing field, theory shows that the selection rule $\Delta L = \pm 1$ for the terms of one emission electron no longer holds exactly because L loses more and more its meaning as angular momentum. Thus in an electric field transitions may take place which would be forbidden in the absence of a field; for example, $S - S$, $S - D$, $P - P$, $P - F$, and so on. The He line λ4388 (Fig. 50) corresponds to the transition $2\,^1P - 5\,^1D$. But in an electric field the neighboring transitions $2\,^1P - 5\,^1P$, $5\,^1F$, $5\,^1G$ likewise take place. These give rise to the lines to the right in Fig. 50. It is seen that these lines gradually vanish toward weaker fields, and also approach positions different from the non-forbidden lines to the left in the figure. For strong fields, the whole pattern tends to become symmetrical, as for the hydrogen-like spectra, because then the splitting is large compared with the separation between $5\,^1P$, ^1D, ^1F, ^1G.

In certain cases the fields due to ions present in a discharge, or even interatomic fields, are sufficient to cause the appearance of such forbidden transitions (cf. also Chapter IV).

Statistical weight. There is no means of further splitting the individual term components present in a magnetic field.[13] They must therefore be regarded as actually simple —that is, no longer degenerate. These different states are

[13] Here it is assumed that the degeneracy between states with different l but equal n for H atoms and H-like ions has already been removed—for instance, by an electric field.

ascribed the same *a priori probability,* or the same *statistical weight;* that is, it is assumed that they will appear equally often under the same conditions. This assumption has always been found to be correct.

As the magnetic field grows weaker and weaker, naturally the equality of the statistical weights of the individual term components does not change. For the limiting case $H \to 0$, groups of such term components coincide. The resultant term which is thus formed has a statistical weight that is as many times larger than the weight of a simple term as the term itself has components in a magnetic field. Hence, if we take the statistical weight of a simple term equal to 1, then *the term with angular momentum J has a statistical weight* $2J + 1$, since this is the number of simple term components of which it consists in a magnetic field—and, therefore, also in the absence of a magnetic field—corresponding to the different possible orientations of J. More generally expressed, the statistical weight of a term is equal to its *degree of degeneracy.*[14]

For two states with different J values, J_1 and J_2, the probability that the atom will be found in one of these states is given by the ratio $(2J_1 + 1) : (2J_2 + 1)$. This is true if the states in question have approximately equal energies so that their Boltzmann factors $e^{-E/kT}$ are equal.

However, not all degeneracies are removed by an *electric* field. Terms with equal positive and negative M have equal energy. Thus, with the exception of $M = 0$, each term in an electric field is doubly degenerate—that is, it still has a statistical weight 2.

An important alteration in the absolute value of the statistical weight results from nuclear spin, and will be discussed further in Chapter V.

Among other applications, statistical weights are of importance in the calculation of the intensities of spectral lines (see Chapter IV), of the specific heat of gases, and of chemical constants.

---

[14] In wave mechanical terms, the statistical weight is, accordingly, equal to the number of independent eigenfunctions belonging to a given energy value.

CHAPTER III

The Building-Up Principle and the Periodic System of the Elements

1. The Pauli Principle and the Building-Up Principle

We have previously considered the terms of atoms with several electrons—in particular, those with several emission electrons. We shall now treat this topic in greater detail and investigate how the energy level diagram and the ground state of any atom can be theoretically derived.

Quantum numbers of the electrons in an atom. A single electron moving in a spherically symmetrical but non-Coulomb field of force (for example, the emission electron of an alkali) can always be characterized by two quantum numbers, the *principal quantum number n* and the *azimuthal quantum number l*. According to quantum mechanics, n can be considered as an approximate measure of the extent of the region in which the electron preferably remains. Different values of n (1, 2, 3, $\cdots$) correspond to widely different energy values. l gives the angular momentum of the electron in its orbit and, for a given value of n, can take all integral values from 0 to $n - 1$. The energy difference between states with different l and equal n is, in general, not so great as that between states with different n. The possible states of an electron can thus be divided into principal groups or levels which differ from one another in their n values, and into sub-groups or sub-levels which have a given n but different l values. This division is clearly indicated in the energy level diagram of lithium (Fig. 24, p. 57). Even for given n and l values, several different states of an electron are possible: first, due to the various possible orientations of the vector l (for example, in a magnetic field), and, second, due to the electron spin $s = \frac{1}{2}$ which can

120

set parallel or antiparallel to a magnetic field (for example, that of l).

In an atom with *several* electrons, the motion of each individual electron can also be regarded, to a first approximation, as a motion in a centrally symmetric but non-Coulomb field of force. This field results from the overlapping of the Coulomb field of the nucleus and the mean field of the other electrons. Therefore, to this approximation a definite value of n and l can also be ascribed to each electron in a complicated atom. The approximation will be particularly good when we are considering a single electron with large n, as is usually the case for most of the higher terms of an atom (terms of an emission electron). Then the action of the remaining electrons may really be described, to a close approximation, as due to their mean field. In contrast to this, if we are dealing with a number of electrons which have equal n and are thus approximately equidistant from the nucleus, taking a mean field gives a relatively poor approximation, since the action of the other electrons on a given electron is strongly dependent on their *momentary* positions. In this case, the field in which the given electron moves can, in general, no longer be considered (even approximately) to be centrally symmetric and the quantum numbers n and l have no longer any exactly definable meaning. In spite of this, they can still be used to obtain the number and type of the terms, on account of the adiabatic law (see Chapter II, section 2).

The *normal state of an atom* is that state in which all the electrons are in the lowest possible orbits. The lowest possible orbit of a single electron in a centrally symmetric field is the $1s$ orbit $(n = 1, l = 0)$, which is also called the K shell. Accordingly, one might perhaps think that, for the normal state of uranium, all the 92 electrons are in this K shell, and analogously for all other atoms. However, such a conclusion can easily be shown to be incorrect; for, if the electron configuration of the ground state of an atom altered regularly with the atomic number, it would obviously be quite impossible to explain the *observed periodicity* of the chemical and spectroscopic properties of the elements. Furthermore, according to this assumption, the ground state of any atom would have to be an S state, which is not the case according to the analysis of the different spectra. For example, B and Al have a ^2P state for the ground state. We have already noted that, in the case of Li, all three electrons are not in the K shell; one (the emission electron) is in a 2s orbit (L_1 shell, $n = 2$, $l = 0$), as can be concluded from a comparison of the Li spectrum with those of Li-like ions (cf. Chapter I, section 5).

Pauli principle. In order to understand the building-up of the periodic system and the periodicity in the properties of the atoms and in their energy level diagrams, we must introduce a new assumption. This is the *Pauli exclusion principle*, which prevents the filling of the various shells with an arbitrary number of electrons. To formulate the principle conveniently, let us imagine the atom to be brought into a very strong magnetic field, which is so strong that not only is the normal Paschen-Back effect operative (uncoupling of L and S), but also the different l_i and the different s_i are uncoupled from one another in such a way that all the l_i and all the s_i are space quantized independently of one another in the direction of the field. That is, for each single electron, the components of l in the direction of the field can take one of the values $m_l = l, l - 1, l - 2,$ $\cdots, -l$, whereas the components of s can take one of the values $m_s = \pm \frac{1}{2}$. The number of possible states, with which we are concerned here, will not be altered by the assumption of a strong magnetic field.

Pauli's principle now states: *In one and the same atom, no two electrons can have the same set of values for the four quantum numbers n, l, m_l, and m_s.*[1]

---

[1] The same conclusions will result if, instead of assuming an extremely strong field, we assume that the interactions between the individual electrons are so reduced that even a weak field produces the independent space quantization of the l_i and the s_i. Moreover, instead of the four quantum numbers n, l,

It follows that only a limited number of electrons can have the same set of values for the quantum numbers n and l. The detailed meaning of this fact will become clear in the following discussion.

The Pauli principle does not result from the fundamentals of quantum mechanics, but is an assumption which, although it fits very well into quantum mechanics, cannot for the time being be theoretically justified.

If $\psi(x_1 y_1 z_1, \cdots, x_n y_n z_n)$ is the eigenfunction of a system containing n electrons, generalizing our previous considerations, we obtain

$$\psi\psi^* \, dx_1 \, dy_1 \cdots dz_n$$

for the probability of finding the system in a configuration with the coordinates of the individual electrons within the limits x_1 and $x_1 + dx_1$, y_1 and $y_1 + dy_1$, $\cdots$, z_n and $z_n + dz_n$. Since there is no way of distinguishing individual electrons, $\psi\psi^*$ must be independent of the numbering of the electrons. Therefore, if any two electrons are exchanged (exchange of the corresponding indices in $\psi\psi^*$), $\psi\psi^* = |\psi|^2$ must remain unaltered. Such is the case either if ψ itself is unaltered or if it simply changes sign; that is, ψ must be symmetric or antisymmetric with respect to an exchange of any two electrons. [For a more rigorous proof, see Condon and Shortley (13); cf. also p. 67.]

The quantum mechanical formulation of the Pauli principle is: *The total eigenfunction of an atom with several electrons must be antisymmetric in all its electrons.* That is, of the two systems of states mentioned above, only the one which is antisymmetric actually occurs. It may be shown that this formulation is identical with the statement of the principle given above.

At first it would appear to follow from this quantum mechanical formulation of the Pauli principle that, of the two term systems of He previously considered, only the antisymmetric, to which the ground state does *not* belong, could occur (Chapter I, section 6).

---

m_l, and m_s, we can also use the quantum numbers n, l, j, and m_j, where j is the total angular momentum of a single electron (that is, $j = l \pm \frac{1}{2}$) and m_j is the component of j in the direction of a field ($m_j = j, j - 1, \cdots, -j$). See Chapter IV. We can easily show that this gives the same number of possible states for an electron; with $n = 2$ and $l = 1$, it gives the following states:

j	$\frac{1}{2}$	$\frac{3}{2}$
m_j	$-\frac{1}{2}, +\frac{1}{2}$	$-\frac{3}{2}, -\frac{1}{2}, +\frac{1}{2}, +\frac{3}{2}$

There are thus six states (see p. 127).

The assumption of electron spin is necessary to explain the fact that actually *both* systems occur. If the spin is included, the total eigenfunction is obtained by combining the hitherto considered total eigenfunction ψ (*co-ordinate function*) with a further eigenfunction β, the *spin eigenfunction*. To a first approximation, the new total eigenfunction $\psi' = \psi \cdot \beta$. Let β^+ be the spin function of a single electron with the spin directed upward, and β^-, correspondingly, the spin function of an electron with the spin directed downward—that is, if the spin was originally directed upward, $|\beta^+|^2$ gives the probability of finding the values $+\frac{1}{2}$ or $-\frac{1}{2}$ for the spin of the electron in any given direction; similarly, if the spin was originally directed downward, the probability will be $|\beta^-|^2$. Consequently there are the following four possibilities for the total spin function of the two electrons 1 and 2:

$$\uparrow\uparrow \quad \beta_1^+\beta_2^+$$
$$\uparrow\downarrow \quad \beta_1^+\beta_2^-$$
$$\downarrow\uparrow \quad \beta_1^-\beta_2^+$$
$$\downarrow\downarrow \quad \beta_1^-\beta_2^-$$

In a magnetic field such as that associated with l, the states represented by the first and fourth eigenfunctions have different energies, which are also different from those of the second and third, although the latter are degenerate with each other. If the mutual interaction of the two spins is taken into account, a splitting of the originally degenerate states into two different states with eigenfunctions $\beta_1^+\beta_2^- + \beta_1^-\beta_2^+$ and $\beta_1^+\beta_2^- - \beta_1^-\beta_2^+$ occurs. This effect is quite analogous to the Heisenberg resonance phenomenon (Chapter I, section 6). We therefore have the following four spin functions of the two electrons:

$$\beta_I = \beta_1^+\beta_2^+$$
$$\beta_{II} = \beta_1^+\beta_2^- + \beta_1^-\beta_2^+$$
$$\beta_{III} = \beta_1^+\beta_2^- - \beta_1^-\beta_2^+$$
$$\beta_{IV} = \beta_1^-\beta_2^-$$

Only one of these eigenfunctions is antisymmetric in the electrons—namely, β_{III}; the others are symmetric. However, the *total eigenfunction* $\psi' = \psi \cdot \beta$ can now (and this is the important point) be antisymmetric for both term systems—that with symmetric as well as that with antisymmetric ψ. We have only to recall that the product of a symmetric and an antisymmetric eigenfunction is antisymmetric, whereas the product of two symmetric or of two antisymmetric functions is symmetric. Then, if the one antisymmetric β is combined with the symmetric ψ, or if one of the three symmetric β's is combined with the antisymmetric ψ, the total eigenfunction ψ' will be antisymmetric; that is, according to the Pauli principle, both term systems can actually appear. (See Table 8.)

TABLE 8

SYMMETRY OF THE EIGENFUNCTIONS OF HELIUM

ψ Co-ordinate Function	β Spin Function	ψ' Total Eigenfunction	Term System
Symmetric	Symmetric Antisymmetric	Symmetric Antisymmetric	(Does not occur) Singlet system
Antisymmetric	Symmetric Antisymmetric	Antisymmetric Symmetric	Triplet system (Does not occur)

The term system whose co-ordinate function is symmetric has a statistical weight of 1 (only *one* spin function β_{III} belongs to it, singlets); the system with antisymmetric co-ordinate function has a weight of 3 (*three* spin functions, triplets). The former corresponds to $S = 0$; the latter, to $S = 1$. The three symmetric spin functions correspond to the three possible orientations $M_S = +1, 0, -1$, of the spin vector $S = 1$ in an external magnetic field or in the field due to the orbital motion when $L \neq 0$.

The occurrence of both term systems is thus entirely due to the existence of spin. However, the latter has nothing to do with their energy difference. This already exists for the co-ordinate functions, without considering spin, and results from the electrostatic interaction of the electrons (see Chapter I, section 6).

The different multiplet systems of atoms with more than two electrons may be obtained by analogous, though more complex, considerations. [Hund in (1d); Condon and Shortley (13).]

Prohibition of intercombinations. A total prohibition of intercombinations exists between states with antisymmetric *total* eigenfunction ψ' and states with symmetric total eigenfunction. This can be shown in the same manner as in Chapter I, section 6. If an atom is once in an antisymmetric state, it must remain in that state for all time. The fact that Pauli's exclusion principle holds for all atoms proves that they are all in the states with antisymmetric total eigenfunction. Transitions to states with *symmetric* total eigenfunction never take place; hence these states do not occur.

The prohibition of transitions between states with symmetric and antisymmetric *co-ordinate* functions ψ_s and ψ_a (the prohibition of transitions between states of different multiplicity) holds only approximately—that is, so long as it is possible to use the separation $\psi' = \psi \cdot \beta$, since then the matrix element R^{nm} (p. 53) can be separated into two factors, one of which depends only upon ψ. The latter factor, as we have seen, is zero for a transition between states with symmetric and antisymmetric ψ, and thus the complete transition probability is zero. As soon as the coupling between spin and orbital angular momentum becomes appreciable, such a separation $\psi' = \psi \cdot \beta$ is no longer strictly possible, and therefore R^{nm} no longer splits into two factors, one of which becomes zero for a combination between two terms of different multiplicities. The smallness of the multiplet splitting shows that the coupling between spin and orbital angular momentum is weak for elements with low atomic number. Consequently the rule prohibiting intercombinations holds almost absolutely for them $(\Delta S = 0)$. With increasing atomic number, it holds less rigorously.

Application of the Pauli principle. Table 9 shows, for the possible states of an electron in an atom, the divisions into groups and sub-groups up to $n = 4$ (cf. scheme, p. 39). The order given is, in general, the energy order of the states. Each of the before-mentioned sub-groups with given n and l is once more subdivided according to the value of m_l. All of the latter sub sub-groups of states have the same energy for a given n and given l value in the absence of a magnetic field. Actually, each of these values (given n, l, m_l) should be once more subdivided into two sub-groups with $m_s = +\frac{1}{2}$ and $m_s = -\frac{1}{2}$. For the sake of simplicity, this subdivision is not carried out in Table 9. Instead, the presence of an electron in a *cell* (n, l, m_l) is represented by an arrow whose direction (up or down) indicates whether m_s is $+\frac{1}{2}$ or $-\frac{1}{2}$. On the basis of the Pauli principle, only two electrons can be in each such cell (n, l, m_l), and then only when they have antiparallel spin directions, since otherwise these two electrons would have the same four quantum numbers n, l, m_l, m_s.

The number of electrons in a sub-group (n, l) is given by the exponent of the symbol representing the sub-group. For example, $(2p)^2$ or $2p^2$ represents two $2p$ electrons. The maximum number of electrons which can have the same n and l and yet not violate the Pauli principle is given by the number of arrows in Table 9 between the corresponding

TABLE 9

POSSIBLE STATES OF AN ELECTRON

	K	L				M									N															
n	1	2				3									4															
l	0	0	1			0	1			2					0	1			2					3						
	s	s	p			s	p			d					s	p			d					f						
m_l	0	0	-1	0	+1	0	-1	0	+1	-2	-1	0	+1	+2	0	-1	0	+1	-2	-1	0	+1	+2	-3	-2	-1	0	+1	+2	+3
m_s	↑↓	↑↓	↑↓	↑↓	↑↓	↑↓	↑↓	↑↓	↑↓	↑↓	↑↓	↑↓	↑↓	↑↓	↑↓	↑↓	↑↓	↑↓	↑↓	↑↓	↑↓	↑↓	↑↓	↑↓	↑↓	↑↓	↑↓	↑↓	↑↓	↑↓
	K	L_1	L_2			M_1	M_2			M_3					N_1	N_2			N_3					N_4						

vertical lines. This maximum number is obviously equal to $2(2l + 1)$, since $2l + 1$ is the number of possible m_l values for a given l. The entrance of any additional electron into such a sub-group (n, l) is forbidden by the Pauli principle, since the additional electron would then necessarily have the same m_l and m_s as one of the electrons already present. When a sub-group or shell contains the maximum number of electrons, it is called a *closed shell*.

The *ground state of an atom* is the one in which all electrons are in the lowest possible energy states. On the basis of the Pauli principle, this is not $(1s)^N$, where N is the total number of electrons, but it is the state in which all the lower shells are filled only so far as the Pauli principle allows. Thus in the ground state not all of the electrons are equivalent; rather, they can be differentiated as *inner* and *outer* electrons. Excited states of an atom result, in general, when the outermost and least firmly bound electron (emission electron) is raised to any of the higher orbits or levels. There are also excited states in which two or more of the outer electrons are simultaneously in higher orbits, or in which one of the inner electrons is raised to an outer orbit (see Chapter IV). However, such states are observed relatively seldom in the optical line spectra of the lighter atoms, but are found more often in the spectra of the heavier elements.

The terms of an atom of nuclear charge $Z + 1$ may be obtained in the following way: the nuclear charge Z of the preceding element in the periodic table in its ground state (or perhaps also in an excited state) is increased by 1, and then an additional electron is added to one of the shells not yet filled. Beginning with hydrogen, the terms of all the elements in the periodic system can be derived in this way (Bohr, Mainsmith-Stoner). The principle underlying this procedure is called the *building-up principle*. It is clear that the electron configurations of the ground states will show a *periodicity*, since, after a certain number of electrons have been added, the outermost electron will be once more, for example, an *s*-electron. Correspondingly, the other configurations of the outer electrons recur periodically.

2. Determination of the Term Type from the Electron Configuration

The above method gives us only the electron configuration (*n* and *l* values of the individual electrons); thus far it does not tell us the term type of the ground state and the excited states. The term type is obtained by adding together the respective angular momentum vectors *l* and *s* of the individual electrons. For this purpose it is necessary to make some definite assumptions about the mutual coupling or interaction of the individual angular momentum vectors.

Russell-Saunders coupling. The assumption that seems to apply to most cases is the *Russell-Saunders coupling*, which we have already used implicitly in the preceding chapter. In this coupling it is assumed that, when several electrons are present in an atom, each with a definite l_i and each with $s_i = \frac{1}{2}$, the individual l_i vectors are so strongly coupled with one another that states with different resultant *L* have very different energies. Further, it is assumed that the individual s_i vectors are so strongly coupled with one another that states with different resultant *S* have a considerable energy difference. As explained in Chapter II, for strongly coupled vectors, only the resultant (in this case

L or S) has an exact meaning as angular momentum. The vectors that are strongly coupled with one another must always be added together first. The resultants L and S, according to the Russell-Saunders coupling, are then less strongly coupled with one another and their resultant is J. Each allowable value of L can be combined with each possible S; that is, the spins can take all orientations which are possible on the quantum theory for each state characterized by a definite value of L. The interaction between L and S gives the multiplet splitting of each term, which without this interaction would be simple.

The Russell-Saunders coupling can be written symbolically:

$$(s_1, s_2, \cdots)(l_1, l_2, \cdots) = (S, L) = J \qquad \text{(III, 1)}$$

It should be noted here that the considerable difference between the energy levels of corresponding terms of different multiplicity (different S) is actually due, not to a strong magnetic interaction of the respective s_i, but to the Coulomb interaction of the electrons and the Heisenberg resonance phenomenon (p. 66), which is entirely independent of spin. The spin merely makes possible the actual appearance of the different term systems (p. 124). In spite of this we can proceed, in practice, *as though* the energy difference were due to the magnetic interaction of the spins.

In Chapter IV we shall consider still another kind of coupling of the individual angular momentum vectors which occurs for heavy elements.

Terms of non-equivalent electrons. Non-equivalent electrons are electrons belonging to different (n, l) subgroups (cf. Table 9). In order to determine the terms resulting from two non-equivalent electrons, we must, first of all, find the possible values of the resultant L. In the case of a p-electron and a d-electron, $L = 3, 2, 1$ (cf. p. 87); that is, the two electrons form F, D, and P terms. The spins of the two electrons can be either parallel or antiparallel. S is therefore 1 or 0, which means that triplet as well as singlet terms result. In all, there will be six terms: ^1P, ^1D, ^1F, ^3P, ^3D, ^3F. Similarly, two non-equivalent p-electrons give the terms: ^1S, ^1P, ^1D, ^3S, ^3P, ^3D.

If a third non-equivalent electron is added, its l must be added vectorially to the previously calculated L; and s must similarly be added to S. If, for example, an s-electron is added to pd, the L values remain the same. The possible S values are now $\frac{1}{2}$, $\frac{1}{2}$, $\frac{3}{2}$; that is, the possible terms are: ^2P, ^2D, ^2F, ^2P, ^2D, ^2F, ^4P, ^4D, ^4F. Two different doublet terms for each L will be formed, since p-electrons and d-electrons with parallel as well as antiparallel spins can give $S = \frac{1}{2}$ with the addition of an s-electron. On the other hand, $S = \frac{3}{2}$ can be obtained in only one way—namely, when all three spins are parallel to one another (quartet). The three spin configurations for $s\,p\,d$ are $\uparrow\downarrow\uparrow$, $\downarrow\uparrow\uparrow$, $\uparrow\uparrow\uparrow$. If the third electron that is added is an f-electron ($l = 3$), the possible L values are $3 \mp 1, 3 \mp 2, 3 \mp 3$ (where the sign $\mp$ indicates vector addition). This gives the following L values: 2, 3, 4; 1, 2, 3, 4, 5; 0, 1, 2, 3, 4, 5　6. As before, the possible S values are $\frac{1}{2}$, $\frac{1}{2}$, $\frac{3}{2}$. Thus we obtain: $^2S(2)$, $^2P(4)$, $^2D(6)$, $^2F(6)$, $^2G(6)$, $^2H(4)$, $^2I(2)$, $^4S(1)$, $^4P(2)$, $^4D(3)$, $^4F(3)$, $^4G(3)$, $^4H(2)$, $^4I(1)$, where the numbers in parentheses indicate the number of the corresponding terms. For example, $^4P(2)$ means two ^4P terms. Even in the above comparatively simple case the total number of terms belonging to the same electron configuration (pdf) is considerable.

These and other examples are given in Table 10 (p. 132).

Terms of equivalent electrons. When we are dealing with equivalent electrons (having the same n and the same l), some of the terms derived for non-equivalent electrons are no longer possible. For example, for two equivalent p-electrons (p^2), not all the terms (^1S, ^1P, ^1D, ^3S, ^3P, ^3D) previously derived for two non-equivalent p-electrons are possible. In considering non-equivalent electrons, we assumed that no account need be taken of the Pauli principle in adding together the individual l and s values; it was supposed that each orientation allowed by the quantum theory did actually occur. This assumption is in fact justified, since, when the electrons have different n or l values, the Pauli principle is already satisfied. When, however, the two electrons have equal n and equal l, that is, when they are equivalent, they must at least differ in their values of m_l or m_s. When, for example, the two p-electrons (p^2) both have l with the same direction, which gives a D term, m_l is the same for both ($+ 1, 0$, or $- 1$) and therefore, according to Pauli's principle, the two electrons cannot both have $m_s = + \frac{1}{2}$, or both $m_s = - \frac{1}{2}$. That is, their spins can only be antiparallel for a D term, giving ^1D only, and ^3D is not possible, although it would be with non-equivalent electrons. Further consideration shows that two equivalent p-electrons give only the terms ^1S, ^3P, ^1D (see below). Similarly, three equivalent p-electrons give ^4S, ^2P, ^2D. These and additional examples are given in Table 11 (p. 132).

Particular mention should be made of *closed shells*—that is, shells in which the maximum number of equivalent electrons is present. In order to fulfill the Pauli principle, all the electrons must be in antiparallel pairs ($S = 0$). In addition, $L = 0$, since the state can be realized in only one way in a magnetic field—namely, with $M_L = \sum m_l = 0$. *Therefore, a closed shell always forms a $^1S_0$ state.*

In deriving the terms of an electron configuration that consists of one or more closed shells and a few additional electrons (for example, $2p^6\, 3s^2\, 3p^3$), the closed shells can be left entirely out of consideration. The terms are the same as for the electrons that are not in closed shells; for, in determining the resultant L and S, the respective l_i can be added together in any desired groups to form partial resultants, and these can be added together to give the total resultant. Since the partial resultants for closed shells are zero, they have no influence on the total resultant.

From the latter statement the following may be derived: the term $^1S_0$ for a closed shell must result when the shell is divided into two parts, the term types for each part derived, and the resulting angular momentum vectors added together. For example, adding the angular momenta of the terms of p^2 vectorially to the corresponding quantities for p^4 must give those for a $p^6\, ^1S_0$ state, that is, zero. From this it follows that the quantum numbers S and L must be the same for these two electron configurations; that is, the terms of the configuration p^4 are the same as those of p^2. This result can also be obtained directly (see Table 11). Generalizing, we can say that *the terms of a configuration x^q are the same as the terms of a configuration x^{r-q} where r is*

the maximum number of x-electrons, that is, $2(2l + 1)$.
(See p. 127.)   For example, the terms of p^5 are the same as
those of p; they give only one ^2P term; or, the terms of d^7
are the same as those of d^3 given in Table 11.

TABLE 10

TERMS OF NON-EQUIVALENT ELECTRONS

Electron Configuration	Terms
$s\,s$	$^1S,\ ^3S$
$s\,p$	$^1P,\ ^3P$
$s\,d$	$^1D,\ ^3D$
$p\,p$	$^1S,\ ^1P,\ ^1D,\ ^3S,\ ^3P,\ ^3D$
$p\,d$	$^1P,\ ^1D,\ ^1F,\ ^3P,\ ^3D,\ ^3F$
$d\,d$	$^1S,\ ^1P,\ ^1D,\ ^1F,\ ^1G,\ ^3S,\ ^3P,\ ^3D,\ ^3F,\ ^3G$
$s\,s\,s$	$^2S,\ ^2S,\ ^4S$
$s\,s\,p$	$^2P,\ ^2P,\ ^4P$
$s\,s\,d$	$^2D,\ ^2D,\ ^4D$
$s\,p\,p$	$^2S,\ ^2P,\ ^2D,\ ^2S,\ ^2P,\ ^2D,\ ^4S,\ ^4P,\ ^4D$
$s\,p\,d$	$^2P,\ ^2D,\ ^2F,\ ^2P,\ ^2D,\ ^2F,\ ^4P,\ ^4D,\ ^4F$
$p\,p\,p$	$^2S(2),\ ^2P(6),\ ^2D(4),\ ^2F(2),\ ^4S(1),\ ^4P(3),\ ^4D(2),\ ^4F(1)$
$p\,p\,d$	$^2S(2),\ ^2P(4),\ ^2D(6),\ ^2F(4),\ ^2G(2),\ ^4S(1),\ ^4P(2),\ ^4D(3),\ ^4F(2),$ $^4G(1)$
$p\,d\,f$	$^2S(2),\ ^2P(4),\ ^2D(6),\ ^2F(6),\ ^2G(6),\ ^2H(4),\ ^2I(2)$ $^4S(1),\ ^4P(2),\ ^4D(3),\ ^4F(3),\ ^4G(3),\ ^4H(2),\ ^4I(1)$

TABLE 11

TERMS OF EQUIVALENT ELECTRONS

Electron Configuration	Terms
s^2	^1S
p^2	$^1S,\ ^1D,\ ^3P$
p^3	$^2P,\ ^2D,\ ^4S$
p^4	$^1S,\ ^1D,\ ^3P$
p^5	^2P
p^6	^1S
d^2	$^1S,\ ^1D,\ ^1G,\ ^3P,\ ^3F$
d^3	$^2P,\ ^2D(2),\ ^2F,\ ^2G,\ ^2H,\ ^4P,\ ^4F$
d^4	$^1S(2),\ ^1D(2),\ ^1F,\ ^1G(2),\ ^1I,\ ^3P(2),\ ^3D,\ ^3F(2),\ ^3G,\ ^3H,\ ^5D$
d^5	$^2S,\ ^2P,\ ^2D(3),\ ^2F(2),\ ^2G(2),\ ^2H,\ ^2I,\ ^4P,\ ^4D,\ ^4F,\ ^4G,\ ^6S$

We shall now derive, in greater detail, the terms of equivalent electrons for a special case. According to the adiabatic law already used, we should be able to derive all possible terms by using any desired alteration of the coupling conditions. In the Paschen-Back effect, L and S are space quantized with respect to the field direction, independently of each other, with components $M_L = L, L - 1, \cdots, - L$, and $M_S = S, S - 1, \cdots, - S$. M_L and M_S represent the components of the total orbital and spin momenta in the field direction. On the other hand, for complete uncoupling of the individual electrons from one another, the individual l_i and s_i are space quantized with components $m_l = l, l - 1, l - 2, \cdots, - l$, and $m_s = \pm \frac{1}{2}$. Under these coupling conditions $\sum m_l$ and $\sum m_s$ represent, respectively, the components of the total orbital and spin angular momenta in the field direction. Therefore, according to the adiabatic law, $\sum m_l$ must equal M_L, and $\sum m_s$ must equal M_S, for all the configurations which the electrons under consideration are allowed, according to the Pauli principle, to assume in the cells of Table 9. Exactly the same M_L and M_S must be obtained as from the L and S values of the resulting terms, and, conversely, these may be derived from the calculated $\sum m_l$ and $\sum m_s$ values.

Table 12 gives the possible configurations for the case of two equivalent p-electrons,[2] as well as the corresponding values $\sum m_l = M_L$ and $\sum m_s = M_S$ (see p. 134).

In order to determine the resulting terms, it is useful to begin with the highest value of $\sum m_l = M_L$, which must be equal to the highest occurring value of L. In the present case, the highest value of M_L is 2 and thus a D term results. Since this M_L occurs only with $M_S = 0$, the term is ^1D. Apart from $M_L = 2$, $M_L = + 1, 0, - 1, - 2$ also belong to this term, each having $M_S = 0$. They are indicated by $\triangle$ in the last column of Table 12. There are two terms each with $M_L = \pm 1$, $M_S = 0$, and three with $M_L = 0$, $M_S = 0$. Which of them is selected for the components of the ^1D term is of no special importance for this derivation. Of the remaining M_L and M_S values, the maximum M_L is $+ 1$ and the largest M_S is $+ 1$. These values must belong to a ^3P term, since only for such a term can the largest values of M_L and M_S be $+ 1$. $M_L = 0$ and $- 1$ also belong to this ^3P term, each of the M_L values having $M_S = + 1, 0, - 1$. Altogether, for ^3P we obtain nine configurations. In Table 12, these are marked $+$. One configuration remains: $M_L = 0$, $M_S = 0$; this is indicated by $\times$. It can give only a ^1S term. Thus, *two*

---

[2] It must be noted that, because of the identity of electrons, the configuration $\uparrow \downarrow$ in a single cell is not different from $\downarrow \uparrow$; whereas, if the two electrons are in different cells, the configuration $\uparrow \downarrow$ is different from $\downarrow \uparrow$. Only the various states—not the electrons themselves—can be identified. This assumption may be considered a supplement to Pauli's principle [cf. Slater (134)].

equivalent p-electrons give the terms ^1D, ^3P, ^1S *and no others.*
The terms of the other configurations listed in Table 11 may be
derived in a similar manner.

TABLE 12

DERIVATION OF TERMS FOR TWO EQUIVALENT p-ELECTRONS

m_l			$\Sigma m_l = M_L$	$\Sigma m_s = M_S$	
$+1$	0	-1			
↑↓			$+2$	0	△
↑	↑		$+1$	$+1$	$+$
↑	↓		$+1$	0	△
↓	↑		$+1$	0	$+$
↓	↓		$+1$	-1	$+$
↑		↑	0	$+1$	$+$
↑		↓	0	0	△
↓		↑	0	0	$+$
↓		↓	0	-1	$+$
	↑↓		0	0	×
	↑	↑	-1	$+1$	$+$
	↑	↓	-1	0	△
	↓	↑	-1	0	$+$
	↓	↓	-1	-1	$+$
		↑↓	-2	0	△

A procedure similar to the one outlined here for equivalent
electrons can also be followed in the case of non-equivalent electrons. However, the method previously used (p. 129) is much
simpler.

If we have a configuration containing equivalent as well as non-
equivalent electrons (for example, p^3sd) the corresponding partial
resultants must be taken from Tables 10 and 11. These are then
added together to give a total resultant in which each term of one
partial configuration (p^3 in the example) is combined with each
term of the other (sd in the example). In general a large number
of terms result. In the above relatively simple example, there
are 28 terms: $^2S(2)$, $^2P(4)$, $^2D(5)$, $^2F(4)$, $^2G(2)$, ^4S, $^4P(2)$, $^4D(4)$,
$^4F(2)$, ^4G, ^6D.

The angular momenta l and s of the individual electrons
have a well-defined meaning only when they influence one
another but slightly (in principle, not at all). If this were
actually the case, all terms with the same electron configu-

ration would have the same energy (cf. p. 83).   Actually
they have not.   In many cases, considerable energy differences occur; these are larger, the larger the interaction.

In this connection two rules operate.   The first was
formulated by Hund: *Of the terms given by equivalent electrons, those with greatest multiplicity lie deepest, and of these
the lowest is that with the greatest L.*   For the cases given in
Table 11, this term is the last one in each line.   The
second rule states: *Multiplets formed from equivalent electrons are regular when less than half the shell is occupied,
but inverted when more than half the shell is occupied.*   For a
proof of this rule, the reader is referred to Condon and
Shortley (13).

Electron distribution with a number of electrons present.
It has already been stated that, when a number of electrons
are present in an atom, the wave mechanical charge distribution is given, to a first approximation, by a superposition
of the charge distributions of the individual electrons (cf.
Fig. 21, p. 44).   It is clear that superposition of the electron distributions of s-electrons, each having a spherically
symmetrical charge distribution, must give a spherically
symmetrical total charge distribution for the resulting S
term.   A more detailed wave mechanical calculation shows
that S terms resulting from somewhat more complicated
electron configurations (possibly containing p-electrons and
d-electrons) also have a spherically symmetrical charge
distribution.   This holds in particular for closed shells,
which always give $^1S_0$ terms; the spherical symmetry holds
rigorously for these shells, even when the interaction of the
electrons is taken into exact account.

The more accurate wave mechanical calculation of the
charge distribution for atoms with a number of electrons is
too complicated to be further considered here.   The Hartree method of self-consistent fields has shown itself to be
particularly useful, but likewise will not be dealt with here.

In Fig. 54 are given the results of such calculations for the *radial charge distribution* curves for the ground states of the Li$^+$, Na$^+$, and K$^+$ ions. Since these ions have closed shells only, the charge distribution will be completely described by the curves. The distribution for the ground state of the hydrogen atom is given (drawn to the same scale) for comparison. Fig. 54 corresponds in all details to the solid curves of Fig. 20 (p. 43). The summation of $r^2\psi_r^2$ over all electrons, $\sum r^2\psi_r^2$, is indicated here; whereas, in Fig. 20, $r^2\psi_r^2$ was drawn, since only one electron was present. The curves in Fig. 54 thus give the mean charge distribution (that is, the sum of the probability densities of

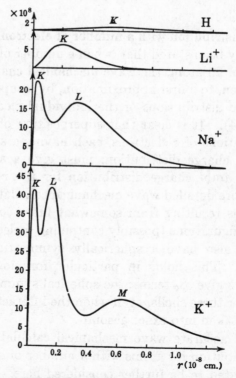

Fig. 54. Radial Charge Distribution for the Ground States of H, Li$^+$, Na$^+$, K$^+$. The curves for Na$^+$ and K$^+$ are drawn according to the work of Hartree and his co-workers (62) and (63); the curve for Li$^+$, according to Pauling and Goudsmit (9). All curves are drawn to the same scale.

the individual electrons) for the given ions, referred to the whole spherical shell of radius r. The charge distribution has pronounced maxima at certain distances from the nucleus. For Li+, there is only one maximum, corresponding to the one closed shell ($n = 1$, K shell). The mean distance of the electrons from the nucleus is 0.28 Å, which is considerably smaller than for the H atom (0.79 Å) because of the greater nuclear charge. At the same time the height of the maximum is greater. This difference is due to the fact that the eigenfunctions have naturally been so *normalized* that the probability of finding an electron somewhere in the atom is equal to the number of electrons; that is, the area under the curves (Fig. 54) must be equal to the number of electrons. In the case of *one* electron, the probability $= 1$.[3] Thus, owing to the contraction in the direction of the abscissae and the increase in the number of electrons, the height of the curves must increase with increasing Z. In the case of Na+ there are two maxima, the first of which is mainly due to the electrons in the K shell, and the second to the closed L shell ($n = 2$). Because of much higher nuclear charge, the mean distance of the K electrons from the nucleus is only 0.07 Å; that of the L electrons, 0.41 Å. K+ shows still another maximum, due to the additional M shell. For the electrons of the M shell, the mean distance is 0.82 Å. The maxima for the K and L shells are again pushed farther inward. Corresponding results are obtained when still more shells are added (Rb+ and Cs+).

It is seen that we can also speak of a *shell structure of the atom* from the wave mechanical viewpoint. Such a state of affairs holds for all atoms and ions. However, the distribu-

---

[3] The normalization is generally so carried out that $\int r^2 \psi_r^2 \, dr = 1$, and not $4\pi \int r^2 \psi_r^2 \, dr = 1$ (where $4\pi r^2 \, dr$ = volume of spherical shell). The factor 4π is introduced into the normalization of the directional part of the eigenfunction. Therefore, for one electron the function $\psi\psi^*$ averaged over the different directions in space is equal to $\frac{1}{4\pi} \psi_r^2$. Thus, we can also say that the curves in Fig. 54 represent $4\pi r^2 \Sigma \psi\psi^*$.

tion of most of the electrons that are not in closed shells is not spherically symmetrical, but is similar to the electron distributions for a single electron given in Fig. 21, p. 44.

3. The Periodic System of the Elements

The electron configurations and the term types of the ground states for all the elements of the periodic system are given in Table 13, pages 140–141 (cf. Table 9).

H (hydrogen). The lowest orbit of the one electron of the H atom is a $1s$ orbit. The ground state is therefore a $^2S_{1/2}$ state. The higher states correspond to the various other pairs of n and l values. They are, according to the value of l, ^2S, ^2P, ^2D, $\cdots$ states. However, for equal n, the states nearly coincide (see Chapter I). The spectrum is a *doublet spectrum*, since $S = s = \frac{1}{2}$. The same is true for He^+, Li^{++}, and so on, except that the terms are 4, 9, $\cdots$ times larger.

He (helium). This element has a nuclear charge 2 and can have 2 electrons. On the basis of the Pauli principle, both electrons can go into the K shell ($n = 1$) only when they have antiparallel spin directions ($\uparrow\downarrow$), since, if the spins were parallel, all four quantum numbers would be the same for the two electrons ($n = 1$, $l = 0$, $m_l = 0$, $m_s = +\frac{1}{2}$). Therefore, in the ground state $S = 0$, and, since both electrons are $1s$ electrons, $L = 0$. Thus the ground state is a ^1S state (closed shell). A triplet state is not given by this electron configuration. An excited state results when an electron (the emission electron) goes to a higher orbit. Then both electrons can have, in addition, the same spin direction; that is, we can have $S = 1$ as well as $S = 0$. Excited triplet and singlet states are possible (orthohelium and parhelium). The lowest triplet state has the electron configuration $1s2s$; it is a $2\,^3S_1$ state. It is the metastable state already referred to (p. 65). The corresponding singlet state is $2\,^1S_0$ and lies somewhat higher.

We can easily see how the two term systems of helium are obtained in this way (cf. Fig. 27, p. 65).

Li (lithium). If an electron with $n = 1$ is added to the helium-like Li^+ ion, this electron would have the same four quantum numbers as one of the electrons already present. This is forbidden by the Pauli principle. The K shell is thus complete with two electrons, and with it also the first period of the periodic system. The third electron can only go into the next shell ($n = 2, l = 0$), or to a still higher shell (see Table 9, p. 127). The Li terms are doublet terms, like those of hydrogen, since $S = s = \frac{1}{2}$. The ground state ($1s^2 2s$) is a $^2S_{1/2}$ term. In the first excited state the emission electron has $n = 2$, $l = 1$ (Table 13); a ^2P state results. The combination of this state with the ground state gives the red resonance line of Li (a doublet like the D lines of Na). The principal quantum number n does not alter in this transition, which according to page 51 is allowed.

Sometimes the electron configuration is written in front of the term symbol in order to give a more accurate representation of the term of an atom containing a number of electrons; for example, for the term just discussed, $1s^2 2p$ ^2P.

Be (beryllium). In the lowest state of the next element, beryllium, the additional electron can have the same quantum numbers $n = 2$, $l = 0$, $m_l = 0$, as the electron previously added in the case of Li, but must then have opposite spin. The ground state of Be is thus ^1S, since all the electrons have $l = 0$ and form pairs (closed shells only). According to the Pauli principle, a corresponding ^3S state (two electrons with parallel spins) does not exist. However, just as soon as one of the outer electrons has quantum numbers n, l different from those of the other, its spin can be either parallel or antiparallel to that of the other. Thus there is a triplet term corresponding to each higher singlet term (for example, $1s^2 2s 3d$ ^3D, ^1D), analogous to He. The L value of the term is equal to the l value of the outermost electron. The singlet and triplet line series ordinarily

TABLE 13

ELECTRON CONFIGURATIONS AND TERM TYPES FOR THE GROUND STATES OF THE ELEMENTS

(Numbers and symbols in parentheses are uncertain.)

Element	K	L		M			N				O					Ground Term
	1s	2s	2p	3s	3p	3d	4s	4p	4d	4f	5s	5p	5d	5f	5g	
1. H	1															$^2S_{1/2}$
2. He	2															$^1S_0$
3. Li	2	1														$^2S_{1/2}$
4. Be	2	2														$^1S_0$
5. B	2	2	1													$^2P_{1/2}$
6. C	2	2	2													$^3P_0$
7. N	2	2	3													$^4S_{3/2}$
8. O	2	2	4													$^3P_2$
9. F	2	2	5													$^2P_{3/2}$
10. Ne	2	2	6													$^1S_0$
11. Na	2	2	6	1												$^2S_{1/2}$
12. Mg	2	2	6	2												$^1S_0$
13. Al	2	2	6	2	1											$^2P_{1/2}$
14. Si	2	2	6	2	2											$^3P_0$
15. P	2	2	6	2	3											$^4S_{3/2}$
16. S	2	2	6	2	4											$^3P_2$
17. Cl	2	2	6	2	5											$^2P_{3/2}$
18. A	2	2	6	2	6											$^1S_0$
19. K	2	2	6	2	6		1									$^2S_{1/2}$
20. Ca	2	2	6	2	6		2									$^1S_0$
21. Sc	2	2	6	2	6	1	2									$^2D_{3/2}$
22. Ti	2	2	6	2	6	2	2									$^3F_2$
23. V	2	2	6	2	6	3	2									$^4F_{3/2}$
24. Cr	2	2	6	2	6	5	1									$^7S_3$
25. Mn	2	2	6	2	6	5	2									$^6S_{5/2}$
26. Fe	2	2	6	2	6	6	2									$^5D_4$
27. Co	2	2	6	2	6	7	2									$^4F_{9/2}$
28. Ni	2	2	6	2	6	8	2									$^3F_4$
29. Cu	2	2	6	2	6	10	1									$^2S_{1/2}$
30. Zn	2	2	6	2	6	10	2									$^1S_0$
31. Ga	2	2	6	2	6	10	2	1								$^2P_{1/2}$
32. Ge	2	2	6	2	6	10	2	2								$^3P_0$
33. As	2	2	6	2	6	10	2	3								$^4S_{3/2}$
34. Se	2	2	6	2	6	10	2	4								$^3P_2$
35. Br	2	2	6	2	6	10	2	5								$^2P_{3/2}$
36. Kr	2	2	6	2	6	10	2	6								$^1S_0$
37. Rb	2	2	6	2	6	10	2	6			1					$^2S_{1/2}$
38. Sr	2	2	6	2	6	10	2	6			2					$^1S_0$
39. Y	2	2	6	2	6	10	2	6	1		2					$^2D_{3/2}$
40. Zr	2	2	6	2	6	10	2	6	2		2					$^3F_2$
41. Cb	2	2	6	2	6	10	2	6	4		1					$^6D_{1/2}$
42. Mo	2	2	6	2	6	10	2	6	5		1					$^7S_3$
43. Ma	2	2	6	2	6	10	2	6	(5)		(2)					$(^6S_{5/2})$
44. Ru	2	2	6	2	6	10	2	6	7		1					$^5F_5$
45. Rh	2	2	6	2	6	10	2	6	8		1					$^4F_{9/2}$
46. Pd	2	2	6	2	6	10	2	6	10							$^1S_0$
47. Ag	2	2	6	2	6	10	2	6	10		1					$^2S_{1/2}$
48. Cd	2	2	6	2	6	10	2	6	10		2					$^1S_0$
49. In	2	2	6	2	6	10	2	6	10		2	1				$^2P_{1/2}$
50. Sn	2	2	6	2	6	10	2	6	10		2	2				$^3P_0$
51. Sb	2	2	6	2	6	10	2	6	10		2	3				$^4S_{3/2}$
52. Te	2	2	6	2	6	10	2	6	10		2	4				$^3P_2$
53. I	2	2	6	2	6	10	2	6	10		2	5				$^2P_{3/2}$
54. Xe	2	2	6	2	6	10	2	6	10		2	6				$^1S_0$
	2	8		18												

140

TABLE 13 (*Continued*)

ELECTRON CONFIGURATIONS AND TERM TYPES FOR THE GROUND STATES OF THE ELEMENTS

(Numbers and symbols in parentheses are uncertain.)

Element	K	L	M	N				O					P						Q	Ground Term
				4s	4p	4d	4f	5s	5p	5d	5f	5g	6s	6p	6d	6f	6g	6h	7...	
55. Cs	2	8	18	2	6	10		2	6				1							$^2S_{1/2}$
56. Ba	2	8	18	2	6	10		2	6				2							$^1S_0$
57. La	2	8	18	2	6	10		2	6	1			2							$^2D_{3.2}$
58. Ce	2	8	18	2	6	10	(1)	2	6	(1)			(2)							$(^3H_4)$
59. Pr	2	8	18	2	6	10	(2)	2	6	(1)			(2)							(^4K)
60. Nd	2	8	18	2	6	10	(3)	2	6	(1)			(2)							(^5L)
61. Il	2	8	18	2	6	10	(4)	2	6	(1)			(2)							(^6L)
62. Sm	2	8	18	2	6	10	6	2	6				2							$^7F_0$
63. Eu	2	8	18	2	6	10	7	2	6				2							$^8S_{7/2}$
64. Gd	2	8	18	2	6	10	7	2	6	1			2							^9D
65. Tb	2	8	18	2	6	10	(8)	2	6	(1)			(2)							(^8H)
66. Dy	2	8	18	2	6	10	(9)	2	6	(1)			(2)							(^7K)
67. Ho	2	8	18	2	6	10	(10)	2	6	(1)			(2)							(^6L)
68. Er	2	8	18	2	6	10	(11)	2	6	(1)			(2)							(^5L)
69. Tm	2	8	18	2	6	10	13	2	6				2							$^2F_{7/2}$
70. Yb	2	8	18	2	6	10	14	2	6				2							$^1S_0$
71. Lu	2	8	18	2	6	10	14	2	6	1			2							$^2D_{3/2}$
72. Hf	2	8	18	2	6	10	14	2	6	2			2							$^3F_2$
73. Ta	2	8	18	2	6	10	14	2	6	3			2							$^4F_{3/2}$
74. W	2	8	18	2	6	10	14	2	6	4			2							$^5D_0$
75. Re	2	8	18	2	6	10	14	2	6	5			2							$^6S_{5/2}$
76. Os	2	8	18	2	6	10	14	2	6	6			2							$^5D_4$
77. Ir	2	8	18	2	6	10	14	2	6	7			2							^4F
78. Pt	2	8	18	2	6	10	14	2	6	9			1							$^3D_3$
79. Au	2	8	18	2	6	10	14	2	6	10			1							$^2S_{1/2}$
80. Hg	2	8	18	2	6	10	14	2	6	10			2							$^1S_0$
81. Tl	2	8	18	2	6	10	14	2	6	10			2	1						$^2P_{1/2}$
82. Pb	2	8	18	2	6	10	14	2	6	10			2	2						$^3P_0$
83. Bi	2	8	18	2	6	10	14	2	6	10			2	3						$^4S_{3/2}$
84. Po	2	8	18	2	6	10	14	2	6	10			2	4						$^3P_2$
85. —	2	8	18	2	6	10	14	2	6	10			2	5						$^2P_{3/2}$
86. Rn	2	8	18	2	6	10	14	2	6	10			2	6						$^1S_0$
87. —	2	8	18	2	6	10	14	2	6	10			2	6					1	$^2S_{1/2}$
88. Ra	2	8	18	2	6	10	14	2	6	10			2	6					2	$^1S_0$
89. Ac	2	8	18	2	6	10	14	2	6	10			2	6	(1)				(2)	$(^2D_{3/2})$
90. Th	2	8	18	2	6	10	14	2	6	10			2	6	(2)				(2)	$(^3F_2)$
91. Pa	2	8	18	2	6	10	14	2	6	10			2	6	(3)				(2)	$(^4F_{3/2})$
92. U	2	8	18	2	6	10	14	2	6	10			2	6	(4)				(2)	$(^5D_0)$

observed (see Chapter I) result from transitions of this emission electron. There can also occur terms for which both outer electrons are in orbits other than the lowest ($n = 2$, $l = 0$). Under these circumstances several terms will, in general, result from a given electron configuration (see section 2 of this chapter). These are the so-called anomalous terms of the alkaline earths, which cannot be arranged in the normal term sequences. (Cf. also Chapter IV —particularly Fig. 61, in which the complete energy level diagram for Be is reproduced.)

B (boron). Again on the basis of the Pauli principle, the fifth electron cannot be added to the so-called L_1 shell ($n = 2$, $l = 0$), but must be added at least to the L_2 shell with $n = 2$, $l = 1$ (cf. Table 9, p. 127). Since all the electrons of boron (except that in the L_2 shell) form pairs (closed shells), a doublet spectrum is normally produced. The ground state is ^2P (not ^2S, as for Li), since now $L = l = 1$. Otherwise the energy level diagram is similar to that for Li. (Cf. the energy level diagram of aluminum in Fig. 73, p. 198, which is quite similar to that of boron.) However, boron can also have terms in which only one electron is in the $2s$ shell, and the other two are in the $2p$ shell or higher orbits. Then all three outer electrons can have parallel spins; that is, S can be $\frac{3}{2}$. Quartet terms and also anomalous doublet terms result. Up to the present time, these quartet terms have not been observed for B, although they are known for C^+, which has the same number of electrons as B, and for Al [Paschen (64)].

C (carbon). In the lowest state of carbon, two electrons are in the $2p$ shell ($l = 1$). According to the preceding section, this gives three terms: ^3P, ^1D, ^1S; of these ^3P is the lowest and is therefore the ground state of the C atom. The ^1D and ^1S terms do not lie very far above the ground state, since they belong to the same electron configuration.

When one of the two emission electrons of the C atom goes from the $2p$ orbit to a higher orbit, normal series of singlet and triplet terms result. The number of term series is, however, much greater than for boron and the preceding elements in the periodic system, since now several terms can result for each electron configuration (Table 10). Fig. 55 gives the energy level diagram for C I, so far as it is known. It is drawn in a manner which differs from that of the preceding energy level diagrams because of the presence of different terms belonging to the same electron configuration. Terms belonging to the configurations $1s^2 2s^2 2p \, np$ ($n = 2$, 3, $\cdots$), $2p \, ns$ ($n = 3$, 4, $\cdots$), and $2p \, nd$ ($n = 3$, 4, $\cdots$)

are placed under one another, with the singlet terms indicated to the left and the triplet terms to the right. When necessary, terms of the same electron configuration are bracketed together. We see from the figure that, for example, six terms result for $2p\,np$ if $n > 2$ (cf. Table 10), and these draw closer together as n increases (cf. p. 84). Apart from these normal terms, additional relatively low-lying terms are possible, which result when an electron is brought from the 2s shell (which is complete in the ground state) to the $2p$ shell, for example, $1s^2 2s 2p^3$. In the energetically lowest term of this configuration all four outer electrons have parallel spins and the result is a $^5S_2$ term,

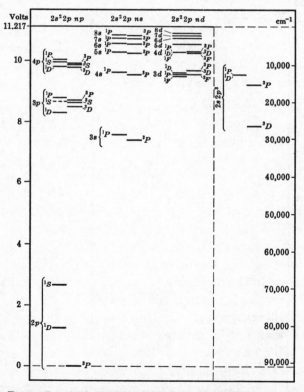

Fig. 55.   **Energy Level Diagram for C I.**   The unobserved $3p\ ^1S$ term is indicated with a dotted line.

which has thus far not been observed. Other terms of the same configuration are represented to the right in Fig. 55.

N (nitrogen). The succeeding element, nitrogen, in its lowest electron configuration has three electrons in the L_2 shell ($2p^3$). According to Table 11, these give the terms ^4S, ^2D, ^2P; of these, according to the Hund rule (p. 135),

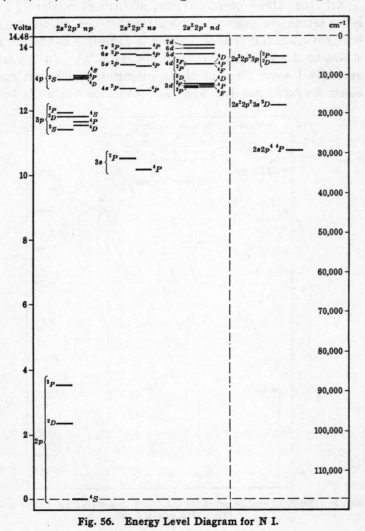

Fig. 56. Energy Level Diagram for N I.

^4S lies lowest and is therefore the ground state of the N atom, in agreement with experiment. In this state all the three $2p$ electrons have parallel spins. Higher excited states result when one electron goes from the $2p$ orbit to a higher orbit. Series of quartet and doublet terms are thereby produced; and the number of term series is again, as with carbon, much larger than for Li.

Fig. 56 represents the N I energy level diagram in a manner similar to that of the C I diagram, Fig. 55. A few terms, drawn to the right of the dotted line, do not go to the normal series limit (cf. Chapter IV). In addition, a term ^4P for which one electron is brought from the $2s$ shell to the $2p$ shell is indicated. If an electron goes from the $2s$ shell to higher orbits, sextet terms can result, since the five electrons can then have parallel spins. Such terms have not yet been observed for N I.

O (oxygen). The lowest possible orbit for the added electron in the case of oxygen is $2p$; hence four equivalent $2p$ electrons are present, and produce the terms ^3P, ^1D, ^1S, just as for carbon (Table 11, p. 132). Again, ^3P is the lowest and is the ground state for oxygen. According to the Pauli principle, the spins of the four outer electrons can never all be parallel in the $2p$ shell. They can, however, all be parallel when one electron is brought from the $2p$ shell into higher shells, and then excited quintet terms, as well as singlet and triplet terms, are formed. The oxygen lines lying in the visible region are combinations of these quintet terms. The energy level diagram of the oxygen atom will be treated in detail in the next chapter (cf. Fig. 59, p. 163).

F (fluorine). For this element, one electron is lacking to complete the L_2 shell. The ground term is therefore the same as for boron with its one electron in the L_2 shell, namely ^2P. The difference now is only that the ^2P ground term of F is an inverted term ($^2P_{3/2}$ lies lower than $^2P_{1/2}$), whereas the ground term for B is regular. This ^2P

term is the sole low-lying term of fluorine. For all other terms, the principal quantum number of at least one electron is raised. Excited doublet and quartet terms then result (cf. the energy level diagram of Cl, Fig. 74, p. 199).

Ne (neon). This element has six $2p$ electrons, and for it the L_2 shell and also the whole L shell are filled. As a result, the ground state is $^1S_0$ (cf. He and Be). Excited states result when one electron goes from the L_2 shell to a higher orbit. As in the case of helium, the energy necessary for this transition is very great, since the principal quantum number must be altered. In addition, for a single electron in an orbit with $n \geqq 3$, the nuclear charge is almost completely shielded by the nearly complete inner L_2 shell, and hence the excited terms are rather hydrogen-like; whereas, for the electrons in the closed $2p$ shell (ground state), the nuclear charge is much less completely shielded, and therefore the ground state lies considerably lower than the corresponding hydrogen term $n = 2$ (cf. Chapter VI). In fact, it actually lies lower than the hydrogen term $n = 1$. The large first excitation potential, together with the term type of the ground state (^1S), *is responsible for the character of an inert gas* (Chapter VI). The excited states of Ne are singlet and triplet states, as for He.

Succeeding periods of the periodic system. On the basis of the Pauli principle, after eight electrons have been added (Ne), no more electrons can enter the L shell, since any additional electron would necessarily have the same four quantum numbers as one of the electrons already present (cf. Table 9, p. 127). The eleventh electron must therefore go into the M shell (with $n = 3$). The lowest possible state has $l = 0$. The ground state of the element Na (with nuclear charge 11) is therefore $1s^2 2s^2 2p^6 3s\ ^2S_{1/2}$. Apart from the insertion of the L shell ($2s^2 2p^6$) and the alteration in principal quantum number, this is exactly the same as for Li.

We understand from the preceding discussion the fundamental reason why the *second* period of the periodic system is completed with Ne (cf. Table 13, p. 140).

As already stated, the number of terms and the term types are not altered by a closed shell. This fact, together with the Pauli principle which first made possible the concept of a closed shell, provides the essential basis for the theoretical explanation of the periodicity of the properties of the chemical elements (cf. Chapter VI, section 3).

Apart from the altered principal quantum number and the built-in closed L shell, the eight elements (Na, Mg, Al, Si, P, S, Cl, A) following Ne have exactly the same electron configurations in the ground state as have the preceding eight elements. According to the building-up principle, the excited states should also be quite analogous, except for a slight difference introduced by the possibility of excitation to a d level without change in principal quantum number. All this is in full agreement with experiment. For the terms of these elements, we need only refer to Table 13.

At argon, the M_1 and M_2 shells ($n = 3$, $l = 0$, 1) are filled; but it can be seen from Table 9 that the whole M shell is not filled at this stage, since l can also be 2. For $l = 2$ (M_3 shell), $m_l = + 2, + 1, 0, - 1, - 2$, and hence there can be ten electrons in the M_3 shell. However, as the argon spectrum shows, the energy necessary to bring an electron from the M_2 shell to the M_3 shell is very great— even somewhat greater than that required to bring an electron into the N_1 shell (4s orbit). The latter, that is, the first excitation potential of argon, is also considerable (11.5 volts), and this, together with the fact that the ground state is a ^1S state, makes argon an inert gas (see above). If another electron is added with a corresponding increase in nuclear charge, it goes into a 4s orbit, since according to the evidence of the argon spectrum the 4s orbit lies lower than 3d. This explains the early occurrence in the periodic system of another alkali metal, namely K, with a ground state ^2S. Thus the third period, as well as the second, contains only eight elements.

For Ca, two electrons are in the 4s orbit. Ca corresponds to Mg, which has two 3s electrons. If after Ca the building-up process should go on as after Mg, we would expect the next electron to enter the 4p shell. But the spectra show

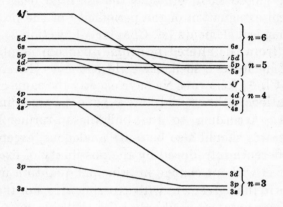

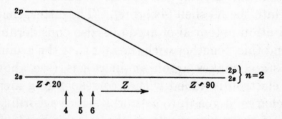

Fig. 57. Rough Representation of the Energies of the Shells for Different Nuclear Charge Z (to Explain the Filling Up of Inner Shells). The arrows at the bottom of the figure (numbered 4, 5, and 6) point to the values of Z at which the fourth, fifth, and sixth periods of the periodic system begin.

that, for the succeeding elements (Sc to Ni), the $3d$ shell is first filled (cf. Table 13). The reason for this is explained in Fig. 57. The energy of the different shells ($n \geqq 2$) is given here very roughly for small (~ 20) and large (~ 90) nuclear charge Z, with a correspondingly altered scale. For large Z, the shells with the same principal quantum number lie relatively close to one another; whereas, with decreasing Z, the field becomes less and less hydrogen-like (particularly for the outer shells) and consequently shells with the same n separate from one another (indicated by the connecting lines), until in some cases they are no longer grouped together.

For example, with small Z, the $3d$ shell lies somewhat above the $4s$ shell (see above). With increasing Z, the $3d$ shell tends to be lower; eventually it is lower than the $4s$ shell. This happens first when $Z = 21$, and therefore the $3d$ shell (M_2) is first filled for the elements following Ca (cf. Table 13). At the same time the $4s$ shell does not always remain filled with two electrons; for example, the Cr I spectrum shows that the lowest term ($^7S_3$), formed from $3d^54s$, is lower than the lowest term from $3d^44s^2$, because of the not very different heights of the $3d$ and $4s$ shells. In the same way the $3d^{10}4s \, ^2S$ term for Cu lies lower than the $3d^94s^2 \, ^2D$ term. Thus the $3d$ shell is completely filled for the ground state ^2S of Cu. In this state Cu, having one s-electron outside the closed shells, is similar to the alkalis. This similarity is in agreement with the common form of the periodic system in which Cu is placed in the alkali column. The succeeding elements (Zn, Ga, Ge, As, Se, Br) have electron configurations and energy level diagrams analogous to those in the second and third periods, apart from an altered principal quantum number for the outer electrons and an additional closed $3p^63d^{10}$ shell (cf. Table 13). The $4s$ and $4p$ shells are completed at Kr, and this ends the first long period of the periodic system with its $(10 + 8)$ elements.

Now the performance begins again, just as at the beginning of the first long period. When more electrons are added with a corresponding increase of nuclear charge, it is not (as might be expected) the 4d or 4f shells that are first filled, but rather the 5s shell, which lies lower for these nuclear charges (cf. Fig. 57). This gives the elements Rb and Sr. The 4d shell lying at about the same height as the 5s shell is then filled for the succeeding elements, Y to Pd (similar to the 3d shell). When this is completed, the next lowest shells, the 5s and 5p shells (see Fig. 57), are filled, and give the elements Ag to Xe, which correspond exactly to the elements Cu to Kr. This completes the fifth period, or second long period, with (10 + 8) elements.

The inner 4f shell is still unoccupied (see Table 13 and Fig. 57). The 4f shell is first occupied after the 6s shell has been broken into by Cs and Ba, and the 5d shell by La. The rare earths then follow, exactly 14 in number, this being the maximum number of electrons in the 4f shell. When this is filled, the 5d shell is filled from Lu to Pt, and then the 6s and 6p shells. The resulting elements, Au to Rn, correspond once more to the elements Cu to Kr. With Rn, the sixth period of the periodic system with its $32 (= 8 + 10 + 14)$ elements is completed. The elements following from the unknown element 87 to uranium correspond to the first elements of the fourth, fifth, and sixth periods. The elements for which a *building-up of inner shells* takes place are grouped within dotted lines in Table 13.[4]

Inert gases (except for He) always occur with the closing of an s^2p^6 group, as seen from Table 13. For $n > 2$, inert

---

[4] It should be noted that the elements Y to Pd do not correspond exactly to the elements Sc to Ni (although in both cases a d shell is built up), since, owing to the approximately equal heights of the s and d shells under consideration (3d and 4s : 4d and 5s), a sort of competition occurs between the two which leads to different results for different principal quantum numbers. Consequently the ground terms are not always completely analogous to one another. For example, the ground state of Pd is the $4d^{10}\, {}^1S_0$ state, whereas the ground state for Ni occurring one period (18 elements) earlier is $3d^8 4s^2\, {}^3F$. This corresponds to the chemical behavior. The elements of these columns of the periodic table have by no means such similar properties as have, for example, the halogens or the alkalis.

gases do *not* follow the completion of a *whole* shell with a given value of n, because of the fact that the d orbits lie considerably higher than the s and p orbits for the same value of n—in fact, just about as high as the s and p orbits having n one higher (see Fig. 57). On account of this, the excitation potential for closed s and p shells is large (inert gases), whereas it is small for elements for which a whole shell with $n > 2$ is filled (for example, Pd, no inert-gas character).

The order of the different *inner* shells for an element of high atomic number is normal (Fig. 57, right). For example, when electrons are added one after another to the lowest possible orbits for a uranium nucleus ($Z = 92$), the nineteenth electron comes into a $3d$ orbit and not into a $4s$ orbit, as with K ($Z = 19$). The normal order for the nineteenth electron is already reached by Sc ($Z = 21$). This is shown by the second spark spectrum of Sc, which has a ^2D state for its ground state and not a ^2S state; that is, the outermost electron (the nineteenth) is here a d-electron and not an s-electron (and similarly in other cases).

A more detailed discussion of the periodic system is given in the following books: Grotrian (8); Pauling-Goudsmit (9); White (12). It has, however, been made quite clear that *the whole periodic system of the elements can be unambiguously derived by using the building-up principle in conjunction with the Pauli principle.* The length of the long and short periods is given exactly, together with the existence of the rare earths, which had previously appeared to contradict the periodicity. The rare earths correspond to the building-up of an inner shell, similar to the Fe, Pd, and Pt groups.

CHAPTER IV

Finer Details of Atomic Spectra

1. Intensities of Spectral Lines

The intensity of an *emission* spectrum line corresponding to the transition from n to m is given by the product:

$$W^{nm}h\nu'_{nm}$$

where W^{nm} is the number of transitions taking place per second in the light source, and $h\nu'_{nm}$ is the energy of the radiated quantum. W^{nm} is the product of N_n, the number of atoms in the initial state n, and A^{nm} the number of transitions per second of an atom. A^{nm} is the so-called *Einstein transition probability*. Thus a knowledge of the two magnitudes A^{nm} and N_n is important in the calculation of intensities.

The intensity of *absorption* for the transition m to n (that is, the absorbed energy per unit time of the frequency ν'_{nm}) is:

$$N_m B^{nm} h\nu'_{nm}\rho_\nu$$

where N_m is the number of molecules in the initial state m, ρ_ν is the radiation density of the frequency ν'_{nm}, and B^{nm} is the transition probability for absorption.

The transition probability for absorption is proportional to the transition probability for emission. According to Einstein, we have:

$$B^{nm} = \frac{c^3}{8\pi h\nu'^3_{nm}} \cdot \frac{g_n}{g_m} \cdot A^{nm} \qquad \textbf{(IV, 1)}$$

where g_n and g_m are the statistical weights of the states n and m.

The transition probabilities can be calculated, according to wave mechanics, from the eigenfunctions belonging to the atomic states taking part in the transition (see p. 52).

From these eigenfunctions can also be obtained the *selection rules*, which will be summarized in the following.

General selection rules (dipole radiation). The selection rule for the total angular momentum [1] is $\Delta J = 0, \pm 1$, with the restriction that $J = 0 \nleftrightarrow J = 0$ ($\nleftrightarrow$ means "cannot combine with"). This holds for any type of coupling (see section 3 of this chapter). For the component M of J in a preferred direction (for example, the direction of a magnetic field), the following rule holds: $\Delta M = 0, \pm 1$, with the restriction that $M = 0 \nleftrightarrow M = 0$ for $\Delta J = 0$ (see p. 104). For Russell-Saunders coupling, which holds at least approximately in the great majority of cases and which we have always used above, $\Delta S = 0$ (prohibition of intercombinations, p. 94). Under the same conditions, the selection rule for the orbital angular momentum L is $\Delta L = 0, \pm 1$. At the same time, Δl must be ± 1 for the electron making the quantum jump (see p. 85).

Special selection rules (dipole radiation). Transitions in which the quantum numbers of only one electron change are always by far the most intense. *Transitions in which two or more electrons jump at the same time are considerably weaker* but are not forbidden by any strict selection rule. In order to formulate the selection rules for such transitions, it is useful to divide the terms of an atom into *even* and *odd* terms, according as $\sum l_i$ is even or odd. The summation is to extend over all the electrons of the atom. The odd terms are distinguished from the even by a superior o added to the term symbol, or sometimes the subscripts g ($= gerade$, meaning "even") and u ($= ungerade$, meaning "odd") are used. For example, the ground state of the O atom, $1s^2 2s^2 2p^4\ ^3P$, is an even state, and may be written simply ^3P or sometimes ^3P_g. The ground state of the N atom, $1s^2 2s^2 2p^3\ ^4S_{3/2}$, is an odd state, and may be written $^4S^o_{3/2}$ or $^4S_{3/2u}$.

The division of the terms into odd and even has the following wave mechanical meaning. As indicated before, the number of nodal surfaces which go through the origin of co-ordinates (the nucleus) is equal to l for the eigenfunction of a single electron; that is, the number is even or odd according as l is even or odd. This means at the same time, however, that the eigenfunction either remains unaltered (l even) or changes sign (l odd) by

---

[1] This rule does not hold for a strong magnetic field or for quadrupole radiation (cf. below).

reflection at the origin (inversion),[2] that is, when $+ x$, $+ y$, $+ z$ are replaced by $- x$, $- y$, $- z$. When several electrons are present, the total eigenfunction is approximately equal to the product of the eigenfunctions of the individual electrons, and it therefore follows that *the total eigenfunction is even or odd according as $\sum l_i$ is even or odd;* that is, remains unaltered by reflection at the origin or changes sign. This property of the eigenfunction holds even when the l_i are no longer approximately quantum numbers (angular momenta), as a more detailed wave mechanical investigation shows [cf. Condon and Shortley (13)].

The transition probability between two states n and m is now given by $\int \psi_n \psi_m^* x \, d\tau$, and correspondingly for the other co-ordinates (see p. 53). The integrand is obviously an odd function when ψ_n and ψ_m are either both even or both odd; that is, the integrand, and with it the value of the integral, change sign by the transformation of co-ordinates $+ x$, $+ y$, $+ z$ to $- x$, $- y$, $- z$. Since, however, the value of an integral cannot possibly change by an alteration of the system of co-ordinates, the above integral must be exactly equal to zero (see similar argument, p. 69). On the other hand, if ψ_n is even and ψ_m is odd, or vice versa, the integrand will be an even function and the integral will generally differ from zero.

Thus the strict selection rule for dipole radiation is: *Even terms can combine only with odd, and odd only with even (Laporte rule).* For the particular case of two electrons i and k, the Laporte rule may be formulated: When $\Delta l_i = \pm 1$, Δl_k must be 0 or $+ 2$ or $- 2$, and vice versa. A special case of the Laporte rule is the *prohibition of the combination of two terms of the same electron configuration.* (For example, according to this, the three lowest terms of the N atom, $1s^2 2s^2 2p^3 \, {}^4S$, ${}^2D$, ${}^2P$ cannot combine with one another.)

Additional special selection rules are: (1) In a strong magnetic field (Paschen-Back effect), $\Delta M_L = 0$, ± 1, and $\Delta M_S = 0$, but ΔJ need no longer be 0, ± 1. (2) For (j, j) coupling (cf. below), $\Delta j_i = 0$, ± 1 for the electron performing the quantum jump.

Forbidden transitions. As we have already noted, transitions violating the above selection rules do sometimes occur with very small intensity. The following are possible grounds for these transgressions:

Case 1. The selection rule under consideration may be true only *to a first approximation.*

Case 2. A transition may be forbidden as dipole radiation but may be allowed as *quadrupole radiation or magnetic dipole radiation,* and may therefore appear, even though very weakly.

---

[2] The nodal surfaces for $l = 3$ (drawn schematically in Fig. 19, p. 41) will help to make this clear. It should be remembered that ψ has opposite signs on different sides of a nodal surface.

Case 3. The selection rules under consideration (for dipole radiation) may be strictly true in the absence of electric or magnetic fields. They may, however, be transgressed when such fields are applied externally or are produced by neighboring atoms or ions (*enforced dipole radiation*).[2a]

Case 1. An example is the selection rule $\Delta S = 0$, which holds unconditionally only under the assumption of vanishing coupling between L and S, and therefore holds less and less rigorously as the coupling between L and S increases; that is, the higher the atomic number and thus the larger the multiplet splitting, the stronger will be the intercombination lines which appear. For an atomic number as high as that of Hg, these forbidden transitions are rather intense (for example, the Hg line 2537 Å).

Case 2. The second case comes into operation with the selection rule $\Delta J = 0, \pm 1$ ($J = 0 \nrightarrow J = 0$) and with the Laporte rule. According to quantum mechanics, these selection rules should actually hold quite accurately. The fact that transitions violating them do appear, though with very small intensity, is due to the possibility of quadrupole radiation or magnetic dipole radiation (cf. Chapter I, p. 54). As stated earlier, quadrupole radiation depends on the integral $\int x^2 \psi_n \psi_m{}^* d\tau$, which (as x^2 is an even function) will always vanish except when ψ_n and ψ_m are both even or both odd. A similar relation holds for magnetic dipole radiation. Hence we have, for these two types of radiations, exactly the opposite selection rule to the Laporte rule, namely: *Even terms combine only with even, and odd only with odd.* From this it follows directly that ordinary dipole radiation, on the one hand, and quadrupole radiation or magnetic dipole radiation, on the other, cannot take part simultaneously in one and the same transition.

Further calculations show that, for *quadrupole radiation*, the selection rule for J is: $\Delta J = 0, \pm 1, \pm 2$, with the addition that $J' + J'' \geqq 2$, where J' and J'' are the J values of the upper and lower states (that is, $J = 0 \nrightarrow J = 0$; $J = \frac{1}{2} \nrightarrow J = \frac{1}{2}$; $J = 1 \nrightarrow J = 0$). For *magnetic dipole radiation:* $\Delta J = 0, \pm 1$; and $J = 0 \nrightarrow J = 0$ (as for ordinary dipole radiation). For L, the selection rules are (Russell-Saunders coupling): $\Delta L = 0, \pm 1, \pm 2$ ($L = 0 \nrightarrow L = 0$) and $\Delta L = 0, \pm 1$, respectively. The selection rule for S is: $\Delta S = 0$, and this holds to the same degree as for ordinary dipole radiation.

To illustrate, terms of the same electron configuration can combine with one another according to the selection rules for quadrupole radiation as well as for magnetic dipole radiation, whereas they could not combine according to the selection rules for ordinary dipole radiation (see above).

The ratios of the intensities of magnetic dipole radiation and quadrupole radiation compared to electric dipole radiation are,

[2a] Two further causes of violations of selection rules have recently been discussed: Case 4: Coupling with the nuclear spin [Mrozowski (158), see also footnote 3, p. 156 and Chapter V], and Case 5: Simultaneous emission of two light quanta [Breit and Teller (159)].

respectively, of the order $10^{-5} : 1$ and $10^{-8} : 1$, provided that there is no intercombination.

Case 3. The occurrence of lines in an electric field which contradict the selection rules $\Delta L = 0$, ± 1, or $\Delta l = \pm 1$ is an example of the third case (enforced dipole radiation). Under these circumstances the intensity of the forbidden lines may even become comparable to the intensity of the allowed lines.

It is important to note that the selection rules for the Zeeman effect for quadrupole, magnetic dipole, and enforced dipole radiation differ from those for ordinary dipole radiation, and also from one another. Consequently an investigation of the Zeeman effect gives an unambiguous criterion for the kind of transition under consideration. Details will not be given here [see Rubinowicz and Blaton (65)].

In *absorption,* forbidden transitions can be observed by using a sufficiently thick layer of absorbing gas. For example, the intercombination line $^1S - ^3P$ of the alkaline earths can be observed in this way. The intensity of the corresponding line for Hg is so great that a very thin layer suffices for the observation (cf. above). Because of the J selection rule, only the component $^1S_0 - ^3P_1$ usually appears.[3] (Cf. the energy level diagram of Hg, p. 202.) The forbidden lines of the alkalis, $1^2S - m\ ^2D$ (for *small* values of m), have also been observed, with small intensity, in absorption. Segrè and Bakker (68) have shown, from a study of the Zeeman effect of these lines, that they are undoubtedly due to quadrupole radiation, and not to enforced dipole radiation. On the other hand, Kuhn (69) has observed the *higher* members of the same series in absorption in the presence of an external electric field, but they have not been observed in the absence of a field. Thus we are dealing here with enforced dipole radiation.

In *emission,* transitions due to enforced dipole radiation are sometimes observed in electric discharges where electric fields are always present (external fields or ion fields). Here, also, it is chiefly the higher members of the series that appear since the higher terms are influenced much more strongly by the Stark effect than the lower (see p. 118). With the alkalis, for example, the series $2P - mP$, $2S - mS$, $2S - mD$ are observed.

On the other hand, forbidden transitions which are not caused by electric fields are more difficult to observe in emission. When

---

[3] By using considerably thicker absorbing layers of Hg (10^7-fold), the forbidden line $\lambda 2269.80$, corresponding to the transition $^1S_0 - ^3P_2$, may also be observed [Lord Rayleigh (66)]. The occurrence of this line contradicts the selection rules for ordinary dipole radiation, as well as those for quadrupole and magnetic dipole radiation. (The upper state is odd, and the lower even.) According to Bowen [cited in (67)], the transition is apparently due to the influence of nuclear spin. The line $\lambda 2655.58$, corresponding to the transition $^1S_0 - ^3P_0$, has been observed in emission [Fukuda (141)]. It also contradicts the above-mentioned selection rules.

the probability for a given transition is extremely small, the corresponding upper state has a very long life (provided no other allowed transitions take place from that state). Therefore in an ordinary light source, before an atom in such a metastable state radiates spontaneously, it has the opportunity to collide many times and thus to lose its excitation energy without radiating (collisions of the second kind, p. 228).[4] This influence of collisions can be kept sufficiently small only under special conditions; for example, at extremely low pressures or by the addition of a gas whose atoms or molecules either are not able to remove the excitation energy of the metastable state or can remove it only with difficulty. Since the life of a state which is actually metastable to dipole radiation is of the order of seconds (as compared to 10^{-8} seconds for an ordinary excited state), it is almost impossible in terrestrial light sources to reach a pressure so low as to avoid the effect of collisions—especially since, at low pressures, collisions with the wall of the vessel lead to loss of excitation energy. However, suitable conditions are present in cosmic light sources.

Bowen (70) first showed that the *nebulium lines*, which had been observed in the spectra of many cosmic nebulae but were long a complete mystery, were to be *explained as forbidden transitions between the deep terms of* O^+ (^4S, ^2D, ^2P), O^{++} (^3P, ^1D, ^1S), *and* N^+ (^3P, ^1D, ^1S). The deep terms of these ions are shown in Fig. 58 (see p. 158). Transitions between them involving dipole radiation are strictly forbidden by the Laporte rule, since they are terms belonging to the same electron configuration: $1s^22s^22p^3$ for O^+, $1s^22s^22p^2$ for O^{++} and N^+. The positions of these energy levels have been known with great accuracy for a long time from allowed combinations with higher terms. Bowen showed that the wave lengths of the forbidden lines, calculated from the combination of these terms, agree exactly (within the limits of experimental accuracy) with the wave lengths of the unexplained nebulium lines. Thus it was proved that the nebulium lines result from forbidden transitions in the O II, O III, and N II spectra, and it was no longer necessary to assume the presence of a new element in these nebulae. Actually, in cosmic nebulae the conditions are extremely favorable for the occurrence of these forbidden transitions. It is estimated that the densities in the nebulae are of the order of 10^{-17} to 10^{-20} gr. per cc. Assuming a plausible value for the temperature (approximately 10,000° K), the time between two collisions suffered by an atom is then 10^1 to 10^4 seconds. Thus, when O^+, O^{++}, or N^+ ions, which certainly are present, go into these low metastable states by allowed transitions

---

[4] If *other* allowed transitions are possible from this state, a forbidden transition is even less likely to occur, since long before that transition the ordinary dipole transition to some other level would have taken place.

from higher states, they remain there uninfluenced until they radiate spontaneously. A large fraction of the more highly excited ions must come eventually into these states, and practically

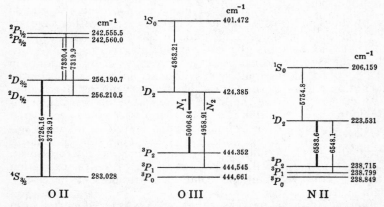

Fig. 58. Origin of the Most Important Nebular Lines (Transitions Between the Low Terms of O II, O III, and N II). The triplet and doublet splitting is drawn to a much larger scale than the rest of the figure. Term values are written to the right. The O III lines, 5006.8 Å and 4958.9 Å, are the most intense nebular lines and are sometimes designated N_1 and N_2.

every ion goes from them to the ground state by radiation. This explains why the nebulium lines are very intense in nebulae, whereas they are not observed in terrestrial light sources, in which the other allowed O II, O III, and N II lines appear strongly.

In the last few years, additional weaker nebular lines have been identified by various investigators in a similar manner as forbidden transitions of S II, S III, Ne III, Ne IV, Ne V, A IV, A V, and Cl III. The identity of a few others still remains doubtful [see Bowen (71)].

In an analogous way, McLennan (72) and Paschen (73) have explained the *green and red auroral lines* as corresponding to forbidden transitions ($^1S \rightarrow {}^1D$ and $^1D \rightarrow {}^3P$, respectively) of the neutral O atom.[5] (Cf. the energy level diagram in Fig. 59.)

According to Condon (74), the intense nebulium lines N_1 and N_2, ascribed to O^{++}, are due to magnetic dipole radiation. Corresponding to this, the component $^1D_2 \rightarrow {}^3P_0$ does not appear (cf. the above selection rules). Since we are dealing at the same

---

[5] This naturally suggests that the lines observed in the spectrum of the solar corona, which have not been found in any terrestrial light sources, may be explained in a similar way as forbidden transitions. However for many years they defied all attempts of identification. Only very recently Edlén (146) [see Swings (147)] succeeded in identifying them with forbidden transitions between the low terms of Fe X, Fe XI, Fe XIII, Fe XIV, Fe XV, Ni XII, Ni XIII, Ni XV, Ni XVI, Ca XII, Ca XIII, Ca XV, A X, and A XIV.

time with an intercombination (singlet—triplet), the mean life of the upper state is even greater than for quadrupole radiation without intercombination. On the other hand, the green auroral line, as well as the corresponding nebular lines $^1D_2 - {}^1S_0$, is due to quadrupole radiation ($\Delta J = 2$, no intercombination).

The auroral lines have also been obtained in the laboratory in suitable light sources [McLennan and Shrum (75); Paschen (73)]; for example, in discharges through argon with a small addition of oxygen. The destruction of the metastable atoms is considerably hindered by the argon. This artificial production of the green auroral line made possible the study of its Zeeman effect. From this it follows definitely that a quadrupole transition is involved [Frerichs and Campbell (76)]. Since it is a singlet transition, the normal Zeeman effect with three components would have been expected for dipole radiation. Actually, two additional components were observed at twice the distance from the middle line—an effect in agreement with the theory for quadrupole transitions.[6]

General remarks on the intensity ratios of allowed lines. Apart from the selection rules by which certain transitions are completely, or almost completely, forbidden, certain theoretical predictions can be made concerning the intensity ratios of allowed lines. In a series of lines which differ in the value of the principal quantum number for the upper state, the intensity generally decreases regularly toward the series limit. Theoretically, the variation in intensity can be calculated according to wave mechanics (see p. 50), and so far as these calculations have been carried out, there is agreement with experiment.

According to the earlier part of this chapter, the intensity depends on the number of atoms in the initial state as well as on the transition probability. In order to ascertain the intensity, two limiting cases may be distinguished:

Case 1. In the case of *thermal equilibrium* or the temperature excitation of the spectral lines, if E_n is the excitation energy of the state n above the ground state, the number of atoms or molecules in the state n is proportional to $e^{-E_n/kT}$ (Boltzmann). However, this rule holds only so

---

[6] The middle component does not appear for exactly transversal or longitudinal observations, but does occur for observations inclined to the direction of the magnetic field.

long as the statistical weight or a priori probability is 1 (cf. p. 119). If the weight is g_n, the probability of finding the state n is g_n times as great; that is, the number of atoms in the state n is proportional to $g_n e^{-E_n/kT}$. If m is a second state with excitation energy E_m, then

$$\frac{N_n}{N_m} = \frac{g_n e^{-E_n/kT}}{g_m e^{-E_m/kT}} \tag{IV, 2}$$

where N_n and N_m are the number of atoms in states n and m, respectively. If m is the ground state of the atom ($E_m = 0$), the number of atoms in the state n becomes:

$$N_n = N_m \frac{g_n}{g_m} e^{-E_n/kT} \tag{IV, 3}$$

The intensity of the line ν_{nm} is proportional to this quantity in the case of thermal equilibrium.

Case 2. In the case of many *electric discharges* where excitation results from collisions with electrons of all possible velocities, the Boltzmann factor plays no very significant part. Or, expressing this in another way, the temperature of the electron gas is so high that $e^{-E/kT}$ can be taken equal to 1 for most of the states in question. Then

$$\frac{N_n}{N_m} = \frac{g_n}{g_m} \tag{IV, 4}$$

Thus, while the states of lowest excitation energy are the most frequent for temperature excitation (owing to the Boltzmann factor), in electric discharges the higher excited states are, within certain limits, approximately as frequent. In both cases, for states with practically equal excitation energies, $N_n/N_m = g_n/g_m$ since $e^{-E_n/kT}$ is then approximately equal to $e^{-E_m/kT}$; that is, the intensities are determined mainly by the statistical weights.

The first doublet of the principal series of the alkalis illustrates the point (for example, the D lines of Na). The lower state is single. The two components of the upper state, $^2P_{3/2}$ and $^2P_{1/2}$, have statistical weights 4 and 2. Owing to the approximately equal excitation energies, for temperature excitation as well as in a discharge, the number of atoms in the $^2P_{3/2}$ state is twice the number in the $^2P_{1/2}$ state. The intensity ratio of the two lines in emission should therefore be 2 : 1, and this actually is observed. The same holds for absorption, since then the number of transition possibilities is twice as great for one component as for the other.

Sum rule. The generalization of these considerations for complicated cases is the *Burger-Dorgelo-Ornstein sum rule: The sum of the intensities of all the lines of a multiplet which belong to the same initial or final state is proportional to the statistical weight $2J + 1$ of the initial or final state, respectively.* By way of illustration the following scheme for a $^2P - {}^2D$ combination may be derived [see Table 14; cf. Figs. 29(b) and 30, p. 74 and p. 75]. The sum of the intensities of the transitions with $^2P_{1/2}$ are to those with $^2P_{3/2}$ as $5 : (1 + 9) = 2 : 4$; that is, in the ratio of the statistical weights. Similarly for ^2D, $(5 + 1) : 9 = 4 : 6$. Conversely, from these two relations the relative intensities may be calculated.

TABLE 14

INTENSITIES FOR A $^2P - {}^2D$ TRANSITION

		$^2D_{3/2}$	$^2D_{5/2}$
	$2J + 1$	4	6
$^2P_{1/2}$	2	5	—
$^2P_{3/2}$	4	1	9

From the sum rule the following general rules can be derived: (a) *The components of a multiplet for which J and L alter in the same manner are more intense than those for which they alter unequally.* (b) *The components belonging to a large J value are more intense than those with small J.* These rules are especially important for the practical analysis of a multiplet (cf. Figs. 31, 33, and 34; see also section 4 of this chapter).

The sum rule is not sufficient for an unambiguous determination of the intensities of compound triplets or higher multiplets. In such cases we must use the *general theoretical intensity formulae* derived by Sommerfeld, Hönl, and de Kronig [see (5a) and (13)], which naturally contain the sum rule. These formulae, as well as the sum rule, hold only for Russell-Saunders coupling (small multiplet splitting). Intensities in more general cases and for non-Russell-Saunders coupling have been treated in recent investigations but this work will not be dealt with here. A discussion of the intensity rules for Zeeman components must also be omitted [consult White (12); Condon and Shortley (13)].

2. Series Limits for Several Outer Electrons, Anomalous Terms, and Related Topics

Series by excitation of only one outer electron. When the outermost or valence electron for an alkali atom is raised to orbits with higher values of n and then allowed to return to a lower state, there result different emission series whose limits correspond to the complete removal of the valence electron. In absorption, only one series of lines (doublets) is obtained, the principal series, whose limit gives directly the ionization potential of the atom. The state of the ion resulting from the removal of the outermost electron has only closed shells; it is the $^1S_0$ ground state (inert gas configuration, see Table 13). This state is single, and therefore the series limit is single; all term series go actually to the same limit. Similar relations hold for the alkaline earths and the earths (boron group), where, likewise, the removal of the outermost electron leads to the ground state of the ion. However, different relations hold for the elements of the carbon group and the following groups. For these elements, the ion which is obtained by removing the outermost electron has an electron configuration which gives excited terms in addition to the ground state. For example, for C the remaining ion can be in a $^2P_{1/2}$ or $^2P_{3/2}$ state; for N, in a ^3P, ^1D, or ^1S state; and so on.

We shall consider in more detail the case of the *oxygen atom*. According to the building-up principle (Chapter III), we can predict the qualitative energy level diagram that will be obtained when we add an additional electron to the lowest electron configuration of the ion, $1s^2 2s^2 2p^3$. In this case the lowest electron configuration of the ion corresponds to three different terms, ^4S, ^2D, and ^2P (as for N). Different term series are thus obtained for the neutral O atom according as the emission electron is added to the terms ^4S or ^2D or ^2P in the different free orbits with various n and l values. The number of terms is thus considerably larger than for Be or B, for example.

If an s-electron is added to the ^4S ground state of the O^+ ion, ^3S and ^5S terms are obtained by vector addition of the l of the added electron to the L of the ion, and of the s to the S (see p. 129 f.). For each of these terms there is an entire series corresponding to the different possible values of the principal quantum number ($n \geqq 3$).

If a p-electron is added to ^4S, a series of ^3P as well as a series of ^5P terms is obtained. According to the Pauli principle, for ^5P the n value of the added p-electron must be at least 3 (see Table 13); but for ^3P, n can also be 2. The state $2p$ ^3P is the

ground state [7] of the O atom.   Similarly, ^3D and ^5D, or ^3F and ^5F
series are obtained by the addition of a d-electron or an f-electron,
respectively.   Parts of these series are shown graphically at the
left of Fig. 59 (terms not observed are indicated by dotted lines).

If an s-electron is added to the excited ^2D state of the ion having
the same electron configuration $(1s^22s^22p^3)$ as ^4S, there result
series of ^1D and ^3D terms whose limit, however, lies above the

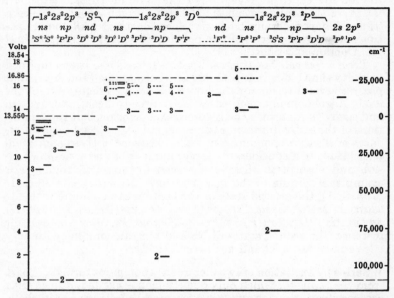

Fig. 59. **Energy Level Diagram of the O Atom, with Different Series
Limits.** The n values given are the true principal quantum numbers of the
emission electron.   The term to the extreme right $(2s2p^5\ {}^3P)$ does not belong
to any of the indicated series limits.   Dotted lines indicate terms not yet
observed.

limit of the previously considered terms by an amount equal to
the excitation energy of the ^2D state of the ion (see Fig. 59, center).
From ^2D, by adding a p-electron further series of terms are obtained: ^1P, ^3P, ^1D, ^3D, ^1F, ^3F; correspondingly, by adding a
d-electron: ^1S, ^3S, ^1P, ^3P, ^1D, ^3D, ^1F, ^3F, ^1G, ^3G.   In an exactly
similar manner, the series ^1P, ^3P, ^1S, ^3S, ^1P, ^3P, ^1D, ^3D, $\cdots$ result
from the ^2P state of the ion (Fig. 59, right), the series limit being
still higher.

In general, the term values are so chosen for atomic spectra
that ionization with the ion left in its *lowest* state corresponds to a
term value 0 and terms of smaller energy are counted positive

---

[7] For simplicity, only the symbol for the emission electron is given.

(see Chapter I).   Terms corresponding to excited ion states which lie above the first ionization limit will thus be *negative*.

When it is necessary to distinguish terms belonging to series with different limits, the term type of the corresponding ion can be included in the designation; for example, $2p^3(^2D)4p\ ^1D_2$, and similarly in other cases.   All terms of the same multiplicity and the same electron configuration resulting from a given term of the ion are called a *polyad*.   For example, all triplet terms, ^3P, ^3D, ^3F, of the configuration $2p^3(^2D)np$ of oxygen would be called a *triad*.   They generally lie fairly close together.   All the transitions between the terms of two polyads are called a *supermultiplet* [cf. Condon and Shortley (13)].

Term series going to different limits (such as have been amplified here for the O atom) appear for all those atoms (and ions) that possess several terms for the lowest electron configuration of the ion.   A great many such cases have already been investigated, and each has confirmed the theoretical conclusion that the separations of the series limits must be equal to the observed term differences of the corresponding ion.   The existence of these additional terms leads to a considerably larger number of line series in emission and absorption than is observed for simpler atoms.   For example, according to the selection rules ($\Delta S = 0$; $\Delta L = 0, \pm 1$; $\Delta l = \pm 1$), the ground state of the O atom can combine with the terms $1s^2 2s^2 2p^3(^4S)\ ns\ ^3S^o$; $2p^3(^4S)\ nd\ ^3D^o$; $2p^3(^2D)\ ns\ ^3D^o$; $2p^3(^2D)$ $nd\ ^3S^o$, $^3P^o$, $^3D^o$; $2p^3(^2P)\ ns\ ^3P^o$; $2p^3(^2P)\ nd\ ^3P^o$, $^3D^o$; whereas, for instance, the ground states of Na and Mg can combine with only *one* term series, $n\ ^2P$ and $n\ ^1P$, respectively.

Series by excitation of two electrons; anomalous terms.   Apart from the terms for which only one electron is excited, other terms are possible for which two (or even more) electrons are in shells other than those for the ground state.   Such terms are actually observed and are called *primed* or *anomalous terms*.   They were first observed for the alkaline earths and the alkaline-earth-like ions.   In their spectra were found multiplets which could not be arranged in the normal triplet series and which did not show the normal structure of a compound triplet.   Fig. 31(*d*), p. 76, shows a spectrogram of an anomalous triplet of Ca, which should be compared with the normal compound triplet in Fig. 31(*b*).   The lower part of Fig. 60 shows the same schematically. The relationships between the separations and between the intensities for a normal compound triplet (see p. 78) are not fulfilled here.   However, these and similar multiplets may be explained (as indicated in Fig. 60) as due to a combination of two ^3P terms with not very different splitting (taking into account the selection rules for J and the intensity rules).   If the explanation is correct, the energy level diagram shows that the separations of the components *a* to *c* and *d* to *f* must be exactly equal.   This is actually observed to be the case and the separation gives the splitting $^3P_2 - {}^3P_1$ of the lower term.   It now appears that this splitting and also the splitting $^3P_1 - {}^3P_0$ (separation of the lines c and e) agree *exactly* with those of the lowest ^3P term of the alkaline-earth metal under consideration (Ca, in Fig. 60) which have been known for a long time. The foregoing means that the lower state of this multiplet is the lowest $sp\ {}^3P$ state.   The upper state is an anomalous term which does not belong to the normal term series and is designated as $^3P'$.

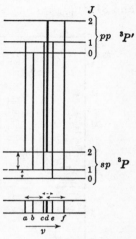

The fact that this anomalous term combines with the known ^3P term, although it is itself a P term,[8] contradicts the selection rule $\Delta L = \pm 1$, which must hold for terms for which only one electron has $l \neq 0$.   It follows that the *anomalous term corresponds to an excitation of two electrons.*   When this is the case, $\Delta L = 0$ is also possible, provided that $\Delta l = \pm 1$ for the one electron making the quantum jump (transition between even and odd terms).   This conclusion is supported by a large number of

Fig. 60.   Origin of an Anomalous Triplet of the Alkaline Earths.

further arguments which cannot be taken up here [consult White (12)].   Agreement with experiment is obtained when the assumption is made that, in the $^3P'$ term, *both* outer electrons are excited for Be to $2p$ orbits, for Mg to $3p$ orbits, for Ca to $4p$ orbits, and so on.   According to the foregoing (p. 131), two equivalent p-electrons give the terms: ^1S, ^3P, ^1D.   Here we are dealing with the ^3P state since it can combine with the $sp\ {}^3P$ term in the way shown in Fig. 60.   Writing the symbols in full, for Be we have the transition $1s^2 2p^2\ {}^3P \rightarrow 1s^2 2s 2p\ {}^3P$; for Ca, $4p^2\ {}^3P \rightarrow 4s4p\ {}^3P$ [see Fig. 31(d)].   Since only *one* electron jumps, these transitions are allowed and are very intense.   Owing to the Laporte rule, the $p^2\ {}^3P$ state cannot be reached by absorption from the $s^2\ {}^1S$ ground state.   It is probably also impossible to excite it directly in a discharge by electron collision from the ground state.   Possibly it is reached through the $sp\ {}^3P$ state by two successive electron collisions.

The two other terms, ^1S and ^1D, with the same configuration, p^2, have likewise been found for Be and for other cases, although their identification is not so certain since they are singlets.

---

[8] The values of J necessary to explain the splitting pattern show that the term cannot be any other than a P term.

The triplet splitting for the anomalous $p^2\ {}^3P$ term must be of approximately the same magnitude as that for the normal $sp\ {}^3P$ term since the p-electrons have the same principal quantum number. This is in agreement with experiment [cf. Figs. 60 and 31(d)].

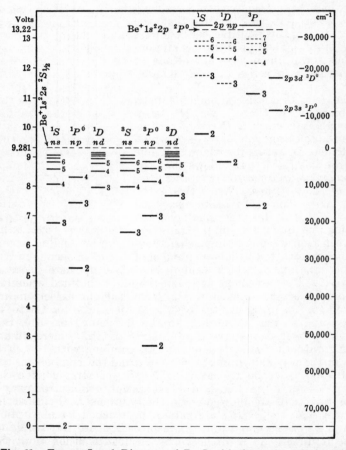

Fig. 61. Energy Level Diagram of Be I with Anomalous Term Series [Paschen and Kruger (78)]. The normal singlet and triplet series are drawn to the left (cf. Fig. 32 for Ca I); the anomalous term series, to the right. The terms drawn with dotted lines have not been observed. Apart from the terms ${}^1S$, ${}^1D$, ${}^3P$, for $n > 2$, the terms ${}^3S$, ${}^3D$, ${}^1P$ are also possible for the configuration $1s^2 2p\ np$, but thus far have not been observed. For $n > 2$, terms of the configurations $2p\ ns$ and $2p\ nd$ are also possible; of these, however, only the first member of each has been observed (indicated at the extreme right of the figure). n is the true principal quantum number.

The observed energies of these anomalous terms correspond also with the theoretical expectations. They should lie, roughly, twice as high above the ground state as the normal sp ^3P term, since *two* electrons have been brought into the $2p$ orbit (for Be) instead of one. An inspection of the Be energy level diagram in Fig. 61 shows that this is actually the case.

The following is another somewhat more accurate estimation of this excitation energy. If the explanation of anomalous terms is correct, we should expect for Be, for example, that the wave number of the transition $1s^2 2s 2p$ ^3P $-$ $1s^2 2p^2$ ^3P would approximately agree with the wave number of the line obtained when one $2p$ electron is left completely out (that is, with the $1s^2 2s$ ^2S $-$ $1s^2 2p$ ^2P transition of the Be$^+$ ion), since it can hardly be assumed that the $2p$ electron can influence the energy of the two terms very differently. Actually, this relation is well fulfilled (see Fig. 61).

Thus the term $1s^2 2p^2$ of Be and the analogous terms of the other alkaline earths and of the alkaline-earth-like ions lie rather close to the first ionization limit. Apart from the term $1s^2 2p^2$, analogues are obviously to be expected for which one electron goes to higher orbits, $3p$, $4p$, and so on (that is, a whole series $1s^2 2p$ np, corresponding to the series $1s^2 2s$ np). The limit of the former series is the ion term $1s^2 2p$; that is, an excited state of the ion quite similar to the foregoing, but with the difference that this term no longer has the same electron configuration as the ground state of the ion. Two members of this series have been found for Be (see Fig. 61). These terms have *negative* term values; that is, they lie above the lowest ionization potential. Due to this, only a few of them have been observed in this and similar cases. Before an atom in such a state can radiate, *pre-ionization* (auto-ionization) usually takes place. (This topic will be discussed further at the end of the present section.) Series of terms corresponding to the above also result when ns or nd replaces np.

Similar anomalous terms have been found for many atoms and ions. Relatively few occur for the lighter elements since they lie, for the greater part, above the lowest ionization limit. However, these terms are very numerous for the heavier elements since, for them, some of the outer shells frequently have not much more energy than the ground state, and hence the energy for the simultaneous transition of two electrons to a higher shell is often not particularly large. That they are so numerous also depends on the fact that the corresponding ion has a large number of low-lying terms. This is one of the reasons for the essentially greater complexity of the spectra of the heavier elements as compared to those of the lighter.

Excitation of inner electrons. Very closely connected with the foregoing are the spectra resulting from the excitation of inner

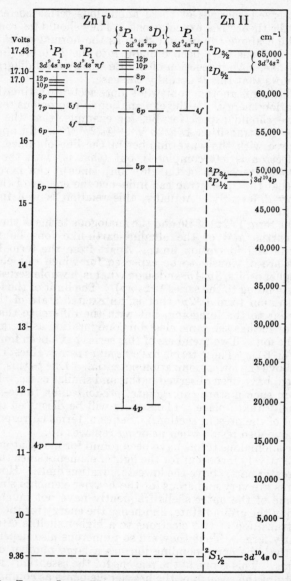

Fig. 62. Energy Level Diagram of Zn I[b] [Beutler and Guggenheimer (80)]. A part of the energy level diagram of Zn II is drawn to the right. The scale of volts to the left starts from the ground state of Zn as zero. The cm⁻¹ scale to the right starts from the ground state of Zn⁺ as zero.

electrons. Such spectra have recently been investigated in detail by Beutler (79). They provide a connecting link between optical and X-ray spectra. As is well known, the latter correspond to transitions involving the innermost electron shells of an atom. Beutler found, in absorption, transitions from the ground state of the atom to states in which one of the electrons of the outermost *closed* shell (which must be designated as an inner electron) goes to a higher orbit. He has designated these spectra I^b spectra, as an extension of the usual designation for the ordinary spectra of neutral atoms as I spectra (for example, Hg I). The essential point is that, contrary to the case just treated, only *one* electron needs to alter its quantum numbers in order to reach the corresponding excited state (I^b term) from the ground state. However, it must be an *inner* electron, and this difference distinguishes such terms from normal terms. Since only one electron has to jump, these terms may be reached by absorption.

An illustration from the *zinc spectrum* will help to make this point clearer. The electron configuration of Zn in the ground state is $1s^2 2s^2 2p^6 3s^2 3p^6 3d^{10} 4s^2$. The normal spectrum results when one electron goes from the $4s$ shell to higher orbits; anomalous terms result when both electrons go from the $4s$ shell to higher orbits. The I^b term series results when one electron goes from the closed $3d$ shell into higher orbits. Such terms lie very high—appreciably higher than the ionization limit of the normal atom. The lowest state to be excited in this way is $\cdots 3d^9 4s^2 4p$. Beutler found a whole series with np ($n = 4, 5, \cdots$), and a corresponding series with nf. Naturally, many terms belong to each configuration (cf. Tables 10 and 11 on p. 132). Of these terms, only three ($^1P_1$, $^3P_1$, $^3D_1$) can be observed in absorption from the ground state ($^1S_0$), because of the selection rules $\Delta J = 0, \pm 1$ ($J = 0 \leftrightarrow J = 0$).[9] Term series with ns or nd in the place of np or nf cannot be observed because of the selection rule $\Delta l = \pm 1$.

Fig. 62 shows the observed Zn I^b terms. All of the predicted terms except the $nf\ ^3D_1$ terms have been observed. The terms lie above the lowest ionization limit of the normal atom. The energy level diagram is drawn from this point up. The energy level diagram of the Zn^+ ion is indicated at the right of the figure. The series limit ($n \to \infty$) of the I^b terms under consideration must correspond to the $3d^9 4s^2$ state of the Zn^+ ion. This is a term of the ion (^2D) for which an inner electron is excited (according to Beutler, a II^b term). A continuous absorption spectrum joins the series limit just as for a normal series, and corresponds to ionization leaving the ion in the II^b state mentioned. In X-ray

---

[9] The deviation from Russell-Saunders coupling is already so great that the selection rules $\Delta S = 0$ and $\Delta L = 0, \pm 1$ no longer hold strictly.

nomenclature this spectrum would be called an *absorption spectrum from the M_3 shell.*

Beutler and his co-workers have already found similar absorption spectra for a large number of atoms. The series limits do not necessarily correspond to a II^b term of the ion. For K, for example, the upper states of a I^b series are $3p^5 4s\ ns$, and this gives the ordinary excited state $3p^5 4s$ of K^+ when $n \rightarrow \infty$.

Naturally there also exist terms which correspond to the excitation of shells lying still farther in. They are correspondingly designated I^c, I^d, $\cdots$. For Tl, absorption lines have been found whose transitions correspond to such terms. These spectra bridge the gap to X-ray spectra and might well be called X-ray spectra.

Summarizing the results of the preceding discussion, we conclude: in theory, *term series of a neutral atom result from the addition of an electron not only to the ground state of a singly charged ion but also to each excited state of the singly charged ion,* whether or not it has the same electron configuration as the ground state, whether it is normal or anomalous, or whether or not it belongs to the b terms. In general, this leads to a great number of terms. The foregoing considerations of course also apply to the spectra of ions.

Term perturbations. Sometimes deviations from the normal positions (expected according to the ordinary series formula) are observed in certain line series belonging to atoms and ions with several emission electrons. These deviations are known as *perturbations.* As an example the $^1F_3$ and $^3F_4$ terms of the Al II spectrum are given to the right and left of Fig. 63. For comparison, the terms $4R/n^2$ are drawn in the center of the figure. They should follow very closely the variation of the F terms of Al II, since F terms are usually hydrogen-like.[10]

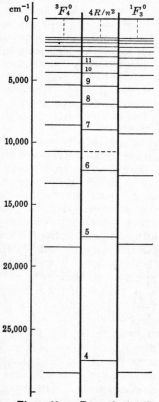

Fig. 63. Perturbed ^3F Terms of Al II Compared with the Hydrogen-like Terms $4R/n^2$ and with the ^1F Terms. The perturbing term is indicated by a dotted line.

----

[10] The factor 4 enters the formula since we are dealing with the first spark spectrum.

We can see that this is largely the case for the $^1F_3$ terms throughout the entire region. On the other hand, for the $^3F_4$ terms this is true only for large and small values of n, whereas pronounced deviations from the normal position appear in the region $n = 5$ to $n = 7$. There is actually one more term present than would be expected.[11]

The reason for this phenomenon is a *resonance process* quite analogous to the Heisenberg resonance for He (p. 66), which led to the energy difference between singlet and triplet terms. When it happens that two terms of different electron configurations of the same atom or ion have approximately the same energy, the states influence each other. In the case of He, the eigenfunctions of the resulting states are mixtures of the eigenfunctions of the two originally degenerate states [$\varphi_1(1)\varphi_n(2)$: electron 2 excited, and $\varphi_n(1)\varphi_1(2)$: electron 1 excited; cf. p. 67]. Similarly, here, a *mixing of the eigenfunctions* results. If ψ_1 and ψ_2 are the zero approximation eigenfunctions of the two states of nearly equal energy with different electron configuration, the eigenfunctions of the two resulting states will be, to a first approximation (as shown by more detailed calculations not given here):

$$\psi_I = a\psi_1 + b\psi_2 \qquad \text{and} \qquad \psi_{II} = c\psi_1 + d\psi_2$$

Thus each of the resulting states has, so to speak, both electron configurations (though not in equal amounts as for He, where $a = b = c$ and $d = -a$). This mixing may also be regarded as an oscillation of the atom between the two states (the two electron configurations). There is at the same time a shifting of both terms away from each other, as for He. Theory shows that these perturbations can occur only between terms which have equal J and, in the case of Russell-Saunders coupling, equal L and S. In addition they must either both be odd or both be even.

In fact, in the example of Al II an anomalous term ($1s^22s^22p^63p3d\ ^3F^o$) is to be expected, and it will be of the same type as the term of the normal $2p^63s\ mf\ ^3F^o$ series and may lie somewhere between $n = 6$ and $n = 7$ (dotted line in Fig. 63, center). Its eigenfunction mixes with that of the neighboring normal terms, and, furthermore, the latter will be displaced away from the position of the perturbing term. The perturbing term itself forms the extra term. On account of the mixing of the eigenfunctions, we cannot ascribe an unambiguous electron configuration to terms in the region of perturbation.

Pre-ionization (auto-ionization). The phenomenon of pre-ionization or auto-ionization [Shenstone (81)] is very closely related to perturbations. As we have already pointed out, many

---

[11] In addition, there is at the same time an abnormally large triplet splitting of the ^3F terms (not shown in Fig. 63).

of the terms resulting from the excited states of an ion (for example, practically all I^b terms) have negative values; that is, they lie higher than the lowest ionization potential of the atom or ion in question. They thus overlap the continuous term spectrum which joins the normal sequence of terms. This is shown schematically in Fig. 64. As in the case of perturbations, we have here two different states of an atom which have the same energy: the discrete anomalous state, and the continuous ionized state with a corresponding relative kinetic energy of ion plus electron (indicated by the dotted arrows in Fig. 64, right). As before, a mixing of the eigenfunctions takes place—that is, an oscillation between the two states of equal energy.

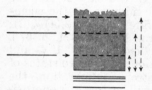

Fig. 64.   Pre-ionization of the Terms Lying above the First Ionization Potential of an Atom or an Ion.   To the left are shown the discrete terms that lie at the same height as the continuum which joins the series of terms drawn to the right.

However, when the system has once oscillated from the discrete state into the continuous state lying at the same height, a return oscillation is not possible, since the electron has already left the atom. This can also be expressed in the following way: A *radiationless quantum jump* takes place from the discrete state to the continuous state lying at the same height (shown by the horizontal arrows in Fig. 64), and results in an *ionization of the atom*. Analogous to a similar phenomenon for molecules (pre-dissociation), this effect should be called pre-ionization but in the literature is usually referred to as auto-ionization.

In the case of perturbations, a shifting of the levels takes place. Similarly here, theory shows that a *broadening of the discrete levels* is to be expected. Actual observations show that lines in which such negative terms participate are in many cases considerably broadened, although in some cases they are sharp (narrow). It may be shown theoretically that the greater the probability of a radiationless transition, the greater the broadening. A noticeable broadening (greater than the normal Doppler breadth) will take place only when the probability of a radiationless transition is very great compared with the probability of a transition to an energetically lower state *with* radiation. This means at the same time that emission lines which originate from levels broadened in this way should be either very weak or entirely missing, a conclusion that agrees completely with experiment. It was stated above that negative terms are very difficult to observe in emission.

We shall now consider why some of the absorption lines are fairly sharp and some of the emission lines are relatively intense even when the above conditions for pre-ionization are fulfilled.

This has, in principle, the same explanation as the facts that some normal lines are strong and others weak, and that the continuous spectrum which joins the absorption series diminishes fairly rapidly in intensity with decreasing wave length.　　The radiationless transition probability depends on the eigenfunctions of the two states involved, in a similar manner to the transition probability with radiation.　　There are also *selection rules for radiationless transitions*.　　It should be noted that in the continua which extend beyond the different term series, the angular momenta S, L, and J retain their meaning unaltered and the property even-odd is also defined.　　The selection rules are the same as for perturbations (see above): $\Delta J = 0$, $\Delta S = 0$, $\Delta L = 0$, *and even terms do not combine with odd*.　　The discrete terms lying above the lowest ionization potential cannot, therefore, go over by a radiationless transition into the continuum joining any arbitrary term sequence; instead, they can go only into specific continua.　　If these definite continua do not exist, pre-ionization cannot occur.　　In addition, the radiationless transition probability becomes smaller with increasing distance from the series limit, since the eigenfunction is a periodic function with a nodal distance (wave length) which becomes smaller and smaller with increasing distance from the limit.　　Therefore the value of the transition integral approaches nearer and nearer to zero.　　This conclusion corresponds to the fact that absorption lines, whose upper states lie at a fairly great distance from a series limit, are very sharp.

Similar radiationless quantum jumps occur also in the X-ray region.　　When a K-electron is removed from an atom by K absorption, the ion is left in a highly excited state (upper state of K_α and K_β).　　This state lies considerably higher than the lowest ionization potential of the ion—actually higher than the ionization energy for the removal of an L-electron.　　Therefore, instead of the atom emitting a K_α quantum as a result of the transition of an electron from the L shell to the K shell, the energy set free by this transition can be used to liberate one of the remaining L-electrons.　　Such a radiationless quantum jump was first discovered by Auger, and is called after him the *Auger effect* or *Auger process*. This name is sometimes used as a general term for all such processes—for atoms as well as molecules.

3. Other Types of Coupling

Thus far we have always used Russell-Saunders coupling (p. 128), which assumes that the interaction of the individual l_i and the individual s_i is so strong between themselves that they combine to give a resultant L and S.　　L and S then combine with a smaller coupling to give a resultant J.　　This assumption holds for a large number of elements, particularly for all the lighter elements, as may be seen from the fact that, for them, the multiplet splitting is usually small compared to the energy difference of the levels having the same electron configuration but different L. The splitting is likewise small compared to the energy difference of corresponding levels which differ only in their multiplicities.

Because of its validity in so many cases, Russell-Saunders coupling forms the basis for the usual nomenclature.

(j, j) **Coupling.** When we assume the opposite case to Russell-Saunders coupling—namely, *not* that there is a strong interaction of the l_i with one another and the s_i with one another, but rather that there is considerable interaction between each l_i and the s_i belonging to it—we obtain so-called (j, j) *coupling:* Each l_i combines with the corresponding s_i to give a j_i, the total angular momentum of the individual electron.[12]   The individual j_i are less strongly coupled with one another and form the total angular momentum J of the atom. Such coupling can be written symbolically:

$$(l_1s_1)(l_2s_2)(l_3s_3)\cdots = (j_1j_2j_3\cdots) = J \qquad \text{(IV, 5)}$$

There is no definite L and S for this coupling. However, J remains well defined. The same holds for M.

Let us consider, as an example, the *configuration ps*, which gives a $^3P_{0\ 1,\ 2}$ and a $^1P_1$ state on the basis of Russell-Saunders coupling. Assuming (j, j) coupling, however, the resultant is formed first from $l_1 = 1$ and $s_1 = \frac{1}{2}$. This gives $j_1 = \frac{3}{2}$ or $\frac{1}{2}$. From the supposition of strong coupling between l and s, these two states have very different energies. j_2 can take only one value, namely, $\frac{1}{2}$, since $l_2 = 0$. Because the coupling between j_1 and j_2 is assumed to be small, we have, to a first approximation, two terms which have equal j_2 and which differ in the two above j_1 values. The two states may be characterized briefly as $(j_1, j_2) = (\frac{3}{2}, \frac{1}{2})$ and $(\frac{1}{2}, \frac{1}{2})$. To the same approximation, we likewise have two terms for Russell-Saunders coupling: one ^1P and one ^3P term. (See Fig. 65, in which the two limiting cases are drawn to the extreme left and right.) When the small (j, j) interaction is taken into account, a slight splitting of each of the two levels, $(j_1, j_2) = (\frac{3}{2}, \frac{1}{2})$ and $(\frac{1}{2}, \frac{1}{2})$, into two components occurs (two possible orientations of j_2 with respect to j_1). For $(\frac{3}{2}, \frac{1}{2})$, J is 2 or 1; for $(\frac{1}{2}, \frac{1}{2})$, J is 1 or 0. For Russell-Saunders coupling, when we allow for the small (L, S) interaction, ^3P splits into its three components, $J = 0, 1, 2$ (Fig. 65, left).

Thus we see that the number of terms is eventually the same for both types of coupling and that the J values are the same also.

---

[12] The component of j in a magnetic field is m_j. For the application of the Pauli principle, in this case it is more convenient to employ n, l, j, and m_j than it is to use n, l, m_l, and m_s (cf. footnote 1, Chapter III).

Hence an unambiguous correlation is possible (dotted lines in Fig. 65). Therefore terms can be designated in the Russell-Saunders manner in spite of the fact that they may have practically (j, j) coupling. However, this method of designation has then only a very limited value. First of all, it no longer corre-

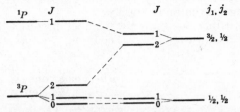

Fig. 65. Relative Positions of the Terms of a *ps* Configuration. To the left, Russell-Saunders coupling; to the right, (j, j) coupling.

sponds to the relative position of the terms. Second, the prohibition of intercombinations $\Delta S = 0$ and the selection rule $\Delta L = 0$, ± 1 no longer hold, since L and S are no longer definite quantum numbers. The terms combine according to the Laporte rule and the selection rules: $\Delta J = 0, \pm 1$; $\Delta j_i = 0, \pm 1$ (see section 1).

For cases in which pp, pd, or other configurations are present instead of the case of one p-electron and one s-electron, the relationships are naturally much more complicated. Neither these nor the completely altered g-formula for Zeeman splitting for (j, j) coupling will be considered further here. [Consult White (12); Condon and Shortley (13).]

Transition cases. Pure (j, j) coupling occurs relatively seldom. Instead, we usually have to deal with transition cases which correspond to the region at the center of Fig. 65. The figure shows that in this region the splitting of the terms does not follow exactly either Russell-Saunders or (j, j) coupling. In Fig. 66 the positions of the first excited ^3P terms and the corresponding ^1P terms of the elements of the carbon group are given. These two terms are due to an electron configuration ps. Carbon has practically pure Russell-Saunders coupling, as has Si. However, Ge, Sn, and Pb approach closer and closer to (j, j) coupling; this effect is indicated especially by the term with $J = 2$, which moves from the neighborhood of the lowest term with $J = 0$ into the neighborhood of the uppermost term with $J = 1$ ($^1P_1$) (see p. 175).

It must be emphasized that, when (j, j) coupling occurs for one term, it need by no means hold for the whole term system of the atom in question. This coupling holds preferentially for excited states. Practically pure (j, j) coupling is present in the above case of an excited state of Pb, but does not hold for its ground state. The outer electrons in the ground state have the configuration p^2; therefore the lowest terms are, in order, ^3P, ^1D, ^1S, just as for C (see p. 142). The triplet splitting, it is true, is considerable, though not so large that the terms cannot be distinguished according to Russell-Saunders. The same holds for Sn and Ge, whereas their excited states (Fig. 66) already approach fairly closely the case of (j, j) coupling (the higher excited states approaching it even more closely).

Thus with increasing atomic number first the higher excited states show a transition to (j, j) coupling, because, for an electron with large principal quantum number, the coupling with the other electrons is rather weak. Even with fairly small atomic number this coupling may be weaker than the coupling of l and s for this electron. Therefore a resultant j is first formed for this electron, which then interacts weakly with the angular momenta of the other electrons. In the case of elements of the carbon group (shown in Fig. 66), only one additional electron is present with $l \neq 0$ (namely, a p-electron). This electron forms its own j, and (j, j) coupling results for large principal quantum numbers of the emission electron. The two j values of the p-electron in the core correspond to the two components of the ^2P ground term of the ion to which the terms of the neutral atom converge.

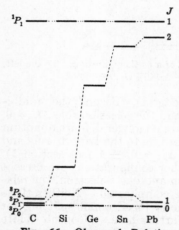

Fig. 66. Observed Relative Positions of the First Excited ^3P and ^1P Terms of Elements of the Carbon Group. Transition from Russell-Saunders to (j, j) coupling. The scale is different for the various elements, but has been so chosen that the separation between each uppermost and lowest term in the diagram is the same for each element.

If several electrons with $l \neq 0$ are present, as well as an emission electron with high n, the former will have Russell-Saunders coupling with one another for a not too high atomic number; that is, they give an L_c and an S_c of the atomic core with a resultant J_c, which will then be weakly coupled with the j of the emission electron. This coupling can be written symbolically:

$$(l_1 l_2 \cdots)(s_1 s_2 \cdots)(l, s) = (L_c, S_c)(l, s) = (J_c, j) = J \quad \textbf{(IV, 6)}$$

Such a case occurs for the excited states of Ne, for example, in spite of a rather small atomic number.

Still other modes of coupling are possible but will not be dealt with here.

When approximation to (j, j) coupling makes it impossible to ascribe definite Russell-Saunders term symbols to the observed terms in a given case, the latter are distinguished by their J value, if necessary with a superior ^{o} added as an upper index to indicate that the term is odd. When the symmetry of the ground state is known, whether a term is odd or even can easily be established on the basis of the Laporte rule, which holds absolutely for any type of coupling.

4. The Interval Rule; Analysis of Multiplets

General remarks concerning the analysis of atomic spectra. According to what has already been said, the analysis of atomic spectra such as the alkali or alkaline-earth spectra, consisting of simple series, presents no difficulties. One needs only to identify among the observed lines those lines that belong to certain series, and then to relate these series according to the theoretical principles. However, the analysis of a complicated spectrum when several outer electrons participate is by no means so simple. It is particularly difficult for the beginner to understand how to pick out the regularities from the perplexing abundance of lines in such a spectrum (cf. Fig. 6, p. 7), how to assign the lines to definite series and definite terms, and how this can ever lead to an unambiguous result. We shall touch on these topics briefly in this section.

First of all, the regularities which have been discussed in earlier chapters and which form the basis of the analysis will be summarized.

1. It must be possible to arrange the lines in *Rydberg series* of the form already given (see also p. 197). The different members of such a series may lie in entirely different spectral regions.

2. Lines belonging to one and the same series show the *same Zeeman effect;* only singlet lines show the normal Zeeman effect.

3. Apart from singlet lines, it should be possible to group the lines together as *multiplets*. [We are disregarding here the case of (j, j) coupling.] The discovery and analysis of such multiplets is the first main task in the analysis of a spectrum. In this step the following points are of importance:

(*a*) In a multiplet, *constant differences* must occur between pairs of lines. This follows from the explanation given previously in connection with compound triplets (p. 78). For example, in the quartet transition for C^+ shown in Fig. 34, the following separations must be exactly equal to one another: $b - a = h - d$, $d - c = g - e$; and, conversely, $d - a = h - b$, $e - c = g - d$. These separations correspond to term differences of the upper and lower states, respectively. When, therefore, the lines of a multiplet are put in a square array (see Table 15) such that lines in each vertical row have lower states with equal J, and those in each horizontal row have upper states with equal J, the differences between the lines in two horizontal or two vertical rows must be exactly constant. The table shows that this is actually the case, within the limits of experimental error. In the scheme only the diagonal from upper left to lower right and the two parallels to it are occupied by lines, due to the selection rule $\Delta J = 0, \pm 1$.

(b) According to our earlier discussion (p. 161), in a multiplet, those transitions for which J and L alter in the same sense are the most intense; of these, the most intense is that with greatest J. Table 15 shows that this rule holds also for the C$^+$ quartet.

TABLE 15

$^4P - ^4D$ TRANSITION FOR C$^+$ [FOWLER AND SELWYN (59)]

(Wave-number differences are given in italic type. Numbers in parentheses are estimated intensities. Superior letters a, b, c, etc., refer to Fig. 34, p. 80.)

	$^4P_{1/2}$		$^4P_{3/2}$		$^4P_{5/2}$
$^4D_{1/2}$	14,729.79(2)^e	*23.73*	14,706.06(0)^c		
	14.82		*14.61*		
$^4D_{3/2}$	14,744.61(2)^g	*23.94*	14,720.67(3)^d	*44.95*	14,675.72(0)^a
			25.10		*25.03*
$^4D_{5/2}$			14,745.77(4)^h	*45.02*	14,700.75(3)^b
					36.30
$^4D_{7/2}$					14,737.05(6)^f

(c) In the Zeeman effect, each multiplet level splits into $2J + 1$ components. The number of components for each *line* is given by the splitting of the upper and lower terms and by the selection rules (II, 12) and (II, 13). Conversely, it is always possible to use the Zeeman splitting to obtain the J values for the upper and lower states of the respective lines. Investigation of the Zeeman effect is, however, not always practicable.

(d) When an investigation of the Zeeman effect is not practicable, an interval rule (discussed in the following) is employed in the determination of J.

Landé interval rule. Under the assumption of Russell-Saunders coupling, the ratios of the intervals in a multiplet can be easily calculated in the following way: The magnetic field produced by L is evidently proportional to $\sqrt{L(L+1)}$, and the component of S in the direction of this field is $\sqrt{S(S+1)} \cos (L, S)$. Therefore from (II, 7), the interaction energy is

$$H \mu_H = A \sqrt{L(L+1)} \sqrt{S(S+1)} \cos (L, S)$$

where A is a constant.   From Fig. 47 (p. 109) it follows [similar to equation (II, 19)] that

$$\cos{(L, S)} = \frac{J(J + 1) - L(L + 1) - S(S + 1)}{2\sqrt{L(L + 1)}\ \sqrt{S(S + 1)}}$$

Consequently the interaction energy is:

$$A\frac{J(J + 1) - L(L + 1) - S(S + 1)}{2}$$

As L and S are constant for a given multiplet term, the intervals between successive multiplet components are in the ratio of the differences of the corresponding $J(J + 1)$ values. But the difference between two successive $J(J + 1)$ values is $2J + 2$. Consequently, for a multiplet term *the interval between two successive components (J and $J + 1$) is proportional to $J + 1$.*   This interval rule was first formulated by Landé.   Deviations from this rule occur with increasing deviation from Russell-Saunders coupling.   According to the interval rule for example, the separations of the components of a ^4D term with $J = \frac{1}{2}, \frac{3}{2}, \frac{5}{2}, \frac{7}{2}$ are in the ratio 3 : 5 : 7.   For the ^4D term of C^+ (Table 15), these separations are 14.72, 25.07, 36.30; and are in the ratio 2.94 : 5 : 7.24. The interval rule is thus verified to a fair approximation in this case, and similarly in other cases.[13]   The multiplet intervals in all the illustrative diagrams have been drawn in accordance with the Landé interval rule.

Example of a multiplet analysis.   In order to locate multiplets in a complicated atomic spectrum, it is necessary first, by systematic trial, to discover pairs of lines with exactly equal wavenumber differences.   As can be seen in Table 15, these pairs usually occur in double sets.   When a number of such double sets have been found, they must be arranged in a scheme similar to the one used in that table.   For a given multiplet, only such double sets come under consideration as have one line in common. In arranging the various pairs in the scheme, one must consider that in all the horizontal rows the wave numbers of the lines decrease or increase continuously from left to right; the same applies, correspondingly, for the vertical columns.   Practically, it is usually easy to arrange the lines in such a scheme when the lines in the spectrum form separated groups (multiplets); however, this is always theoretically possible even when different multiplets overlap one another.

Table 16 gives such a scheme for a multiplet of Fe, which is shown in Fig. 6 (p. 7).   As can be seen, the wave-number differences (given in italic type in the table) of pairs of lines, such

---

[13] An exception is provided, for example, by He (see footnote 2, Chapter II).

as $i - g$ and $f - c$, agree exactly. To be sure, the separations $h - g$ and $m - d$ occur only once. Nevertheless, that the lines h and m belong to the multiplet follows from the fact that the same differences appear for other Fe multiplets having the same upper or lower states.

TABLE 16

Fe I MULTIPLET [LAPORTE (82)]

(Wave-number differences are given in italic type. Numbers in parentheses above the wave numbers of the lines are estimated intensities. Superior letters a, b, c, etc., refer to Fig. 6, p. 7.)

J	i		$i+1$		$i+2$		$i+3$		$i+4$
k	$(40)^h$ 25,966.89								
	104.51								
$k+1$	$(40)^g$ 25,862.38	*168.92*	$(60)^i$ 26,031.30						
	215.52		*215.53*						
$k+2$	$(10)^c$ 25,646.86	*168.91*	$(60)^f$ 25,815.77	*257.73*	$(80)^k$ 26,073.50				
			294.45		*294.45*				
$k+3$			$(8)^b$ 25,521.32	*257.73*	$(60)^e$ 25,779.05	*351.30*	$(125)^l$ 26,130.35		
					411.21		*411.19*		
$k+4$					$(5)^a$ 25,367.84	*351.32*	$(15)^d$ 25,719.16	*448.50*	$(200)^m$ 26,167.66

The types of terms combining with one another must now be determined. We know that J increases or decreases by 1 for successive horizontal and vertical rows. The direction of increasing J is determined by observing the direction of increasing separation of the lines in the horizontal and vertical rows, since, according to the interval rule, the multiplet intervals increase with increasing J. The relative values of J are, therefore, those given in Table 16. They include a constant i or k, which is thus far undetermined. The absolute values of J are obtained when the ratio of successive intervals for the upper and lower states is calculated. In the present case, the numbers, for the upper state, 104.51, 215.53, 294.45, 411.20, are approximately in the ratio $1 : 2 : 3 : 4$; whereas those for the lower state, 168.92, 257.73, 351.31, 448.50, are in the ratio $2 : 3 : 4 : 5$. From this it follows that $i = 1$ and $k = 0$. Consequently, the J values of the upper state are: 0, 1, 2, 3, 4; those of the lower state are: 1, 2, 3, 4, 5. When $L > S$, the number of term components is $2S + 1$. In the present case this number is 5, and therefore $S = 2$. The supposition that, here, $L > S$ follows from the fact that the two states have an equal number of components, although they have different J values.[14] With $S = 2$ and with the above J values, we find that $L = 2$ in the upper state and that $L = 3$ in the lower state. The transition is thus a $^5F - ^5D$ transition. The intensities provide a check on the correctness of the J and L values (see above).

The foregoing considerations do not alter when the upper and lower states are interchanged; that is, when Table 16 is reflected at the diagonal through the upper left corner. A decision as to which is the upper or the lower state can be obtained only by comparison with other multiplets of the same spectrum or by absorption experiments. The arrangement actually used in the table was verified in both ways. Since the ν values in a vertical row in Table 16 decrease with increasing J in the upper state, it follows that the upper state is an *inverted* term. The same holds, in a similar manner, for the lower state. Thus, for both terms, the components with smallest J lie highest.

After a large number of multiplets of the same spectrum have been analyzed in this way, we can arrange similar terms in *Rydberg series: $R/(m + a)^2$* (see p. 55). Terms for which this arrangement is possible differ from one another only in the principal quantum number of one electron. The energy level diagram of the atom is thus obtained, and, when sufficient terms of a Rydberg series are known, the ionization potential can be obtained very accurately by extrapolation to $n = \infty$. (Cf. Chapter VI, section 1.) When the carrier (emitter) of the spectrum is known, a qualitative energy level diagram may be constructed on the basis of the building-up principle, and then the observed combinations may be arranged in this diagram.

---

[14] The number of components for $L < S$ is $2L + 1$. Two terms with equal S can, therefore, have the same number of components less than $2S + 1$ only when they have the same L; that is, the same J values.

CHAPTER V

Hyperfine Structure of Spectral Lines

When individual multiplet components are examined with spectral apparatus of the highest possible resolution (interference spectroscopes, large concave gratings in the higher orders), it is found that in many atomic spectra each of these components is still further split into a number of components lying extremely close together. This splitting is called *hyperfine structure*. The total splitting is only of the order of 2 cm^{-1} (that is, in the visible region of the spectrum approximately 0.4 Å) and is in many cases considerably smaller. In Fig. 67(a), (b), and (c) we give as illustrations the "lines": 4122 Å of Bi I (photogram), 5270 Å of Bi II, and 4382 Å of Pr II.

As we have seen in the preceding chapters, the assumption of orbital and spin angular momenta of the individual electrons of an atom explains completely the multiplet structure thus far mentioned. It is, however, difficult to imagine an additional degree of freedom of the extra-nuclear electrons of an atom which would account for the still further splitting (hyperfine structure) just mentioned. We are therefore led to assume (following Pauli) that this *hyperfine structure is caused by properties of the atomic nucleus*. This assumption is confirmed by a more thorough investigation of the phenomenon.

The influence of the nucleus may be due either to its mass (*isotope effect*), or to a new property, an intrinsic angular momentum or *nuclear spin*, which can be considered similar to the electron spin. Both influences have been found.

1. Isotope Effect

As is well known, most chemical elements consist of a number of isotopic atoms, each of which has an approximately whole-number atomic weight. Different isotopes of an element have the same number and arrangement of extra-nuclear electrons, and consequently have the same coarse structure for their spectra. They are, however, distinguished from one another by their mass.

Isotope effect for the H atom. We have seen in Chapter I that, because of the simultaneous motion of nucleus and electron about the common center of gravity, the Rydberg constant depends on the nuclear mass. The H spectrum thus depends upon the nuclear mass. Urey and his co-workers first found (1932) that each of the Balmer lines H_α, H_β, H_γ, and H_δ has a very weak companion on the short wave-length side at distances of 1.79, 1.33, 1.19, and 1.12 Å, respectively. The wave lengths of the additional lines agree completely (within the limits of experimental error) with the values obtained from the Balmer formula when the Rydberg constant for a mass 2 is used instead of for a mass 1 (p. 21). The calculated separations are 1.787, 1.323, 1.182, and 1.117 Å. The existence of the hydrogen isotope of mass 2 (heavy hydrogen) was first shown in this way. It should perhaps be added that the heavier isotope is present to the extent of only 1 in 5000 in ordinary hydrogen.

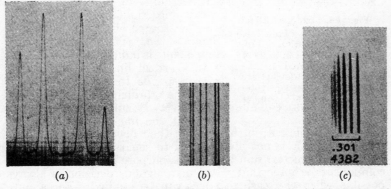

(a)   (b)   (c)

Fig. 67. Hyperfine Structure of Three Spectral Lines. (a) Photogram of the " line " 4122 Å of Bi I, with 4 components. Total splitting 0.44 Å [Zeeman, Back, and Goudsmit (83)]. (b) Spectrogram of the " line " 5270 Å of Bi II, with 6 components. Total splitting 1.37 Å [Fisher and Goudsmit (84)]. (c) Spectrogram of the " line " 4382 Å of Pr II, with 6 components. Total splitting 0.30 Å [White (85)].

Isotope effect for more complicated atoms. As soon as several electrons are present, the isotope effect can no longer be calculated in such a simple manner as for the H atom. We shall discuss here only the qualitative results. The fine structure of the Li resonance line, which is not a simple doublet, was explained a number of years ago as due to the isotopic shift of Li^6 and Li^7 [Schüler and Wurm (86)]. This interpretation has been verified by the intensity ratio of the corresponding lines in the hyperfine structure pattern, which agrees with the abundance ratio of the isotopes.

Another case that was among the first to be explained is the Ne spectrum, part of the lines of which consist of two components. Apart from the somewhat rare isotope Ne^{21}, Ne has two principal isotopes, Ne^{20} and Ne^{22}, whose abundance ratio (9 : 1) agrees with the intensity ratio of the two line components and to which the two line components are thus to be ascribed. This interpretation was further confirmed by the separation of the two isotopes by diffusion [Hertz (87)]. The separated isotopes show only the one or the other component of the doublet.

It might be expected that with increasing atomic number the isotope effect would become smaller, since the motion of the nucleus becomes more and more unimportant. However, it has actually been found [Schüler and Keyston (88); and others] that even for elements of rather high atomic number a noticeable isotope effect is present, which is of the same order of magnitude as the influence of nuclear spin. (Cf. section 2 of this chapter.) As an example, Fig. 68 shows schematically the isotope effect of the 6215 Å "line" of Zn. The intensity of the components is indicated by the height of the vertical lines in the diagram. It corresponds to the abundance of the three [1] principal isotopes: Zn^{64}, Zn^{66}, Zn^{68}. Worth noticing is the fact that the lines of the three isotopes lie equidistant, in the order of their masses.

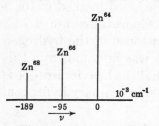

Fig. 68. Isotope Effect for the 6215 Å "Line" of Zn II (Schematic). Frequency differences in units of 10^{-3} cm^{-1} referred to the most intense line (right) are given as abscissae. Total splitting < 0.2 cm^{-1} [Schüler and Westmeyer (89)].

In general, it is not always easy to separate the two effects (isotopy and nuclear spin). For this purpose the intensity of the components is important. An unambiguous decision is always possible when the Zeeman effect can be studied. For a pure isotope effect, each of the individual components will show the Zeeman effect for the extranuclear electrons quite independently

---

[1] The much rarer isotope Zn^{67} has been observed for another line, $\lambda 7479$.

of one another, whereas hypermultiplets, resulting from nuclear spin, should show an essentially different Zeeman effect (see below). Apart from this, it is naturally possible to make an unambiguous differentiation when the spectra of separated or partly separated isotopes can be investigated. In this way the isotope effect in the hyperfine structure of Pb has been carefully investigated by using leads from different radioactive origins (with different atomic weights and therefore different proportions of the individual isotopes). [See Kopfermann (90).]

A quantitative explanation of the isotope effect is not simple, since, with the exception of the H atom, it is not given merely by the altered Rydberg constant. A detailed wave mechanical calculation shows that, for the lighter atoms (Li, Ne, and so forth), an explanation can be obtained on the basis of different masses alone and is at least of the right order of magnitude [Hughes and Eckart (91); Bartlett and Gibbons (92)]. However, for the heavier elements, the effect is traced back to the *change of nuclear radius with mass* [Pauling and Goudsmit (9); Bartlett (93)].

In this connection it is interesting to note that Schüler and Schmidt (135) found in the case of samarium that the three even isotopes Sm^{150}, Sm^{152}, Sm^{154} do not give equidistant lines as do the isotopes of Zn (Fig. 68) and practically all other elements. The separation of Sm^{150}—Sm^{152} is double that of Sm^{152}—Sm^{154} Since the usual isotope shift for heavy nuclei is due to a regular increase in nuclear radius (cf. above), the large change between Sm^{150} and Sm^{152} points to a larger than usual increase in radius, which may indicate a fundamental change in the building-up of the nucleus at this atomic weight.

2. Nuclear Spin

In many cases the isotope effect is not sufficient to explain the hyperfine structure. The number of hyperfine structure components is often considerably greater than the number of isotopes. In particular, elements which have only one isotope in appreciable amount also show hyperfine structure splitting. This is, for example, the case with Bi and Pr (cf. Fig. 67). Likewise, the number of components of different lines is frequently quite different for one and the same element. These hyperfine structures can be quantitatively explained, however, when it is assumed (as for the electron) that the *atomic nucleus possesses an intrinsic angular momentum with which is associated a magnetic moment*. This angular momentum can have different magnitudes for different nuclei and also, of course, for different isotopes of the same element.

Magnitude of the nuclear spin and its associated magnetic moment. If it is assumed that wave mechanics holds for nuclei, the nuclear spin can be only an integral or half-integral multiple of $h/2\pi$. We write for it $I(h/2\pi)$, where I is the quantum number of the nuclear angular momentum,[2] which can be integral or half integral. For the simplest nucleus, the *proton*, investigations of the H_2 molecule (spectrum, specific heat) have shown that its spin I equals $\frac{1}{2}$. The proton has therefore the same angular momentum as the electron. Naturally, different values might be expected for heavier nuclei since they contain, among other component parts, several protons.

A magnetic moment is associated with the nuclear spin (as with electron spin), since the nucleus is also electrically charged and the rotation of electrically charged particles gives rise to a magnetic moment. Classically, the magnetic moment resulting from the rotation of charges is $(e/2mc)p$ (see Chapter II). For an angular momentum $p = 1\, h/2\pi$ and $m =$ the mass of the electron, one *Bohr magneton* results (BM). If we substitute the mass of the proton for m and if $p = 1\, h/2\pi$, we obtain a magnetic moment of $1/1840$ BM, which is called one *nuclear magneton* (NM). Therefore, classically, the magnetic moment of the proton should be $\frac{1}{2}$ NM, or 1840 times smaller than that of the electron, which should similarly be $\frac{1}{2}$ BM. Actually, this relationship holds for neither the proton nor the electron. Analogous to the procedure with the extranuclear electrons, the discrepancy is formally explained by introducing a *nuclear g-factor* and putting the magnetic moment of the nucleus equal to:

$$g\,\frac{e}{2m_pc}\,I\,\frac{h}{2\pi} = g \cdot I \text{ NM}$$

---

[2] The more accurate formula for the magnitude of the nuclear angular momentum is $\sqrt{I(I+1)}\, h/2\pi$, just as for J (see p. 88). For the sake of simplicity, we shall use the expression $I(h/2\pi)$ in what follows.

where m_p is the proton mass. Note that g is counted positive when the magnetic moment falls in the direction of the nuclear spin (as is generally to be expected for the rotation of positive charges), and is counted negative when it falls in the opposite direction.

Since the g values for the nuclei are numbers of the order of 1, the magnetic moment of the nucleus is always about 2000 times smaller than that of the electron.

Vector diagram allowing for nuclear spin. Previously L and S were combined to give the total angular momentum J of the extranuclear electrons. Now J and I must similarly be combined to give a resultant, in order to obtain the *total angular momentum F of the whole atom, including nuclear spin.* As before, the corresponding quantum number F can take values

$$F = J + I, J + I - 1, J + I - 2, \cdots, |J - I| \quad \textbf{(V, 1)}$$

This gives, in all, $2J + 1$ or $2I + 1$ different values, according as $J < I$, or $J > I$.
Fig. 69(a) shows the addition for the case of $J = 2$, $I = \frac{3}{2}$. It corresponds completely to the addition of $L = 2$ and $S = \frac{3}{2}$ in Fig. 37 (p. 89).

Because of the magnetic moment of the nucleus, a coupling between J and I results (similar to that noted previously between L and S) and produces a precession of the vector diagram (Fig. 70) about the total angular momentum F as axis. Due to this, a small energy difference between states with

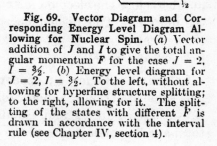

Fig. 69. **Vector Diagram and Corresponding Energy Level Diagram Allowing for Nuclear Spin.** (a) Vector addition of J and I to give the total angular momentum F for the case $J = 2$, $I = \frac{3}{2}$. (b) Energy level diagram for $J = 2, I = \frac{3}{2}$. To the left, without allowing for hyperfine structure splitting; to the right, allowing for it. The splitting of the states with different F is drawn in accordance with the interval rule (see Chapter IV, section 4).

different F exists. However, since the magnetic moment of the nucleus is approximately 2000 times smaller than that of the electron, the precession is 2000 times slower than that of L and S about J (also indicated in Fig. 70), and correspondingly the energy differences are very much smaller. These are the small differences observed in the hyperfine structure of spectral lines. Fig. 69(b) shows the energy level diagram of the term with $J = 2$ and $I = \frac{3}{2}$.

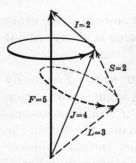

Fig. 70. Precession of the Angular Momentum Vectors about the Total Angular Momentum F for the Component $F = 5$ of a $^5F_4$ Term with $I = 2$. The solid-line ellipse shows the precession of I and J about F. The dotted-line ellipse shows the much faster precession of L and S about J, taking place at the same time.

From equation (V, 1), it follows that in general the *number of hyperfine structure components* of which an atomic term consists is different for different terms of the same atom. Terms with $J = 0$ are always single. If $I = \frac{1}{2}$, all other terms show a splitting into two components. If I is greater than $\frac{1}{2}$, terms with $J < I$ have $2J + 1$ components, whereas those with $J > I$ have $2I + 1$ components (cf. above).

The greater the nuclear magnetic moment, the greater will be the splitting. The latter is also dependent on the type of atomic state under consideration. For example, if the emission electron is in an s orbit, the splitting is much greater than for a p orbit with the same principal quantum number, since the electron in an s orbit approaches closer to the nucleus. This dependency can be calculated in detail theoretically, but will not be taken up further here [consult Condon and Shortley (13)].

Selection rule for F; appearance of a hypermultiplet. The same selection rule holds for the total angular momentum F [see Pauling and Goudsmit (9)] as holds for the total angular momentum of the extranuclear electrons:

$$\Delta F = \pm 1, 0 \quad \text{and} \quad F = 0 \not\leftrightarrow F = 0 \quad \text{(V, 2)}$$

From this it follows that a hypermultiplet, although its splitting is much smaller, will have a similar appearance to an ordinary multiplet (cf. Figs. 29 and 31, p. 74 and p. 76), particularly since the same interval rule holds for both.

In Fig. 71(a), (b), and (c), energy level diagrams for those lines of Bi I, Bi II, and Pr II are shown whose spectrograms have already been given on page 183. The spin of the Bi nucleus is $I = \frac{9}{2}$. In the upper and lower states of

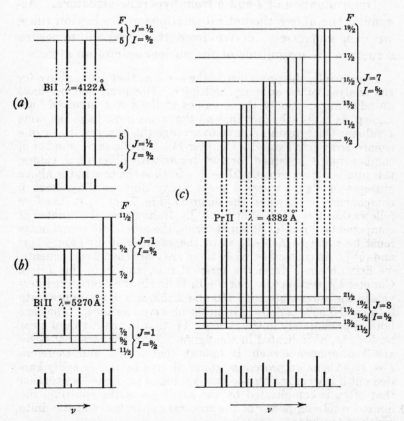

Fig. 71. Energy Level Diagram Showing the Hyperfine Structure for the Three Spectral Lines Reproduced in Fig. 67. (a) Bi I $\lambda 4122$ line. (b) Bi II $\lambda 5270$ line (upper and lower states must be interchanged). (c) Pr II $\lambda 4382$ line.

the Bi I line λ4122, $J = \frac{1}{2}$; for the Bi II line λ5270, $J = 1$ in both states. This gives in the first case 4 components, and in the second case 7 components. The J values are not known exactly for the Pr II line λ4382, but must, at any rate, be very large. With $I = \frac{5}{2}$ and the assumption that the splitting is exceedingly small in the lower state, 6 line components result; of these, 4 consist of 3 unresolved components each, and one consists of 2 unresolved components [see Fig. 71(c)].

Determination of I and g from hyperfine structure. Assuming the above theoretical relations and selection rules, we can, conversely, derive from the observed hyperfine structure the magnitude of the nuclear spin of an atom.

In principle, the procedure is the same as that given above for the analysis of an ordinary multiplet. However, here we have an advantage: usually the J values of the terms involved [3] are known, as is also the fact that all the terms must have the same I value. Once again we have to arrange the hypermultiplet in a square array (cf. Table 16, Chapter IV). If the same number of components is obtained for two terms with different J values, this number gives directly $2I + 1$. Such is the case in the above example of Pr II, where a great many different lines have 6 components, as shown in the diagram [Fig. 71(c)]. It therefore follows that $I = \frac{5}{2}$ [cf. White (85)]. If, however, the number of components varies for different terms, the number of components must be equal to $2J + 1$, as in the example of Bi [Fig. 71(a) and (b)]. In such cases, when there are more than 2 components, we first obtain F from the interval rule, and from this I (see Chapter IV, section 4). For the Bi II line in the figure, the intervals in the lower state are 1.756 and 2.152, and in the upper state 0.459 and 0.562, as derived from the observed pattern. They are both approximately in the ratio 9 : 11; that is, the F values must be $\frac{7}{2}$, $\frac{9}{2}$, $\frac{11}{2}$, as indicated in the figure. From the fact that there are 3 components each, it follows that $J = 1$ and therefore $I = \frac{9}{2}$. A similar procedure could always be rather easily carried out if it were not for the overlapping of the lines—a situation that often is complicated by the smallness of the splitting, the limited resolving power of the spectral apparatus, and the finite width of the lines.

---

[3] Conversely, with a known nuclear spin, we can determine the J values of unanalyzed multiplets by investigating their hyperfine structure.

When the value of the nuclear spin I has been obtained, the
g-factor and the magnetic moment of the nucleus can be derived
from the magnitude of the splitting by using the theoretical
formulae.

Zeeman effect of hyperfine structure.   In a magnetic field a
space quantization of F takes place precisely as given above for J.
The quantum number M_F of the component of the angular
momentum in the field direction can take only the following
values:

$$M_F = F, F - 1, F - 2, \cdots, - F \qquad (V, 3)$$

The $2F + 1$ values of M_F correspond to states of different energies
in a magnetic field.   Because of the precession of J and I about F
(see Fig. 70), the direction of the magnetic moment of the extranuclear electrons lies, *on the average,* in the direction of F.   The
energy differences of the $2F + 1$ states with different M_F are
thus of the same order of magnitude as for the ordinary Zeeman
effect [cf. formula (II, 14)].   As before, the states are equidistant.
With increasing field strength, the precession of F about the field
direction becomes faster and the energy difference between the
various term components becomes greater.   Fig. 72 shows, to the
left, the splitting of the two hyperfine structure components of a
term with $J = \frac{1}{2}$ and $I = \frac{3}{2}$ in a weak field.   (The order of the
components with $F = 1$ is the inverse of the order with $F = 2$,

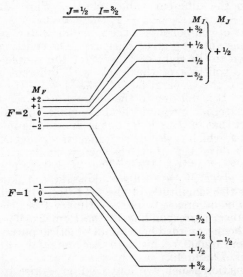

**Fig. 72.   Zeeman Splitting of the Hyperfine Structure Components $F = 1$
and $F = 2$ of a Term with $J. = \frac{1}{2}, I = \frac{3}{2}$.**   To the left, the splitting is in a
weak field; to the right, in a strong field.

since in the first case J is antiparallel to F.)   On the basis of the selection rule $\Delta M_F = \pm 1, 0$ $(M_F = 0 \nleftrightarrow M_F = 0$, for $\Delta F = 0$), which is analogous to (II, 12) and (II, 13), each individual component of a hypermultiplet gives a Zeeman splitting corresponding completely to the spectrograms previously given for the anomalous Zeeman effect (Fig. 39).   In actual investigations this effect is scarcely ever observed, since the hyperfine structure splitting itself is generally close to the limit of possible resolution (see however the more recent work of Rasmussen (148) and Jackson and Kuhn (149).

When the magnetic field is so great that the velocity of precession of F about the field direction becomes greater than that of J and I about F, a *Paschen-Back effect* takes place, as for ordinary multiplet structure.   In the case of hyperfine structure, on account of the weakness of the coupling between J and I, the Paschen-Back effect occurs at very much lower field strengths than for ordinary multiplet structure. J and I are then space quantized in the field direction independently of one another and with components M_J (corresponding to M, above) and M_I. The space quantization of J gives the ordinary Zeeman effect studied in Chapter II, with line separations which, with sufficient field strength, are considerably greater than those of the field-free hyperfine structure components.   Each term with a given M_J is, however, once more split into a number of components corresponding to the different values of M_I.   Since M_I can take values $I, I - 1, I - 2, \cdots, - I$, there are $2I + 1$ components. This number of components is the same for all terms of an atom, since I is constant for a given nucleus.   The splitting in a strong field is shown to the right of Fig. 72 for the simple case $J = \frac{1}{2}$, $I = \frac{3}{2}$.   The splitting of the levels with different M_I is small compared to the separation of the levels $M_J = + \frac{1}{2}$ and $M_J = - \frac{1}{2}$.   It is not due to the interaction of the nuclear spin I with an external magnetic field H, since this is 2000 times smaller than that of J with H; but is due to the interaction between I and J, which is also present in a strong magnetic field and contributes a term $A M_J M_I$ to the energy, similar to the ordinary Paschen-Back effect (p. 113).   The $2I + 1$ components of a term with a given M_J are thus equidistant. A is the constant determining the magnitude of the field-free hyperfine structure splitting.   The difference from the ordinary Paschen-Back effect is that the term corresponding to the term $2ho M_S$ of equation (II, 21) can be disregarded here for all practical purposes, because of the factor 1/2000.   This also accounts for the difference between Figs. 72 and 49.

For a transition which, without field, gives rise to one hypermultiplet, the selection rules in a strong field are: $\Delta M_J = 0, \pm 1$ [identical with (II, 12)] and $\Delta M_I = 0$ (corresponding to $\Delta M_S = 0$).   The first of these rules gives the ordinary anomalous Zeeman effect if at first we disregard nuclear spin.   Because of nuclear spin, however, each of the magnetic levels with a certain

M_J value has $2I + 1$ equidistant components, the separations being different in the upper and lower states. Therefore, considering the selection rule $\Delta M_I = 0$, each anomalous Zeeman component is split into $2I + 1$ lines. This splitting does not depend upon the field strength so long as the latter is sufficiently great to produce an uncoupling of J and I. Thus, simply *by counting up the number of line components, the nuclear spin I can be determined* quite unambiguously from photographs in a sufficiently strong magnetic field. This elegant method for the determination of nuclear spin from hyperfine structure was first employed by Back and Goudsmit for Bi. In a strong magnetic field each of the Zeeman components of Bi consists of 10 components due to nuclear spin, and therefore I must be equal to $\frac{9}{2}$ (a result already obtained above, though with less certainty, from the interval rule).

Statistical weight. It follows from the foregoing discussion that a hyperfine structure term with a given F has a statistical weight $2F + 1$. In hypermultiplets, this statistical weight is important for the determination of intensity ratios, which in turn serve as a check on the analysis of hyperfine structure.

The *total statistical weight* of a term with a given value of J (that is, the total number of single components in a magnetic field, if nuclear spin is included) is:

$$(2J + 1) \times (2I + 1)$$

since we have seen that in the Paschen-Back effect each Zeeman term (single without nuclear spin) splits into $2I + 1$ components. The statistical weight is thus increased, by a factor $2I + 1$, over that previously given (p. 119) where nuclear spin was not allowed for. As this factor is the same for all states of an atom, our earlier discussion of intensities in ordinary multiplets still applies.

Determination of nuclear spin by the Stern-Gerlach experiment. Rabi and his co-workers, employing the foregoing considerations on the Zeeman effect of hyperfine structure, have developed a very beautiful method for the determination of nuclear spin with the aid of atomic rays. For example with the alkalis, disregarding nuclear spin and using any arbitrary field strength, there will be a splitting of an atomic ray into two rays ($M_J = +\frac{1}{2}$ and $M_J = -\frac{1}{2}$), because of the ^2S ground state. If a nuclear spin is present, for a weak field, F (not J) is space quantized. In this case the magnetic moment of the atom has, on the average, the direction of F, and therefore the atomic ray is split into $2F + 1$ (not $2J + 1$) components, where F is the largest of the possible F values (for $J = \frac{1}{2}$ and $I = \frac{3}{2}$, there are 5 components instead of 2).

On the other hand, in a strong field the components of the magnetic moment (which are the deciding factors in the splitting of the ray) take only two values, given by $M_J = +\frac{1}{2}$ and $M_J = -\frac{1}{2}$. The magnetic moment connected with I does not have any appreciable influence on the splitting of the atomic ray, because of the uncoupling of J and I. Thus a splitting into only two rays takes place. Using a strong inhomogeneous field, Rabi and his co-workers first produce such a splitting into two rays. One of the rays is shielded off, and the remaining ray (which may have, for example, $M_J = +\frac{1}{2}$) contains atoms with $M_I = I$, $I - 1, \cdots, - I$. All such atoms, however, have practically the same magnetic moment and, therefore, practically the same deflection. This ray is then sent through a second field, which is weak and extremely inhomogeneous. When the second field is so weak that no Paschen-Back effect can take place, I is no longer uncoupled from J, and there occurs a comparatively large splitting into as many rays as there are M_F values in the ray. There are just $2I + 1$ values of M_F, since the states which had $M_J = -\frac{1}{2}$ in a strong field are no longer present. In this way the magnitude of the nuclear spin is found simply by counting up the number of component atomic rays, as in the Zeeman effect for hyperfine structure. For Na, Rabi and Cohen (94) have found $I = \frac{3}{2}$ (see Fig. 72).

If the variation in the splitting pattern of the atomic ray in the transition from weak to strong fields is investigated in greater detail, the nuclear magnetic moments may also be determined, since the uncoupling of J and I is reached sooner for smaller magnetic moment (cf. above). A more direct method consists in the application of the ordinary Stern-Gerlach experiment either to atoms whose outer electrons have zero magnetic moment, or to diatomic molecules with zero magnetic moment which contain the atoms in question. Much more accurate results have been obtained more recently by Rabi and his coworkers (150) (151) (152) by means of the molecular beam magnetic resonance method.

The results of these procedures for individual nuclei will be given here only for the proton and the deuteron, the nucleus of the heavy hydrogen atom. The *proton*, whose spin $I = \frac{1}{2}$, gives a value of 2.7896 NM [see (151) and (152)], which is remarkably high; whereas the magnetic moment of the *deuteron*, whose spin $I = 1$, is only 0.8565 NM [see (151) and (152)]. *Results;* mentioned methods are listed in Table 17. For the sake of completeness, values obtained by band spectroscopic methods have also been included in the table.

Importance of nuclear spin in the theory of nuclear structure. It is clear that significant conclusions as to the structure of the nucleus may be obtained from the determination of nuclear spin and the magnetic moment belonging to it, just as a fundamental knowledge of the arrangement of the extranuclear electrons was

TABLE 17

OBSERVED VALUES FOR NUCLEAR SPIN

Z	Isotope	I	Z	Isotope	I	Z	Isotope	I
1	H¹	1/2	36	Kr⁸⁶	0	59	Pr¹⁴¹	5/2
	H²	1	37	Rb⁸⁵	5/2	62	Sm?	1/2
2	He⁴	0		Rb⁸⁷	3/2	63	Eu¹⁵¹	5/2
3	Li⁶	1	38	Sr⁸⁶	0		Eu¹⁵³	5/2
	Li⁷	3/2		Sr⁸⁷	9/2	65	Tb¹⁵⁹	3/2
4	Be⁹	1/2(?)		Sr⁸⁸	0	67	Ho¹⁶⁵	7/2
6	C¹²	0	39	Y⁸⁹	1/2	69	Tm¹⁶⁹	1/2
7	N¹⁴	1	41	Cb⁹³	9/2	70	Yb¹⁷¹	1/2
8	O¹⁶	0	42	Mo⁹²,⁹⁴	0		Yb¹⁷³	5/2
9	F¹⁹	1/2		Mo⁹⁵	1/2(?)	71	Lu¹⁷⁵	7/2
10	Ne²⁰	0		Mo⁹⁶	0		Lu¹⁷⁶	≥7
	Ne²²	0		Mo⁹⁷	1/2(?)		Lu¹⁷³,¹⁷⁷	7/2(9/2?)
11	Na²³	3/2		Mo⁹⁸,¹⁰⁰	0	72	Hf¹⁷⁷,¹⁷⁹	1/2(?)
12	Mg²⁴	0(?)	47	Ag¹⁰⁷	1/2		Hf¹⁷⁸,¹⁸⁰	0
13	Al²⁷	5/2		Ag¹⁰⁹	1/2	73	Ta¹⁸¹	7/2
15	P³¹	1/2	48	Cd¹¹⁰	0	74	W¹⁸²	0
16	S³²	0		Cd¹¹¹	1/2		W¹⁸³	1/2(?)
17	Cl³⁵	5/2		Cd¹¹²	0		W¹⁸⁴	0
	Cl³⁷	5/2		Cd¹¹³	1/2		W¹⁸⁶	0
19	K³⁹	3/2		Cd¹¹⁴	0	75	Re¹⁸⁵	5/2
	K⁴¹	3/2		Cd¹¹⁶	0		Re¹⁸⁷	5/2
20	Ca⁴⁰	0(?)	49	In¹¹³	9/2(?)	77	Ir¹⁹¹	1/2
21	Sc⁴⁵	7/2		In¹¹⁵	9/2		Ir¹⁹³	3/2
23	V⁵¹	7/2	50	Sn¹¹⁷	1/2	78	Pt¹⁹⁴	0
25	Mn⁵⁵	5/2		Sn¹¹⁹	1/2		Pt¹⁹⁵	1/2
27	Co⁵⁹	7/2	51	Sb¹²¹	5/2		Pt¹⁹⁶	0
29	Cu⁶³	3/2		Sb¹²³	7/2	79	Au¹⁹⁷	3/2
	Cu⁶⁵	3/2	52	Te¹²⁶	0	80	Hg¹⁹⁸	0
30	Zn⁶⁴	0		Te¹²⁸	0		Hg¹⁹⁹	1/2
	Zn⁶⁶	0		Te¹³⁰	0		Hg²⁰⁰	0
	Zn⁶⁷	5/2	53	I¹²⁷	5/2		Hg²⁰¹	3/2
	Zn⁶⁸	0	54	Xe¹²⁹	1/2		Hg²⁰²	0
31	Ga⁶⁹	3/2		Xe¹³¹	3/2		Hg²⁰⁴	0
	Ga⁷¹	3/2		Xe¹³²	0	81	Tl²⁰³	1/2
33	As⁷⁵	3/2		Xe¹³⁴	0		Tl²⁰⁵	1/2
34	Se⁷⁸	0		Xe¹³⁶	0	82	Pb²⁰⁴	0
	Se⁸⁰	0	55	Cs¹³³	7/2		Pb²⁰⁶	0
35	Br⁷⁹	3/2	56	Ba¹³⁵	3/2		Pb²⁰⁷	1/2
	Br⁸¹	3/2		Ba¹³⁶	0		Pb²⁰⁸	0
36	Kr⁸²	0		Ba¹³⁷	3/2	83	Bi²⁰⁹	9/2
	Kr⁸³	9/2		Ba¹³⁸	0	91	Pa²³¹	3/2
	Kr⁸⁴	0	57	La¹³⁹	7/2			

obtained from the evaluation of their angular momenta. However, the relationships for nuclei are more difficult to find since, for each nucleus, only one nuclear spin can be determined—that belonging to the lowest state of the nucleus. Excited nuclear states occur only for natural or artificial disintegration processes and cannot be investigated optically—or, at least, only with great difficulty. It is due to this that we have not yet made much progress with the systematization of the spin values occurring for different nuclei (representation by the spin of the individual nuclear components). For speculative work in this field, Schüler (100), Landé (101), Bartlett (102), and Bethe and Bacher (138) should be consulted.

Apart from conclusions regarding the spin and the magnetic moment of the nucleus and also the nuclear radius, the investigation of hyperfine structure may provide information about a possible *asymmetry* of the nucleus, as was recently pointed out by Schüler and Schmidt (139). In some cases there occur in hypermultiplets deviations from the interval rule which are ascribed to a *quadrupole moment of the nucleus*—that is, to a deviation from spherical symmetry.

CHAPTER VI

Some Experimental Results and Applications

1. Energy Level Diagrams and Ionization Potentials

In earlier chapters, examples have been given of a number of energy level diagrams obtained from analyses of corresponding line spectra. They were the energy level diagrams of the atoms H (Fig. 13); He (Fig. 27); Li (Fig. 24); K (Fig. 28); Be (Fig. 61); Ca (Fig. 32); C (Fig. 55); N (Fig. 56); O (Fig. 59). In order to show at least one example from each of the columns of the periodic table, the energy level diagrams of Al I and Cl I are reproduced in Figs. 73 and 74 (pp. 198 and 199).

In addition, the energy level diagram of Hg, which is important for many practical applications, is reproduced in Fig. 75 (p. 202). It is qualitatively similar to Ca (Fig. 32), except that the triplet splitting is very much larger (cf. also the Hg spectrogram in Fig. 5, p. 6).

Finally, Fig. 76 shows the energy level diagram of Ni I as an illustration of the complicated term spectrum of one of the elements for which a building-up of inner shells takes place (see p. 203).

If for an atom several terms T of the same series have been found, they can be represented by a *Rydberg formula:*

$$T = A - \frac{(Z - p)^2 R}{(m + a)^2} \qquad \textbf{(VI, 1)}$$

where T is measured against the lowest term (m = running number, $Z - p$ = number of charges of core; see pp. 55 and 60 f.). In order to calculate the two unknown constants A and a, at least two members of the term series must be known, although more known terms are preferable. For $m \rightarrow \infty$, $T = A$; that is, the constant A empirically found is the *ionization potential* of the atom or ion in question measured in cm^{-1}. If an absorption series is observed for the atom, A is the wave number of the series limit (cf. p. 59). The results obtained in this way for the various elements are given in Table 18 (pp. 200–201), which contains not only the ionization potential of the normal atoms (column I) but also that of the single- and multiple-charged ions (columns II to V). Higher ionization potentials than the fifth are not included, although they are known in a few

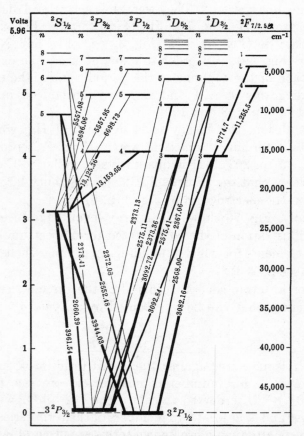

Fig. 73. Energy Level Diagram of Al I [Grotrian (8)]. n is the true principal quantum number of the emission electron. Only the normal doublet terms are indicated, all of which go to the same limit. Series of anomalous terms (doublets and quartets) have been observed by Paschen (64).

cases. The evaluation of ionization potentials is particularly important for practical applications.[1]

Energy level diagrams of atoms and ions with one, two, and three valence electrons are given fairly completely in Grotrian (8). Complete tables of all terms of atoms and ions observed up to 1932 have been collected by Bacher and Goudsmit (22), whose data have been used for most of the energy level diagrams reproduced in this book.

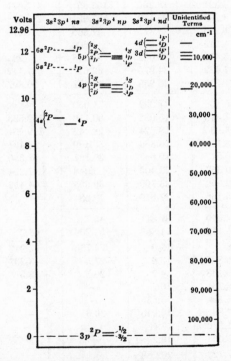

Fig. 74. Energy Level Diagram of Cl I [Kiess and de Bruin (103)]. Terms belonging to the same electron configuration are drawn under one another. Apart from the ground state, the different multiplet components are not drawn separately in the diagram.

---

[1] For the sake of completeness, there are included in Table 18 some values of ionization potentials which have been obtained by other methods (electron collision measurements, and so on) for want of spectroscopic data. Uncertain values are indicated by $\sim$.

TABLE 18

IONIZATION POTENTIALS OF THE ELEMENTS (IN VOLTS)

All values are based on the new conversion factor 1 volt = 8067.5 cm^{-1} (see p. 10).   Uncertain or estimated values are indicated by $\sim$.

Element	I	II	III	IV	V
1 H	13.595	—	—	—	—
2 He	24.581	54.405	—	—	—
3 Li	5.390	75.622	122.427	—	
4 Be	9.321	18.207	153.85	217.671	—
5 B	8.296	25.119	37.921	259.31	340.156
6 C	11.265	24.377	47.866	64.478	392.0
7 N	14.545	29.606	47.609	77.4	97 87
8 O	13.615	35.082	55.118	77.28	113.7
9 F	17.422	34.979	62.647	87.142	114.22
10 Ne	21.559	40.958	63.427	96.897	126.43
11 Na	5.138	47.292	71.650	—	—
12 Mg	7.645	15.032	80.119	109.533	
13 Al	5.985	18.824	28.442	119.961	154.28
14 Si	8.149	16.339	33.489	45.131	166.5
15 P	10.977	19.653	30.157	51.356	65.01
16 S	10.357	23.405	35.048	47.294	62.2
17 Cl	12.959	23.799	39.905	54.452	67.8
18 A	15.756	27.619	40.68	$\sim$61	$\sim$78
19 K	4.340	31.811	45.7	—	—
20 Ca	6.112	11.868	51.209	67.2	—
21 Sc	$\sim$6.7	$\sim$12.9	24.753	73.913	91.8
22 Ti	6.835	$\sim$13.6	$\sim$27.5	43.237	99.84
23 V	6.738	14.2	$\sim$26.5	$\sim$48.5	$\sim$64
24 Cr	6.761	$\sim$16.7	—	—	$\sim$73.0
25 Mn	7.429	15.636	—	—	$\sim$76.0
26 Fe	7.86	16.240	30.6	—	—
27 Co	7.876	17.4	—	—	—
28 Ni	7.633	18.2	—	—	—
29 Cu	7.723	20.283	—	—	—
30 Zn	9.392	17.960	$\sim$39.7	—	—
31 Ga	5.997	20.509	30.7	64.1	—
32 Ge	8.126	15.93	34.216	45.7	93.43
33 As	10.5	20.2	27.297	50.123	62.61
34 Se	9.750	21.691	34.078	42.900	73.11
35 Br	11.844	$\sim$19.2	35.888	—	—
36 Kr	13.996	$\sim$26.5	36.94	$\sim$68	—

TABLE 18 (*Continued*)

IONIZATION POTENTIALS OF THE ELEMENTS (IN VOLTS)

All values are based on the new conversion factor 1 volt = 8067.5 cm^{-1}
(see p. 10).   Uncertain or estimated values are indicated by $\sim$.

Element	I	II	III	IV	V
37 Rb	4.176	27.499	$\sim$47	$\sim$80	—
38 Sr	5.693	11.026	—	—	—
39 Y	$\sim$6.6	12.4	20.5	—	$\sim$77
40 Zr	6.951	14.03	24.10	33.972	
41 Cb	—	—	24.332	—	$\sim$50
42 Mo	7.383	—	—	—	61.12
45 Rh	$\sim$7.7	—	—	—	—
46 Pd	8.334	19.9	—	—	—
47 Ag	7.574	21.960	36.10	—	—
48 Cd	8.991	16.904	38.217	—	—
49 In	5.785	18.867	28.030	58.037	—
50 Sn	7.332	14.629	30.654	40.740	81.13
51 Sb	8.64	$\sim$18.6	24.825	44.147	55.69
52 Te	9.007	21.543	30.611	37.817	60.27
53 I	10.44	19.010	—	—	—
54 Xe	12.127	21.204	32.115	$\sim$46	$\sim$76
55 Cs	3.893	32.458	$\sim$35	$\sim$51	$\sim$58
56 Ba	5.2097	10.001	—	—	—
57 La	5.614	11.43	19.17	—	—
58 Ce	$\sim$6.57	—	19.70	36.715	—
62 Sm	5.6	$\sim$11.4	—	—	—
63 Eu	5.67	11.24	—	—	—
64 Gd	6.16	—	—	—	—
70 Yb	6.25	12.11	—	—	—
74 W	7.98	—	—	—	—
76 Os	$\sim$8.7	—	—	—	—
77 Ir	9.2	—	—	—	—
78 Pt	9.0	$\sim$19.3	—	—	—
79 Au	9.223	20.1	—	—	—
80 Hg	10.434	18.752	34.5	$\sim$72	$\sim$82
81 Tl	6.106	20.423	29.8	50.8	—
82 Pb	7.415	15.04	32.1	38.97	69.7
83 Bi	—	16.7	25.56	45.3	56.0
86 Rn	10.746	—	—	—	—
88 Ra	5.278	10.145	—	—	—
90 Th	—	—	29.5	—	—

2. Magnetic Moment and Magnetic Susceptibility

Magnetic moment of an atom. According to the discussion of the Zeeman effect in Chapter II, the magnetic moment $\mathbf{\mu}_J$ of an atom in a given state has the average magnitude

$$\mathbf{\mu}_J = \sqrt{J(J+1)}\, g\mu_0$$

where μ_0 is the Bohr magneton (p. 103) and g is the Landé

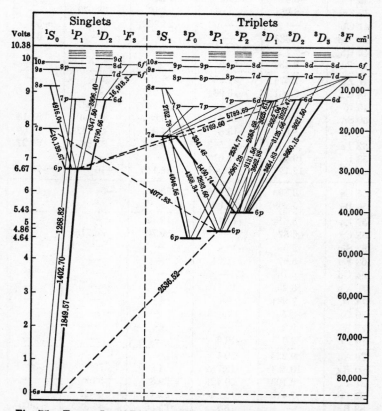

Fig. 75.   Energy Level Diagram of Hg I [Grotrian (8)].   The wave lengths of the more intense Hg lines are given (cf. Fig. 5, p. 6).   The symbols $6p$, etc., written near each level, indicate the true principal quantum number and the l value of the emission electron.

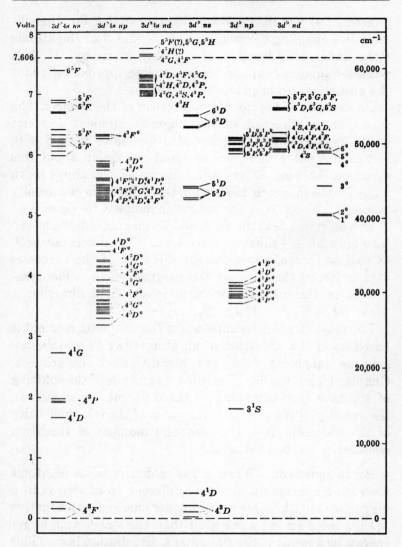

Fig. 76. Energy Level Diagram of Ni I [Russell (104)]. In general, the individual multiplet components are drawn separately, except for a few positions where too many terms nearly coincide with one another. Different terms of the same electron configuration (drawn above one another) do not usually go to the same limit. The lowest series limit (lowest ionization potential) is indicated by a dotted line.

g-factor. $\mathfrak{y}_J$ has the opposite direction to *J*. For Russell-Saunders coupling *g* depends on *J*, *L*, and *S* of the atomic state under consideration in the way given by (II, 15). Russell-Saunders coupling holds to a close approximation for the ground states of practically all atoms.

On account of the double magnetism of the electron, the *instantaneous* direction of the magnetic moment does not generally fall in the direction of *J* for states with $S \neq 0$, but carries out a more or less rapid precession about this direction (cf. Figs. 47 and 48). However, the above mean value for the magnetic moment in the *J* direction can usually be used.[2] For $J = 0$, the magnetic moment becomes 0.

In a magnetic field the atom and its magnetic moment can take only $2J + 1$ different directions. The precession of *J*, as well as that of $\mathfrak{y}_J$, about the direction of the magnetic field is faster, the stronger the magnetic field. The component of the magnetic moment in the field direction is $Mg\mu_0$ ($M = J, J - 1, J - 2, \cdots, - J$).[3]

The most direct determination of the magnetic moment is based upon the deflection of an atomic ray in an inhomogeneous magnetic field (see Stern-Gerlach experiment, Chapter II, section 3). From the magnitude of the splitting of the rays (corresponding to the different orientations), the velocity of the rays, and the value of the inhomogeneity of the magnetic field, the magnetic moment of the atom considered can be evaluated.[4]

Paramagnetism. When a gas which consists of atoms possessing a magnetic moment different from zero is in a magnetic field, the states with smaller energy (with negative *M*) are more strongly occupied than the states with larger energy, as a result of the Boltzmann distribution law. This

---

[2] For accurate investigations, the component of the magnetic moment which is at right angles to *J* must sometimes be taken into account. [Cf. Van Vleck (36).]

[3] Often the maximum value of these components, $Jg\mu_0$, is given as the magnetic moment of the atom (and not the component $\mathfrak{y}_J$ in the direction of *J*).

[4] Primarily one measures the components of the magnetic moment in the field direction and not μ_J itself (see footnote 3, above).

means that *the atoms align preferentially with their magnetic moment in the field direction,* as would be expected. The stronger the magnetic field, the greater will be the energy difference for the various orientations in the field and, therefore, the greater the difference in the number of atoms occupying each state. For a given field, the difference in these numbers will be greater, the lower the temperature, since the arrangement of the atoms will be less hindered by unordered heat motion. The fact that in the presence of a magnetic field, on the average, more atoms will align with their magnetic moments parallel to the field direction than antiparallel to it results in a *magnetic moment per unit volume,* **P**, whose action is added to that of an external field and which can be experimentally determined. The gas is *paramagnetic.* **P** (the intensity of magnetization) is proportional, to a first approximation, to the field strength **H**, and is inversely proportional to the absolute temperature **T**. The proportionality factor depends mainly on the magnitude of the magnetic moment of the atom considered. The theoretical formula for a not too large **H** and a not too small **T** is: [5]

$$P = \frac{J(J+1)g^2\mu_0^2 N_L}{3kT} H = \frac{\mu_J^2 N_L}{3kT} H \qquad \textbf{(VI, 2)}$$

where N_L is the number of molecules per cc. The coefficient of **H**

$$\kappa = \frac{J(J+1)g^2\mu_0^2 N_L}{3kT} = \frac{\mu_J^2 N_L}{3kT} \qquad \textbf{(VI, 3)}$$

is called the *paramagnetic susceptibility.*[6] It is inversely

---

[5] An additional term independent of temperature occurs in the more accurate formula. This term is due in part to the influence of the component of **u** perpendicular to **J** (mentioned in footnote 2, above), and in part to diamagnetism (see p. 207). In most cases, though not in all, this term is negligible compared to the main term given in (VI, 2).

[6] Very often, instead of κ, the molar susceptibility is given:

$$\chi = \kappa \frac{G}{\rho}$$

where G is the molecular weight and ρ is the density. In order to obtain χ, in formula (VI, 3) N, the number of molecules per mol, is substituted for N_L.

proportional to the temperature (*Curie's law*). The paramagnetic behavior of a substance in the gaseous state can be predicted according to (VI, 2) and (VI, 3) when J and g have been determined from the spectrum; or, conversely, from (VI, 3) an experimental value for the magnetic moment μ_J of an atom may be derived (cf. Table 19, p. 209).

Paramagnetic saturation. The Zeeman splitting in the magnetic fields practically attainable is so small that for room temperatures (and, increasingly, for higher temperatures) the energy difference between the levels $M = +J$ and $M = -J$ is exceedingly small compared to kT. Consequently, under these conditions, the difference in the numbers of atoms occupying these two states is very small. At room temperature and $H = 20,000$ oersted, for the alkalis, for which $J = S = \frac{1}{2}$ and $g = 2$, the ratio of the number of atoms oriented parallel and antiparallel to the field is 100 : 99.1. The orienting of the atoms in the direction of the field increases with increasing field strength and decreasing temperature. When $M = -J$ for all atoms, a further increase in the magnetic moment per unit volume (P) in the direction of the field is no longer possible—that is, a state of *paramagnetic saturation* is reached. At room temperature, the field strength necessary for the production of this state (in contrast to ferromagnetic saturation) is so great that it cannot be realized (cf. the above example). Saturation can be reached only at very low temperatures. However, all substances whose atoms have a magnetic moment different from zero are then in the solid state (see below).

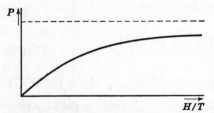

Fig. 77. **Dependence of Magnetization** P **on Field Strength and Absolute Temperature,** H/T **(Langevin).** The dotted horizontal line corresponds to paramagnetic saturation.

atoms have a magnetic moment different from zero are then in the solid state (see below).

Fig. 77 gives the dependence of the magnetization P on H/T, according to a formula of Langevin.[7] Formula (VI, 2) applies only to the linear part of the curve near the origin. It is seen that, with increasing H/T, P does not increase above a limiting value corresponding to saturation.

Diamagnetism. Apart from the orienting effect which the magnetic field has upon the individual atomic magnetic dipoles, the field also exerts an *induction* effect on all atoms; that is, a current flowing in a closed circuit is induced in each atom, in accordance with the Faraday law of induction. This current, of course, arises from an acceleration or retardation of the electrons in their orbits superimposed on the ordinary motion of the electrons. The superimposed induction currents are so directed that their magnetic moment is in the opposite direction to the external field. Thus, in contrast to the paramagnetic directional effect, the diamagnetic induction effect produces a magnetic moment per unit volume *antiparallel* to the field. This effect is, however, very small and can be conveniently observed only when no paramagnetic directional effect is present—that is, when the atom considered has no magnetic moment ($J = 0$). This is the case for all inert gases as well as for most molecular gases.

Paramagnetism of ions in solutions and in solids. Very few atoms having $J \neq 0$ (that is, atoms having a magnetic moment) occur free in the gaseous state; thus the above theoretical results can be tested only for a few gases. Up to the present time, measurements of susceptibility have been carried out only on the vapors of the alkali metals. These measurements agree, within the limits of experimental error, with formula (VI, 3), where $J = S = \frac{1}{2}$ and $g = 2$ [Gerlach (105)].

Because of the difficulty of investigating other para-

---

[7] This formula is derived according to the classical theory. Allowing for the quantum theory makes necessary only a slight correction. [Cf. Van Vleck (36).]

magnetic atoms in the gaseous state, we have to resort to the investigation of paramagnetic ions in solutions and in crystals to test the theory.   However, most salts and solutions of salts are diamagnetic, since the ions present in them have the inert gas configuration, $J = 0$ and thus $\mu_J = 0$. Examples are Na^+, Ca^{++}, O^{--}, Cl^-, and so on.   (See also section 3 of this chapter.)   However, ions with a magnetic moment $(J \neq 0)$ do occur for those elements in which a building-up of inner shells is taking place (see Chapter III). The corresponding salts and their solutions are consequently paramagnetic.   The rare earths, for example, usually occur as trivalent ions, which generally do not have the inert gas configuration (inner $4f$ shell is not filled; cf. Table 13, p. 141).   The resulting state of the ion usually has $L \neq 0$, $S \neq 0$, $J \neq 0$ and, therefore, $\mu_J \neq 0$.   The paramagnetism shown by the salts and salt solutions of the rare earths follows, very nearly, the Curie law:

$$\kappa = \frac{\text{constant}}{T}$$

From this observation it must be concluded that these ions in solution or in the crystal have the possibility of orienting themselves more or less freely, as have atoms in the gaseous state.   Such a conclusion is plausible in view of the fact that, in solutions and, similarly, in crystals, the individual ions are rather widely separated from one another either by the diamagnetic solvent or by other larger ions which are themselves diamagnetic (for example, SO_4^{--} and water of crystallization).   There is also the further fact that the magnetic moment is produced by *inner* electrons.   Even quantitatively, there is close agreement between the observed susceptibilities and the values calculated, according to (VI, 3), from the J and g values for the ground state of the ion.   To be sure, the ground states of the rare-earth ions have, for the most part, not yet been determined spectroscopically; they can, however, be theoretically predicted on the basis of the building-up principle and the Hund rule (p. 135).

In Table 19 the ground states and the number of electrons present in the incomplete $4f$ shell are given. The g values, as obtained from the Landé g-formula, are listed also, together with $g\sqrt{J(J+1)}$. According to the foregoing $g\sqrt{J(J+1)}$ is the magnetic moment of the ion in units of μ_0. In the column next to these calculated values appear the means of the experimental values for the magnetic mo-

TABLE 19

CALCULATED AND OBSERVED VALUES FOR THE MAGNETIC
MOMENTS OF THE RARE EARTH IONS

Ion	State	g	μ_J IN UNITS OF μ_0	
			Calculated Value $g\sqrt{J(J+1)}$	Observed Value
La^{+++}	$^1S_0$	$\%$	0.00	Diamagnetic
Ce^{+++}	$4f$ $^2F_{5/2}$	$\%$	2.54	2.51
Pr^{+++}	$4f^2$ $^3H_4$	$\frac{4}{5}$	3.58	3.53
Nd^{+++}	$4f^3$ $^4I_{9/2}$	$\frac{8}{11}$	3.62	3.55
Il^{+++}	$4f^4$ $^5I_4$	$\frac{3}{5}$	2.68	—
Sm^{+++}	$4f^5$ $^6H_{5/2}$	$\frac{2}{7}$	0.84	1.46
Eu^{+++}	$4f^6$ $^7F_0$	$\%$	0.00	3.37
Gd^{+++}	$4f^7$ $^8S_{7/2}$	2	7.94	8.0$_0$
Tb^{+++}	$4f^8$ $^7F_6$	$\frac{3}{2}$	9.72	9.3$_3$
Dy^{+++}	$4f^9$ $^6H_{15/2}$	$\frac{4}{3}$	10.65	10.5$_5$
Ho^{+++}	$4f^{10}$ $^5I_8$	$\frac{5}{4}$	10.61	10.4
Er^{+++}	$4f^{11}$ $^4I_{15/2}$	$\frac{6}{5}$	9.60	9.5
Tm^{+++}	$4f^{12}$ $^3H_6$	$\frac{7}{6}$	7.56	7.3$_5$
Yb^{+++}	$4f^{13}$ $^2F_{7/2}$	$\frac{8}{7}$	4.53	4.5
Lu^{+++}	$4f^{14}$ $^1S_0$	$\%$	0.00	Diamagnetic

ments. The latter have been obtained by different authors from observations of magnetic susceptibilities of the solid sulphates $M_2(SO_4)_3,8H_2O$, according to formula (VI, 3). With the exception of Sm^{+++} and Eu^{+++}, the agreement is very satisfactory. The discrepancies in these two cases have been completely accounted for by a refinement of the theory, proposed by Van Vleck·and Frank [cf. (36)], who have calculated as values for these ions 1.55 and 3.40.[8]

When the susceptibilities of the ions in the iron series from Sc to Ni are calculated in the same way, at first no agreement with experimental values is obtained. This apparent discrepancy is due to the fact that, for these ions, the multiplet splitting in the ground state is so small that, at room temperature, not only the lowest component but also the higher components are present in appreciable amount. Consequently, we must calculate the magnetic moment for all the components. The mean values obtained by using suitable weighting (corresponding to the Boltzmann factor) agree more closely with experimental values, insofar as accurate data are available. [Cf. Hund (7); Van Vleck (36).]

Magnetocaloric effect; production of extremely low temperatures. The paramagnetism of ions (in particular, the fact that this paramagnetism follows the Langevin-Curie law to very low temperatures even in the solid state) has recently led to an important application—namely, the production of extremely low temperatures (following a suggestion of Giauque and Debye).

When a magnetic field is applied to a paramagnetic substance, there is at the first instant a uniform distribution of the magnetic moments over all possible directions. In order that an atom, whose magnetic moment was originally antiparallel to the field direction, may be able to align itself in the field direction, energy must be taken away—the amount being greater, the stronger the field. This removal of energy is accomplished only by thermal collisions or, in the case of solids, by heat vibrations. The heat energy is thereby raised, and consequently a *rise in temperature* takes place when a magnetic field is applied. This is called the *magnetocaloric effect*. Corresponding to the fact already

---

[8] Their calculations involve making a more exact allowance for the fact that the instantaneous direction of the magnetic moment does not coincide with J (see p. 204) and that, further, other multiplet components of the ground state are excited at the room temperature at which observations are made. Correspondingly, the values of the magnetic moment for Sm^{+++} and Eu^{+++} given above are only effective values and do not represent the magnetic moment of the free atom in the ground state, as the values for the other ions do for which the correction mentioned makes no appreciable difference.

mentioned that in the stationary state at room temperature only a very small percentage of the atoms take a preferred direction in a magnetic field, the magnetocaloric effect is so small at room temperature that it cannot be observed.[9] With decreasing temperature, the amount of heat produced becomes more and more noticeable compared to the total heat content of the body. The effect has actually been observed at very low temperatures.

The converse of this process—that is, a *cooling by adiabatic removal of the magnetic field*—has also been observed and is due to the consumption of energy in reproducing the completely unordered direction distribution of the individual elementary magnets. This cooling effect has recently been used for the production of extremely low temperatures.

To simplify matters, let us suppose that the ions have $J = \frac{1}{2}$ so that only two magnetic sub-levels $M = +\frac{1}{2}$ and $M = -\frac{1}{2}$ are present. Due to the interaction with the inhomogeneous electric and magnetic field in the crystal (the field between the ions), there exists a small energy difference ΔE_0 between the two sub-levels, even for $H = 0$. Only those substances are useful for the magnetic cooling method for which ΔE_0 is so small that, even for the lowest temperatures reached by the ordinary methods (of the order of 1°K), approximately the same number of atoms are in the two sub-states.

If now a sufficiently strong magnetic field H is applied, the splitting between the levels $M = +\frac{1}{2}$ and $M = -\frac{1}{2}$ becomes much larger [namely, $2\mu_0 H$; cf. equation (II, 7)], and therefore, if thermal equilibrium has been reached— that is, if the heat produced by the ordinary magnetocaloric effect has been taken away—most of the atoms will be in the state $M = -\frac{1}{2}$ and only a very small fraction ($e^{-2\mu_0 H/kT}$) in the state $M = +\frac{1}{2}$. If at this stage the field is removed, at the first instant, even for $H = 0$, most of the atoms are in the state $M = -\frac{1}{2}$ and energy has to be supplied from

---

[9] A magnetocaloric effect is observed for ferromagnetic substances at room temperature. The theory of this effect is rather more complicated.

the heat vibrations of the crystal lattice in order to reach the equilibrium distribution of the atoms between the $M = +\frac{1}{2}$ and $M = -\frac{1}{2}$ states—that is, the temperature of the substance is lowered. The decrease in temperature is considerable since, as can be shown, the energy of the lattice vibrations is small compared to ΔE_0. However, this method only works if ΔE_0 is sufficiently small, because for large ΔE_0, even at zero field, the equilibrium distribution gives most of the atoms in the state $M = -\frac{1}{2}$. Thus, only substances such as the rare-earth salts that obey Curie's law to very low temperatures are suitable for the process. In this way de Haas and Wiersma (106) have reached a temperature as low as 0.0044°K.

At zero field the ratio $N_{+1/2} : N_{-1/2}$ of the number of atoms in the states $M = +\frac{1}{2}$ and $M = -\frac{1}{2}$ is given by $e^{-\Delta E_0/kT}$, which for suitable substances is appreciably smaller than 1 only for temperatures $\ll 1°$K. If $N_{+1/2} : N_{-1/2}$ is < 1, it means that the substance has a magnetic moment and therefore conversely, by measuring the magnetic moment, $N_{+1/2} : N_{-1/2}$ can be measured and the temperature determined according to the relation

$$\frac{N_{+1/2}}{N_{-1/2}} = e^{-\Delta E_0/kT} \tag{VI, 4}$$

For the field H, $N_{+1/2} : N_{-1/2} = e^{-2\mu_0 H/kT_i}$ where T_i is the initial temperature (about 1°K). For large H values, $e^{-2\mu_0 H/kT_i}$ is much smaller than $e^{-\Delta E_0/kT_i}$. Since, at the first instant after removing the field, $N_{+1/2} : N_{-1/2}$ is unchanged ($= e^{-2\mu_0 H/kT_i}$), the apparent temperature T_a [which corresponds to the $N_{+1/2} : N_{-1/2}$ value according to (VI, 4)] is much lower than T_i because $\Delta E_0 \ll 2\mu_0 H$. T_a can be immediately calculated from

$$e^{-\Delta E_0/kT_a} = e^{-2\mu_0 H/kT_i}$$

which means that

$$T_a = \frac{\Delta E_0 \cdot T_i}{2\mu_0 H} \tag{VI, 5}$$

Due to the fact mentioned above that the heat energy of the lattice vibrations is very small compared to ΔE_0, the true temperatures obtained after equilibrium has been reached are not very different from the T_a values.[10] It is seen from equation (VI, 5) that T_a is lower, the smaller ΔE_0 and the larger H.

---

[10] Recently Heitler and Teller (142) have shown that at temperatures below 1°K the heat exchange is so slow that usually equilibrium between lattice vibrations and ΔE_0 is not reached. This would mean that the observed

3. Chemical Applications

Periodicity of chemical properties. In Chapter III it was shown how the periodicity of the spectroscopic properties of the elements of the periodic system results from the building-up principle together with the Pauli principle. In other words, it was explained how, at certain intervals, elements recur with qualitatively the same energy level diagrams and, therefore, qualitatively the same spectra. These periods coincide with the periods of chemical properties, on the basis of which the periodic system was originally formulated. This circumstance—that chemically similar elements are also spectroscopically similar—strongly suggests that the foundation of spectroscopic periodicity on the building-up principle likewise provides the foundation for chemical periodicity. Some general grounds for the fact that such is actually the case will first be given.

The chemical properties of an element depend, without doubt, on the behavior of the *outer* electrons of the atom, since when atoms approach, these outer electrons strongly influence one another. This leads to chemical reaction, molecule formation, and the formation of liquids or solids. The *inner* electrons are mainly inoperative in chemical processes, since they are much more tightly bound than the outer electrons (because of higher effective nuclear charge). The energies necessary to influence appreciably the inner electrons are thus very much greater, as is shown by the higher spark spectra and the X-ray spectra. Apart from that, the distance of the inner electrons of an atom from the electrons of another atom is greater and, therefore, the extent of the interaction is necessarily smaller than for the outer electrons.

Naturally the nucleus and the inner electrons do indirectly influence the chemical properties of atoms. The nucleus is

---

low temperatures refer to the orientation of J only (ratio $N_{+1/2} : N_{-1/2}$), whereas the lattice vibrations still correspond to a higher temperature. But, since the energy of the lattice vibrations does not form an appreciable part of the total heat content, one is yet justified in claiming that these low temperatures have been reached.

responsible, by its charge, for the total number of electrons of an atom, and the inner electrons affect the energy relationships of the outer electrons by a partial shielding of the nuclear charge. Apart from that, the nuclear mass can sometimes influence reaction velocity.

The chemical properties of an element are thus essentially the properties of the outer electrons of an atom [11] and must depend on the arrangement of these electrons, on their quantum numbers, on the way in which their angular momentum vectors are added together—that is, on just those quantities which we can predict theoretically on the basis of the building-up principle and which we can evaluate empirically with the help of spectra. The foregoing is the real reason why spectroscopically similar elements are also chemically similar, and why chemical periodicity and spectroscopic periodicity coincide.

In principle it must, therefore, be possible to derive theoretically all the chemical properties of any atom, with the help of the complete energy level diagram obtained from spectra (including electron configurations). Up to the present time, on account of mathematical difficulties, no great progress has been made toward the completion of this program.

Although the complete theory is not yet developed, it is already possible to draw, from the observed energy level diagrams of some of the elements, a number of conclusions of importance in chemistry and to obtain an understanding of some of the characteristic properties of these elements. It is not the object of this book to give a complete treatment of these applications. Instead, we shall discuss a few characteristic examples from which it will be realized that even the more complicated considerations of the previous chapters are of importance for a fuller understanding of certain chemical facts.

Types of chemical binding (valence). The chemical behavior of an atom is characterized mainly by its *valence*

---

[11] This connection was first recognized by Kossel.

number, or *valency;* that is, the number of univalent atoms
with which an atom can enter into chemical combination
at the same time (or double the number of divalent atoms,
and so on). An atom has often several valencies. For
example, Cl has valencies of 1, 3, 5, and 7.

Two main types of chemical valence must be distinguished. (1) It has been found that the members of one
large group of chemical compounds—in particular, the in-
organic salts—are built up from positive and negative
ions. The forces which hold them together are the ordinary
Coulomb forces of attraction between positive and negative
charges. This type of compound is called an *ionic compound* or a *heteropolar compound.* The term *electrovalent
compound* is also used. In order to understand the formation of these compounds, it is first of all necessary to consider in greater detail the *ionization potential* (position of
the ground term). (2) In contrast to these ionic compounds are the compounds belonging to the second large
group—for example, the elementary molecules H_2, O_2, N_2;
most organic molecules; and others which are built up not
from ions but from atoms. Because of this structure, they
are called *atomic* or *homopolar compounds.* The term
covalent compound is also used. An actual understanding
of the forces holding these atomic compounds together was
first made possible by quantum mechanics. For this purpose it is necessary to take account of the *term type of the
ground state* of the atom, together with the type and position
of the other low-lying terms.

The ionization potential. In Table 18 (p. 200) are listed
the first and higher ionization potentials obtained spectroscopically for the elements. The dependence of the ionization potential of the neutral atom on the atomic number is
given graphically in Fig. 78. The most noticeable regularity is that the curve has a steep maximum for the inert
gases and a minimum for the alkalis. The opposite chemical behavior of these two groups of elements is due largely

to this fact.   The underlying reason for it is that the alkalis have a single electron outside closed shells, whereas the inert gases have no electrons outside closed shells.   An electron can be removed from a closed shell only with difficulty; a single electron in an outer shell is, on the other hand, easily removable.

For a single electron outside closed shells, the nuclear charge is so completely shielded that Z_{eff} is approximately 1. Therefore the energy of this outer electron corresponds approximately to that for hydrogen in an orbit with the corresponding principal quantum number.   Apart from $n = 1$, these energies (term values) are small (of the order of 3 volts), and consequently the ionization potentials of the alkalis are also small, since for them $n \geqq 2$.   The decrease in ionization potential in the alkali group is explained by the increase in n.   On the other hand, for the inert gases and also, though to a somewhat less degree, for the halogens (which have completely or nearly completely closed outer shells), the nuclear shielding for an electron in such a shell is very much smaller, since all the electrons in the shell are at approximately the same distance from the nucleus. Therefore the ionization potential is very much greater than it would be for a single electron with the same principal quantum number.

The ionization potentials of the other elements lie between those of the alkalis and the halogens.   For the alkaline earths the first ionization potential is somewhat greater than for the alkalis, but the second ionization potential is still comparatively small for the same reason that the first ionization potential of the alkalis is small.   Therefore the alkaline earths can occur relatively easily as doubly charged positive ions (in contrast to the alkalis).   Correspondingly, the elements of the third column may occur as triply charged ions.

Electron affinity.   While the alkalis, alkaline earths, and earths easily give up electrons to form positive ions, the

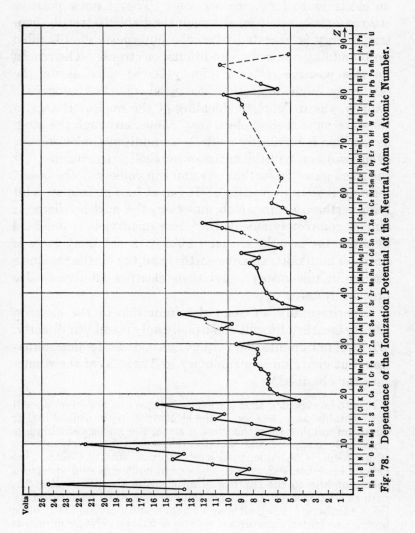

Fig. 78. Dependence of the Ionization Potential of the Neutral Atom on Atomic Number.

halogens and the elements of the oxygen group readily take on electrons to form *negative* ions. They have a positive *electron affinity;* that is, although they are electrically neutral, energy is liberated when the outermost shell is filled up by adding one or two additional electrons. The reason for this positive electron affinity is the same as for the relatively high ionization potential of the halogens— namely, the incomplete shielding of the nuclear charge in the outermost shell of electrons. Thus, although the atom as a whole is obviously neutral, an additional electron (or even two) can be held in the outer shell. In contrast, for the inert gases no further electron can come into the outermost shell (Pauli principle). It can at best go into an orbit lying farther out, in which, however, the nuclear charge is almost completely shielded. Consequently, it is not held in this orbit and the electron affinity of the inert gases is zero. The alkalis, alkaline earths, and the earths are quite similar in this respect, and their electron affinity is also practically zero.

Experimentally an exact determination of the electron affinity is rather difficult and usually only possible indirectly. We shall not go into the various methods for its determination, but give simply a summary in Table 20 of the results thus far obtained.[12]

It is to be expected that the excited states of a negative ion will not be stable since, as soon as the electron is in an orbit of higher quantum number than the ground state, the nuclear shielding is practically complete and therefore the additional electron is no longer held. Consequently discrete electron affinity spectra have never been observed. Even the continuous emission spectrum corresponding to the capture of an electron by a neutral atom, such as a halogen atom, has not yet been observed with certainty [cf. Oldenberg (112)], although Franck and Scheibe (113) have been successful in showing the reverse of this process: a *continuous absorption spectrum by negative ions* (electron affinity spectrum). Negative ions are present in high concentrations in solutions of the alkali halides. Scheibe (114) found that, in all solutions con-

---

[12] Compare the corresponding table by Mulliken (111), and a paper on the electron affinity of iodine by Sutton and Mayer (110).

TABLE 20

ELECTRON AFFINITIES

Element	ELECTRON AFFINITY		Reference
	Volts	kcal./mol.	
H	0.7155 4.9	16.50 17.27	(57) (153)
F	4.13	95.3	(107)
Cl	3.72	85.8	(154)
Br	3.49	80.5	(155)
I	3.14	72.4	(156)
O	3.07	70.8	(157)
S	2.8	65	(108)

taining the I⁻ ion, there occur two relatively small continuous absorption bands whose separation is 7600 cm⁻¹. This separation agrees exactly with the doublet separation of the iodine atom in the ground state as found spectroscopically. According to Franck and Scheibe, the explanation is, therefore, that by light absorption an electron is separated from the iodide ion in the solution. The energy required for this varies according as the I atom remains in a $^2P_{3/2}$ state or a $^2P_{1/2}$ state (two series limits; see Chapter IV, section 2). The difference is just equal to the doublet separation. One would therefore expect two positions of absorption (continua) corresponding to the two different processes. This is found experimentally. The absolute positions of the continua can also be correctly calculated by a more detailed treatment of the process (allowing for hydration and so on). Analogous effects are found for Br⁻ and Cl⁻. This is one of the few cases in which the elementary act in a light absorption process in solution has been unambiguously explained.

Ionic compounds. The small ionization potentials of the alkalis, alkaline earths, and earths are responsible for their *electropositive* chemical character; the considerable electron affinity of the halogens and the elements of the oxygen group, for their *electronegative* character. Owing to the Coulomb attraction between ions, the elements of these two groups form typical ionic compounds with one another. In solution they occur as positive and negative ions, respectively. The number of electrons that an atom can easily give up or take on decides the number of partners with which it can form such ionic compounds, and is known as the *heteropolar valency* (electrovalency). The maximum numerical value of this valency depends on the *number of electrons present outside closed shells, or on the number of electrons lacking to make up a closed shell.* The alkalis which have one electron in an unclosed shell are correspondingly univalent. On the other hand, the alkaline earths (for example, Ca) have two easily removable electrons which are outside closed shells (cf. Table 18, p. 200). These two electrons can therefore be taken up either by an electronegative atom lacking two electrons for a closed shell (for example, O or S) or by two atoms each lacking one electron (for example, Cl). The alkaline earths are therefore divalent. Thus it can be understood, for example, that CaO and $CaCl_2$ are formed, but not CaO_2 or $CaCl_3$. The singly positively charged Ca^+ can, however, form a moderately stable compound with Cl^-, as observation of the compound CaCl shows. Similarly, the earths B, Al, Ga, In, Tl have a maximum valency of 3, but can have valencies of 1 and 2, as observed for Ga and In. Correspondingly, the halogens are univalent, since they lack one electron for a closed shell; and the elements of the oxygen group are divalent, since they lack two electrons for a closed shell.

On the basis of the Pauli principle, a given number of electrons lying outside a closed shell or required to make up a closed shell recur periodically in the system of elements as the atomic number increases. The same is therefore true for heteropolar valence. This shows very clearly the value of the Pauli principle for an understanding of the periodicity of the chemical properties of elements.

In the early development of the subject it was generally assumed that all chemical compounds were more or less ionic (Kossel); that is, that their component parts were bound together as ions.[13] For example, according to this assumption, in CCl_4 four singly charged negative Cl ions

---

[13] Cf. van Arkel and de Boer (37).

should be bound to a C ion with four positive charges, and correspondingly in other cases. We know now, however, that apart from this ionic binding there is also *true atomic binding*, in which the components are bound to one another as atoms (see below). In principle, a given number of atoms (or ions), such as C + 4Cl, can form one and the same molecule either in a state with atomic binding or in one with ionic binding. The molecule will be an ionic compound or an atomic compound in the ground state according to which state has the lower energy. We can therefore say qualitatively that an ionic compound is more probable, the smaller the difference between the ionization potentials involved (for CCl_4, for example, the work to remove the four outer electrons of C) and the electron affinity of the negative ion or ions. A consideration of the following *cycle* may help to make this clear.

$$CCl_4 \xrightarrow{\; -290 \text{ kcal.} \;} C + 4\,Cl$$

$$+\,3358 \text{ kcal} \nwarrow \qquad \swarrow\; -3068 \text{ kcal.}$$

$$C^{++++} + 4\,Cl^-$$

The energy required to transform $C + 4\,Cl$ into $C^{++++} + 4\,Cl^-$ is: 148.0 - (4 × 3.72 = 133.1 volts or 3068 kcal. (cf. Tables 18 and 20). On the other hand, it is known that 12.5 volts or 290 kcal. are required to split CCl_4 into $C + 4Cl$. If the ground state of CCl_4 really originated from ions, (3068 + 290) kcal. should be set free when it is formed from ions. We can, however, calculate the theoretical amount of energy which would be set free by the combination of a singly positively charged ion with a singly negatively charged ion, on the basis of the Coulomb law ($V = e^2/r_0$), using a plausible value for the smallest separation of the two ions r_0. This energy is at most 8 volts or 185 kcal. If we had a fourfold positively charged ion and a fourfold negatively charged ion, the energy would be $4 \times 4 = 16$ times as great. However, in dealing with C^{++++} and $4\,Cl^-$, the mutual repulsion of the Cl^- ions must be taken into account. A more detailed calculation shows that a value 12 times that for singly charged ions should be used. This gives 96 volts or 2200 kcal., which is considerably smaller than the above 3340 kcal. CCl_4 cannot therefore be an ionic compound.

Corresponding considerations for NaCl lead to quite different conclusions. The analogous cycle is given below.

$$
\begin{array}{ccc}
& - \text{ 97 kcal.} & \\
\text{NaCl} & \xrightarrow{\hspace{2cm}} & \text{Na} + \text{Cl} \\
+ \text{ 129.7 kcal.} \nwarrow & & \swarrow - \text{ 32.7 kcal.} \\
& \text{Na}^+ + \text{Cl}^- &
\end{array}
$$

The work required to transform $Na + Cl \rightarrow Na^+ + Cl^-$ is now only 32.7 kcal., and, since the heat of reaction for $Na + Cl \rightarrow NaCl$ is 97 kcal., 129.7 kcal. would be obtained by combining $Na^+ + Cl^- \rightarrow NaCl$. This is, however, quite a plausible value for the amount of energy that would be liberated by bringing together two such ions. It is thereby shown that NaCl, in contrast to CCl_4, may very well be an ionic compound. That it really is an ionic compound receives confirmation from the fact that the observed heat of reaction agrees quite well with the results of quantitative calculations by Born and Heisenberg for such an ionic compound. This is apart from other evidence such as the dissociation into ions in solution.

The foregoing considerations cover only the investigation of the question whether a *free molecule in the gas state* is an ion molecule or an atom molecule. However, the same do not necessarily apply to the compound in the liquid state or in aqueous solution or in the crystal state. The free molecule of HCl, for example, is certainly an atomic compound. However, in aqueous solution it is dissociated into $H^+ + Cl^-$ AgCl is an atomic compound in the vapor state, but in the solid it forms an ionic lattice. The reason for this difference is that in the lattice *several* ions exert an attractive force on a given ion. Consequently, the amount of energy liberated per mol by the coming together of the ions to form a lattice (*lattice energy*) is relatively much greater than the energy set free in the formation of an ionic molecule in the gas state. Therefore in the solid state the ionic linkage may sometimes give a lower energy state than the atomic linkage, though the reverse is true for the gaseous state. The difference between an aqueous solution and the gas state (for example, for HCl) is due mainly to the *hydration* of the ions—that is, to the fact that a number of water molecules are arranged about each ion, their dipoles being radially directed. This means a considerable gain in energy for the ionic state and is the main reason for the dissociation into ions. In spite of this, CCl_4 does not occur in the ionic form in the liquid, solid, or dissolved states, because of the highly endothermic nature of the ionic state of the free molecule.[14]

Atomic compounds (homopolar valence). The fact that neutral atoms can attract one another strongly, as shown by the formation of such molecules as H_2 and N_2, could not be understood on the basis of the Bohr model. An explanation for this fact was first provided by quantum mechanics. In particular, the *saturation* of homopolar valencies was difficult to explain on the old theory (for example, that a hydrogen molecule no longer attracts a third hydrogen atom) in contrast to ionic binding where saturation is easily explained purely classically as electrical neutralization.

The first successful theoretical attack on the treatment of homopolar chemical binding was made by Heitler and London (115). For the simplest case dealt with, that of H_2, they found that *two normal H atoms attract each other only when the spins of the two electrons are antiparallel to each other; whereas they repel each other when the spins are parallel.* The value of the heat of dissociation of the molecule obtained theoretically agrees approximately with experiment.

According to this theory, the large binding energy is caused, not by the interaction of the spins, but by a resonance process similar to that for the He atom (see p. 67). At large separations

[14] Further examples and details may be found in Rabinowitsch and Thilo (38).

of the two atoms a degeneracy is introduced by the equivalence of the two electrons, since the state: electron 1 with nucleus A, and electron 2 with nucleus B (see Fig. 79), has the same energy as the state: electron 2 with nucleus A and electron 1 with nucleus B (*exchange degeneracy*). The eigenfunctions belonging to these states are: $\varphi_A(1)\varphi_B(2)$ and $\varphi_A(2)\varphi_B(1)$, where φ_A and φ_B are hydrogen eigenfunctions referred to A and B, respectively (see p. 39). As the two atoms approach each other, an *exchange* of the two electrons takes place with increasing frequency [transitions from $\varphi_A(1)\varphi_B(2)$ to $\varphi_A(2)\varphi_B(1)$, and conversely]; that is, a periodic transition from the one state to the other results. Just as for He, this process can be represented as the superposition of two stationary vibrations:

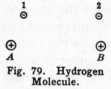

Fig. 79. Hydrogen Molecule.

$$\psi_s = \varphi_A(1)\varphi_B(2) + \varphi_A(2)\varphi_B(1)$$
$$\psi_a = \varphi_A(1)\varphi_B(2) - \varphi_A(2)\varphi_B(1)$$

Wave mechanically the system can be in only one of the two states, *either* the state characterized by ψ_s *or* the state characterized by ψ_a. The former remains unchanged by the exchange of electrons 1 and 2 (is *symmetric* in the electrons); the latter changes sign (is *antisymmetric*). Just as in the case of He, the two states have different energies E_s and E_a, the energy difference being greater, the greater the coupling (that is, the smaller the separation of the nuclei). In contrast to He, here the state ψ_s has smaller energy. Fig. 80 shows the variation of E_s and E_a with changing nuclear separation. In the same way as for He, the influence of the spin consists, not in its effect on the energy, but in its effect through the Pauli principle. According to that principle, the total function must always be antisymmetric in all the electrons (see p. 123). Therefore only the state ψ_a with energy E_a can be realized without spin. But, as Fig. 80 shows, E_a increases continuously with decreasing nuclear separation, which means *repulsion* of the two atoms. However, since by including the spin function the total eigenfunction can be made antisymmetric even for the symmetric co-ordinate function (in the same way as for He), the symmetric state ψ_s with energy E_s can yet occur. E_s first decreases with decreasing separation, and an *attraction* (molecule formation) takes place (lower curve in Fig. 80). The minimum of E_s (the potential energy for the motion of the nuclei) corresponds to the equilibrium position of the nuclei. Quantitative calculations yield the right value for the equilibrium distance, known accurately from the H_2 spectrum, as well as for the heat of dissociation (separation of the minimum from the asymptote). According to the Pauli principle, ψ_s can occur only with the antisymmetric spin function—that is, with antiparallel spin directions of the two electrons (↑↓); whereas ψ_a can occur only with parallel spin directions (↑↑). The former is a singlet state; the latter, a triplet.

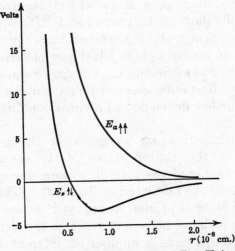

Fig. 80. Dependence of the Potential Energy of Two H Atoms on Nuclear Separation.

The extension of the Heitler-London calculation for H_2 to more general cases has shown that the deciding factor for the *homopolar valence* of an atom is the multiplicity of its ground state or its low-lying terms, or, expressed in another way, the *number of unpaired electron spins*. According to Heitler and London, this latter number is directly equal to the valency of the atomic state considered. It is equal to $2S$ where S is the quantum number of the resultant spin. We can therefore say that *the valency is one less than the multiplicity*.

Correspondingly, He and the other inert gases have a valency 0 in accord with experiment, since their ground state is a singlet state. The alkalis have a valency 1 (doublets). The alkaline earths should again have valency 0 in the ground state (^1S). However, there is an excited triplet state ($S = 1$) lying not far above the ground state, and therefore the alkaline earths can sometimes have a homopolar valency [15] of 2. The earths have as ground state ^2P and, thus, a valency 1. There is, however, a quartet state lying not very high above the ground state $(1s^2 2s 2p^2\ {}^4P)$; that is, a state with three free valencies. Carbon is divalent in the ground state ^3P. Again the observed *tetravalency* of C is traced back by Heitler and London to an *excited state* in which one electron is brought from a 2s orbit to a 2p orbit, the $1s^2 2s 2p^3\ {}^5S$ state (see p. 143), for which all four outer electrons have parallel spins. The theory is further developed in a corresponding manner for other elements.

The multiplicities and valencies for the ground states and some of the excited states of the elements of the different columns of the periodic system according to this representation are tabulated in Table 21. The valency in the ground state is printed in heavy, boldface type. It is especially worthy of note that, whereas the elements of the O and F groups have a number of different valencies, in agreement with experiment, the elements O and F themselves show only the valencies 2 and 1, respectively, of the ground state. This is naturally explained by the fact that, to raise their multiplicity, an electron must be brought into a shell with higher principal quantum number, whereas with the other elements in the same columns this is not necessary.

TABLE 21

HOMOPOLAR VALENCY

Group in Periodic System	I Alkalis	II Alkaline Earths	III Earths	IV Carbon Group	V Nitrogen Group	VI Oxygen Group	VII Halogens
Multiplicity	2	1 3	2 4	1 3 5	2 4 6	1 3 5 7	2 4 6 8
Valency	**1**	**0** 2	**1** 3	**0** 2 4	**1** 3 5	**0** 2 4 6	**1** 3 5 7

It is furthermore important to note that for any one column either only even or only odd valencies occur, since

---

[15] Practically, this homopolar valence is of no importance, since most compounds of the alkaline earths are ionic.

only odd or only even multiplicities occur. An *alternation law* holds for the homopolar valence just as for multiplicities: *For an even number of electrons the valency is even, whereas for an odd number of electrons it is odd.*

The *saturation of homopolar valencies* follows naturally from this representation as a *saturation of the spins*—a pairing off in antiparallel pairs. If an additional H atom approaches an H_2 molecule having antiparallel spins, no additional pair is formed and consequently there is no further gain in energy—that is, no bonding action. More complicated cases can be treated in a similar way.

The Heitler-London mode of representation is thus in principle simple, but its use involves some fundamental difficulties which must now be mentioned. The Heitler-London theory is rigorously derived only for atoms which are in S states and is true for these only when there are no other atomic states in the neighborhood. The calculations for P states do not lead to any simple results. Actually, P states occur quite frequently as ground states, and there often are, also, other states in the neighborhood of the ground state (for example, for C, N, and O).

Because of these difficulties, two further methods for the treatment of homopolar binding have been worked out: the method of Slater and Pauling, and the method of Hund and Mulliken.

Slater and Pauling calculate the interaction of the individual electrons of the different atoms instead of the interaction of the atomic states. From this point of view the chemical behavior of an atom depends not so much on the term type as on the *electron configuration*. Terms with the same electron configuration are treated as one state. Using this method of treatment, one can deduce the fact that certain valencies always occur at a definite angle to one another; for example, in H_2O the two OH directions are approximately at right angles to each other, and similarly for the three NH directions in NH_3. The tetrahedral symmetry of the four valence directions for C is obtained by taking into account the electron configuration sp^3 as well as s^2p^2.

The Hund-Mulliken method attempts to explain chemical binding from a consideration of the behavior of individual electrons in the field of the different nuclei (*many-center problem*).

A detailed discussion of these modern valence theories will not be attempted here. [See Hund in (1*d*); Pauling-Wilson (32); Sponer (39).] All that we wished to show was that *the chemical behavior of an element depends on the term types and electron configurations of its lower energy states* —that is, on the angular momenta of the atom. Thus a knowledge of the energy level diagram of an element is of great importance for an understanding of its chemical behavior.

Activated states and collisions of the second kind; elementary chemical processes. So-called *activated states* of atoms and molecules often play a very important part in chemical reactions. These are simply excited atomic or molecular states. The excitation energies are the energies of activation. Owing to their larger energy content, excited atoms (or molecules) have in general a much higher reactivity than normal atoms. Furthermore, there is the additional effect that excited states often have more free valencies than the ground state (see above). In such cases the atom is more reactive, the smaller the excitation energy to this state. The inert gases are distinguished by a particularly high first excitation energy. They are therefore entirely unreactive in the ground state.[16]

A knowledge of the spectroscopically obtained excitation energies of atoms (and molecules) is thus of particular importance for the understanding of *elementary chemical processes*. A few examples will be considered briefly. A

---

[16] The first excited state of He is at 20 volts. When helium has been brought to this state—for example, by an electric discharge—it has a very high reactivity and can form a molecule with a second normal He atom. This is shown by the He_2 bands emitted by the discharge.

systematic treatment is possible only with the help of a more complete knowledge of molecular spectra and molecular structure than can be assumed here.

When a collision between two atoms or molecules occurs, we distinguish between *collisions of the first and the second kind.* In collisions of the first kind a *change of kinetic energy of translation into excitation energy* takes place by collision (corresponding to excitation by electron collision); that is, a process:

$$A + B + \text{kinetic energy} \rightarrow A + B^* \qquad \textbf{(VI, 6)}$$

where A and B are two different (or identical) atoms in the ground state and B^* is the atom B in an excited state. The necessary kinetic energy may be present if the temperature is sufficiently high or if the atoms are artificially accelerated, possibly as ions [17] (excitation by atom or ion collision). Collisions of the second kind (Klein-Rosseland) are more important for our purpose. They include not only the exact reverse of collisions of the first kind; that is, a process:

$$A + B^* \rightarrow A + B + \text{kinetic energy} \qquad \textbf{(VI, 7)}$$

but also all other *processes in which an atom or molecule gives up excitation energy by colliding with another partner;* for example:

$$A + B^* \rightarrow A^* + B \qquad \textbf{(VI, 8)}$$

The conversion of excitation energy into chemical energy— for example, into the dissociation energy of a molecule—is a further possibility.

The most thorough investigations of such collisions of the second kind have been made for Hg. When a number of Hg atoms have been brought into the excited $^3P_1$ state by irradiating the Hg vapor with the 2537 Å line (see Fig. 75, p. 202), the Hg vapor reradiates the 2537 line as fluorescence. If now Tl vapor, for example, is added to the Hg vapor, it is observed that Tl lines occur in the fluorescence spectrum

---

[17] We might also think of atoms or molecules with a particularly high velocity resulting from a chemical reaction.

as well as the Hg 2537 line [Franck and Cario, see (1c)]. Only those Tl lines occur whose excitation energy is less than that of the Hg $^3P_1$ state. Apparently the collision process

$$Hg(^3P_1) + Tl(^2P_{1/2}) \rightarrow Hg(^1S_0) + Tl^* \qquad (VI, 9)$$

has taken place. Such a process is called *sensitized fluorescence.* Any excess excitation energy of the Hg over that of the metal atom is changed into kinetic energy of the two partners after collision.

When gases whose excitation energy for fluorescence is greater than that of the line 2537 Å (for example, He, H_2, O_2, CO, N_2) are added to the Hg vapor, naturally no sensitized fluorescence appears, although an increasing *quenching of the fluorescence* takes place with increasing pressure. This quenching can have different origins. Either the whole excitation energy can be converted to inner energy by collision without leading to subsequent radiation; or the Hg can go from the $^3P_1$ state to the metastable $^3P_0$ state by collision and only the small difference in energy be transferred to the collision partner; or, finally, a chemical reaction can take place.[18] All these cases have been observed. By O_2, for example, a transfer of $Hg(^3P_1)$ atoms into the ^1S ground state is brought about[19]; by N_2, a transfer to the metastable $^3P_0$ state.[20] The case of Hg vapor plus hydrogen has particularly interesting and important chemical applications. In this case the quenching of the fluorescence of 2537 Å is particularly strong and the $Hg(^3P_1)$ atoms are transferred directly to the ground state. At the same time atomic hydrogen is found to be present. Two elementary processes

---

[18] The case of the exact reverse (VI, 7) of the collision of the first kind might have been expected for the inert gases which cannot take up inner energy of the order of the excitation energy of $Hg(^3P_1)$. Actually, this process of changing the total excitation energy into kinetic energy of the collision partner takes place very seldom, and hence has not yet been proved with certainty. See Hamós (118).

[19] Part of the O_2 reacts chemically with excited Hg: $Hg^* + O_2 \rightarrow HgO + O$. See Bonhoeffer and Harteck (119).

[20] The evidence that metastable Hg atoms are produced may be obtained, for example, by investigating the absorption of Hg lines having this state as the lower state.

are assumed in order to explain this:

$$Hg(^3P_1) + H_2 \rightarrow Hg(^1S_0) + H + H + \text{kinetic energy} \quad \textbf{(VI, 10)}$$
$$Hg(^3P_1) + H_2 \rightarrow HgH + H + \text{kinetic energy} \quad \textbf{(VI, 11)}$$

That the second process occurs as well as the first is shown by the observation of the HgH spectrum [see (120); (121)]. The excitation of the resulting HgH follows by a second collision process, as in sensitized fluorescence:

$$Hg(^3P) + HgH \rightarrow Hg(^1S) + HgH^*$$

The process (VI, 11) is the prototype of an elementary chemical process for which the excitation energy of the colliding partner is the deciding factor. The reaction (formation of HgH from Hg + H$_2$) would not be possible at ordinary temperatures without excitation, since it would be much too strongly endothermic.

Exactly the same elementary processes (VI, 10) and (VI, 11) are possible with the metastable $^3P_0$ state, and have in fact been observed when N$_2$ as well as H$_2$ was added to Hg vapor, the N$_2$ causing preferentially a transfer from $^3P_1 \rightarrow {}^3P_0$.

Two general laws are of importance for these elementary processes. The first one states that *for a collision of the second kind, the yield is greater, the less the energy which needs to be thereby converted to translational energy* [see (122); (123)]. Thus we find, for the Hg sensitized fluorescence of metal vapors, that those lines are particularly intense whose excitation energy is approximately the same as that of the Hg($^3P_1$) state, or possibly of the Hg($^3P_0$) state. Similarly, the strongest quenching on the Hg fluorescence is exerted by those added gases which have a corresponding excitation energy. A theoretical basis for this law has been given by Kallmann and London (124).

The second general law is that, for a collision, *the total spin of the two collision partners must remain unaltered* before and after the collision [Wigner (125)]. For example, Beutler and Eisenschimmel (126) found that in the collision of excited Kr in the ^3P state with normal $Hg(^1S_0)$, triplet terms are preferentially excited in the Hg when the Kr returns to the singlet ground state by collision:

$$Kr(^3P) + Hg(^1S) \rightarrow Kr(^1S) + Hg \text{ (triplet state)}$$

Thus before and after collision the total spin $S = 1$. Collisions of the second kind in which Kr alters its multiplicity but not the Hg occur much less often. The basis for this prohibition of intercombinations is the same as for transitions within a single atom involving radiation (see p. 125). This prohibition also holds to the same approximation as the ordinary intercombination rule, becoming less and less strict for higher atomic numbers.

In all collision processes in which excited atoms take part, the *lifetimes* of the excited states are important since the collision must occur before a transition to the ground state takes place with radiation. Therefore metastable states are often more effective than states which are not metastable and which have a life only of the order of 10^{-8} sec., particularly when not every gas kinetic collision is effective or when an interaction of *two* excited atoms is necessary for the process.

We have considered above what is really an elementary chemical process—namely, ·the dissociation of H_2 by excited Hg. We shall now consider two further examples of important elementary processes in which excited atoms play a role.

Investigations of molecular spectra have shown that, by irradiation of O_2 with light of wave length below 1750 Å, a normal O atom in the ^3P state and an excited O atom in the ^1D state are produced [see Herzberg (127); cf. Fig. 59, p. 163]. The resulting O atoms react with the molecules present, and this leads, for example, to ozone formation. However, this reaction has not yet been explained with certainty. When hydrogen is added to the oxygen, the O atoms can also react with H_2 molecules [cf. Neujmin-Popov (128)]. The reactions which might be expected to take place are:

$$O(^3P) + H_2 \rightarrow OH + H - 1.3 \text{ kcal.} \qquad \textbf{(VI, 12)}$$

$$O(^1D) + H_2 \rightarrow OH + H + 43.8 \text{ kcal.} \qquad \textbf{(VI, 13)}$$

Reaction (VI, 12) is weakly endothermic; it therefore does not generally occur, and this has in fact been shown in experiments by Harteck and Kopsch (129), who used atomic O produced in an electric discharge. The observed H_2O or H_2O_2 formation by irradiation of an O_2–H_2 mixture is thus probably due to reaction (VI, 13), in which the excited metastable $O(^1D)$ atom brings the activation energy directly with it. Similar experiments have been done with $NO_2 + H_2$ [Schumacher (130)]. We know from the spectrum that NO_2 decomposes into $NO + O(^3P)$ by irradiation with light in the region 3800 Å but, in contrast to this, gives $NO + O(^1D)$ by irradiation with light < 2450 Å [Herzberg (131)]. Thus again the above two reactions can take place if hydrogen is added. It was found that no water formation takes place by irradiation at the longer wave length, although such formation does take place by irradiation with the light of shorter wave length.

One of the photochemical reactions most often investigated is the formation of HCl from $H_2 + Cl_2$. It is known from the molecular spectrum that the primary process is:

$$Cl_2 + h\nu \rightarrow Cl(^2P_{3/2}) + Cl(^2P_{1/2})$$

Thus there result one Cl atom in the ground state and one in an excited metastable state [cf. the energy level diagram in Fig. 74 (p. 199)]. When the Cl atom collides with an H_2 molecule, the reaction $Cl + H_2 \rightarrow HCl + H$ is possible. With Cl in the ground state this reaction is about one kcal. endothermic, and will therefore, in general, not take place at room temperature. On the other hand, the reaction is exothermic for the excited Cl atom in the $^2P_{1/2}$ state (excitation energy 2.5 kcal.) formed by irradiation of Cl_2 with light, and can therefore very well take place in this case.

Thus we have considered two elementary chemical reactions which are encountered in experiment and which can, in general, take place *only with excited atoms*.   It is clear that a full discussion of these reactions was possible only after the excitation energy of the states had been evaluated by means of the somewhat complicated analyses of the corresponding atomic spectra.

In conclusion it should perhaps be mentioned that an accurate determination of the *heats of dissociation* of the molecules O_2, N_2, the halogen molecules, and others was first possible after the atomic excitation energies had been evaluated.   A knowledge of the values of these heats of dissociation is obviously of extreme importance in discussing elementary chemical processes and in calculating the heat evolution of individual reactions.

BIBLIOGRAPHY

Bibliography

I. HANDBOOKS, MONOGRAPHS, TEXTBOOKS, TABLES

1. Geiger-Scheel, Handbuch der Physik (Springer, Berlin, 1928–33):
   (a) Vol. 19: Herstellung und Messung des Lichtes.
   (b) Vol. 21: Licht und Materie.
   (c) Vol. 23, Part 1 (second edition): Quantenhafte Ausstrahlung.
   (d) Vol. 24, Part 1 (second edition): Quantentheorie.
2. Wien-Harms, Handbuch der Experimentalphysik (Akad. Verlagsges., Leipzig, 1927–31):
   (a) Vol. 21: Anregung der Spektren, Apparate und Methoden der Spektroskopie, Starkeffekt.
   (b) Vol. 22: Zeeman-Effekt, Ergebnisse und Anwendungen der Spektroskopie, Raman-Effekt.
   (c) Supplement, Vol. 1: W. Weizel, Bandenspektren.
3. E. C. C. Baly, Spectroscopy (Longmans, Green & Co., London, 1924–27).
4. Kayser-Konen, Handbuch der Spektroskopie (Hirzel, Leipzig, 1905–33).
5. A. Sommerfeld:
   (a) Atomic Structure and Spectral Lines (Methuen, London, 1934).
   (b) Wave Mechanics (Methuen, London, 1930).
6. E. Back and A. Landé, Zeeman-Effekt und Multiplettstruktur der Spektrallinien (Springer, Berlin, 1925).
7. F. Hund, Linienspektren und periodisches System der Elemente (Springer, Berlin, 1927).
8. W. Grotrian, Graphische Darstellung der Spektren von Atomen und Ionen mit ein, zwei und drei Valenzelektronen (Springer, Berlin, 1928).
9. L. Pauling and S. Goudsmit, The Structure of Line Spectra (McGraw-Hill, New York, 1930).
10. A. E. Ruark and H. C. Urey, Atoms, Molecules and Quanta (McGraw-Hill, New York, 1930).
11. H. Kuhn, Atomspektren (Hand- und Jahrbuch der chemischen Physik, Vol. 9, I.) (Akad. Verlagsges., Leipzig, 1934).

12. H. E. White, Introduction to Atomic Spectra (McGraw-Hill, New York, 1934).
13. E. U. Condon and G. H. Shortley, The Theory of Atomic Spectra (Cambridge University Press, 1935).
14. K. W. Meissner, Spektroskopie, Sammlung Göschen Nr. 1091 (de Gruyter, Berlin, 1935).
15. H. Lundegårdh, Die quantitative Spektralanalyse der Elemente, Parts I and II (G. Fischer, Jena, 1929 and 1934).
16. W. Gerlach and E. Schweitzer, Foundations and Methods of Chemical Analysis by the Emission Spectrum (Hilger, London, 1932).
17. Wa. Gerlach and We. Gerlach, Clinical and Pathological Applications of Spectrum Analysis (Hilger, London, 1935).
18. W. J. Crook, Metallurgical Spectrum Analysis with Visual Atlas (Stanford University Press, 1935).
19. F. Twyman, The Practice of Spectrum Analysis (Hilger, London, 1933).
20. H. Kayser, Tabelle der Hauptlinien der Linienspektra aller Elemente (Springer, Berlin, 1926).
21. H. Kayser, Tabelle der Schwingungszahlen (Hirzel, Leipzig, 1925); corrections Phys. Rev. 48, 98 (1935).
22. R. F. Bacher and S. Goudsmit, Atomic Energy States (McGraw-Hill, New York, 1932).
23. K. K. Darrow, Introduction to Wave Mechanics (Bell System Technical Publications, New York, 1927).
24. A. Haas, Wave Mechanics and the Quantum Theory (Constable, London, 1931).
25. A. Landé, Wellenmechanik (Akad. Verlagsges., Leipzig, 1930).
26. J. Frenkel, Wave Mechanics, Elementary Theory (Oxford University Press, 1932).
27. L. de Broglie, An Introduction to the Study of Wave Mechanics (Methuen, London, 1929).
28. A. March, Die Grundlagen der Quantenmechanik (Barth, Leipzig, 1931).
29. E. U. Condon and P. M. Morse, Quantum Mechanics (McGraw-Hill, New York, 1929).
30. H. A. Kramers, Die Grundlagen der Quantentheorie (Akad. Verlagsges., Leipzig, 1933).
31. E. Fues, Einführung in die Quantenmechanik (Akad. Verlagsges., Leipzig, 1935).
32. L. Pauling and E. B. Wilson, Introduction to Quantum Mechanics (McGraw-Hill, New York, 1935).

33. M. Born and P. Jordan, Elementare Quantenmechanik (Springer, Berlin, 1930).
34. W. Heisenberg, Physical Principles of the Quantum Theory (Chicago University Press, 1930).
35. P. A. M. Dirac, Principles of Quantum Mechanics (Oxford University Press, 1930).
36. J. H. Van Vleck, The Theory of Electric and Magnetic Susceptibilities (Oxford University Press, 1932).
37. A. E. van Arkel and J. H. de Boer, Chemische Bindung als elektrostatische Erscheinung (Akad. Verlagsges., Leipzig, 1930).
38. E. Rabinowitsch and E. Thilo, Periodisches System, Geschichte und Theorie (Enke, Stuttgart, 1930).
39. H. Sponer, Molekülspektren und ihre Anwendung auf chemische Probleme (Springer, Berlin, 1936).

II. References to Individual Papers [1]

40. E. H. Melvin, Phys. Rev. **37**, 1230 (1931).
41. G. Herzberg, Ann. Physik (4) **84**, 565 (1927).
42. H. Kuhn, Z. Physik **76**, 782 (1932).
43. J. Curry, L. Herzberg, and G. Herzberg, Z. Physik **86**, 348 (1933).
44. R. T. Birge, Phys. Rev. **40**, 319 (1932).
45. R. T. Birge, Nature **134**, 771 (1934).
46. J. A. Bearden, Phys. Rev. **47**, 883 (1935).
47. R. C. Williams and R. C. Gibbs, Phys. Rev. **45**, 491 (1934).
48. H. Bethe, Phys. Rev. **47**, 633 (1935).
49. H. Mark and R. Wierl, Z. Physik **60**, 743 (1930).
50. F. London, Naturwiss. **17**, 516 (1929).
51. H. E. White, Phys. Rev. **37**, 1416 (1931).
52. W. Elsasser, Z. Physik **81**, 332 (1933).
53. O. Betz, Ann. Physik **15**, 321 (1932).
54. G. Collins and W. C. Price, Rev. Sci. Inst. **5**, 423 (1934).
55. H. B. Dorgelo, Physica **6**, 150 (1926).
56. G. W. Kellner, Z. Physik **44**, 91 (1927).
57. E. A. Hylleraas, Z. Physik **65**, 209 (1930).
58. W. Heisenberg, Z. Physik **38**, 411 (1926).
59. A. Fowler and E. W. H. Selwyn, Proc. Roy. Soc. London, Ser. A **120**, 312 (1928).
60. R. Ladenburg, Physik. Z. **30**, 369 (1929).

[1] Only papers which have been directly used in the text are given here, and of these the older ones are listed only occasionally.

61. J. S. Foster, Proc. Roy. Soc. London, Ser. A 114, 47 (1926); 117, 137 (1927).
62. R. W. James, I. Waller, and D. R. Hartree, Proc. Roy. Soc London, Ser. A 118, 334 (1928).
63. D. R. Hartree, Proc. Roy. Soc. London, Ser. A 141, 282 (1933).
64. F. Paschen, Ann. Physik 12, 509 (1932).
65. A. Rubinowicz and J. Blaton, Erg. Exakt. Naturwiss. 11, 176 (1932).
66. Lord Rayleigh, Proc. Roy. Soc. London, Ser. A 117, 294 (1927).
67. L. D. Huff and W. V. Houston, Phys. Rev. 36, 842 (1930).
68. E. Segrè and C. J. Bakker, Z. Physik 72, 724 (1931).
69. H. Kuhn, Z. Physik 61, 805 (1930).
70. I. S. Bowen, Astrophys. J. 67, 1 (1928).
71. I. S. Bowen, Rev. Mod. Phys. 8, 55 (1936).
72. J. C. McLennan, Proc. Roy. Soc. London, Ser. A 120, 327 (1928).
73. F. Paschen, Z. Physik 65, 1 (1930).
74. E. U. Condon, Astrophys. J. 79, 217 (1934).
75. J. C. McLennan and G. M. Shrum, Proc. Roy. Soc. 108, 501 (1925).
76. R. Frerichs and J. S. Campbell, Phys. Rev. 36, 151, 1460 (1930).
77. H. Beutler, Z. Astrophys. 9, 387 (1935).
78. F. Paschen and P. G. Kruger, Ann. Physik (5) 8, 1005 (1931).
79. H. Beutler, Z. Physik 86, 495 (1933).
80. H. Beutler and K. Guggenheimer, Z. Physik 87, 176 (1933).
81. A. G. Shenstone, Phys. Rev. 38, 873 (1931).
82. O. Laporte, Z. Physik 23, 135 (1924).
83. P. Zeeman, E. Back, and S. Goudsmit, Z. Physik 66, 1 (1930).
84. R. A. Fisher and S. Goudsmit, Phys. Rev. 37, 1057 (1931).
85. H. E. White, Phys. Rev. 34, 1391 (1929).
86. H. Schüler and K. Wurm, Naturwiss. 15, 971 (1927).
87. G. Hertz, Naturwiss. 20, 493 (1932).
88. H. Schüler and J. E. Keyston, Z. Physik 70, 1 (1931).
89. H. Schüler and H. Westmeyer, Z. Physik 81, 565 (1933).
90. H. Kopfermann, Z. Physik 75, 363 (1932).
91. D. S. Hughes and C. Eckart, Phys. Rev. 36, 694 (1930).
92. J. H. Bartlett and J. J. Gibbons, Phys. Rev. 44, 538 (1933).
93. J. H. Bartlett, Nature 128, 408 (1931).
94. I. I. Rabi and V. W. Cohen, Phys. Rev. 43, 582 (1933).

95. R. Frisch and O. Stern, Z. Physik **85**, 4 (1933).
96. I. Estermann and O. Stern, Z. Physik **85**, 17 (1933).
97. I. I. Rabi, J. M. B. Kellogg, and J. R. Zacharias, Phys. Rev. **46**, 157 (1934).
98. I. Estermann and O. Stern, Phys. Rev. **45**, 761 (1934).
99. I. I. Rabi, J. M. B. Kellogg, and J. R. Zacharias, Phys. Rev. **46**, 163 (1934).
100. H. Schüler, Z. Physik **88**, 323 (1934).
101. A. Landé, Phys. Rev. **46**, 477 (1934).
102. J. H. Bartlett, Jr., Phys. Rev. **45**, 847 (1934).
103. C. C. Kiess and T. L. de Bruin, Bur. Stand. J. Res. **2**, 1117 (1929).
104. H. N. Russell, Phys. Rev. **34**, 821 (1929).
105. W. Gerlach, Atti Congr. Intern. dei Fisici **1**, 119 (1927).
106. W. J. de Haas and E. C. Wiersma, Physica **2**, 325 (1935).
107. J. E. Mayer and L. Helmholtz, Z. Physik **75**, 19 (1932).
108. J. E. Mayer and M. Maltbie, Z. Physik **75**, 748 (1932).
109. W. W. Lozier, Phys. Rev. **46**, 268 (1934).
110. P. P. Sutton and J. E. Mayer, J. Chem. Phys. **3**, 20 (1935).
111. R. S. Mulliken, J. Chem. Phys. **2**, 782 (1934).
112. O. Oldenberg, Phys. Rev. **43**, 534 (1933).
113. J. Franck and G. Scheibe, Z. Physik Chem., Abt. A, Haberband, p. 22 (1928).
114. G. Scheibe, Z. Elektrochem. **34**, 497 (1928).
115. W. Heitler and F. London, Z. Physik **44**, 455 (1927).
116. J. Franck and G. Cario, Z. Physik **17**, 202 (1923).
117. W. Hanle and K. Larché, Handbuch der Radiologie, Vol. **VI**, Part 1, 115 (1933).
118. L. v. Hamòs, Z. Physik **74**, 379 (1932).
119. K. F. Bonhoeffer and P. Harteck, Grundlagen der Photochemie (Dresden, 1933).
120. E. Gaviola and R. W. Wood, Phil. Mag. **6**, 1191 (1928).
121. H. Beutler and E. Rabinowitsch, Z. Physik. Chem., Abt. B **8**, 403 (1930).
122. J. Franck, Naturwiss. **14**, 211 (1926).
123. H. Beutler and B. Josephy, Z. Physik **53**, 747 (1929).
124. H. Kallmann and F. London, Z. Physik. Chem., Abt. B **2**, 207 (1929).
125. E. Wigner, Göttinger Nachr. 375 (1927).
126. H. Beutler and W. Eisenschimmel, Z. Physik Chem., Abt. B **10**, 89 (1930).
127. G. Herzberg, Z. Physik. Chem., Abt. B **4**, 223 (1929).
128. N. Neujmin and B. Popov, Z. Physik. Chem., Abt. B **27**, 15 (1934).

129. P. Harteck and U. Kopsch, Z. Physik. Chem., Abt. B 12, 327 (1931).
130. H. J. Schumacher, J. Amer. Chem. Soc. 52, 2804 (1930).
131. G. Herzberg, Erg. Exakt. Naturwiss. 10, 207 (1931).
132. J. S. Foster, J. Frank. Inst. 209, 585 (1930).
133. H. Rausch v. Traubenberg and R. Gebauer, Z.f.Phys. 54, 307; 56, 254 (1929).
134. J. C. Slater, Phys. Rev. 34, 1293 (1929).
135. H. Schüler and Th. Schmidt, Z.f.Phys. 92, 148 (1934).
136. A. H. Rosenthal, Z.f. Astrophys. 1, 115 (1930).
137. S. Goudsmit and T. J. Wu, Astrophys. J. 80, 154 (1934).
138. H. A. Bethe and R. F. Bacher, Rev. Mod. Phys. 8, 172 (1936).
139. H. Schüler and Th. Schmidt, Z. Physik 94, 457 (1935).
140. Th. Haase, Ann Physik 23, 657 (1935).
141. M. Fukuda, Sci. Pap. Inst. Physic. Chem. Res. 4, 171 (1926).
142. W. Heitler and E. Teller, Proc. Roy. Soc. 155, 629 (1936).
143. J. M. B. Kellogg, I. I. Rabi, and J. R. Zacharias, Phys. Rev. 50, 472 (1936).
144. R. T. Birge, Rep. on Prog. in Phys. 8, 90 (1941). Rev. Mod. Phys. 13, 223 (1941).
145. R. T. Birge, Phys. Rev. 60, 766 (1941).
146. B. Edlén, Arkiv. f. Matem. Astr. och Fys. 28, B No. 1 (1941). Z. f. Astrophys. 22, 30 (1942).
147. P. Swings, Astrophys. Journ. 98, 116 (1943).
148. E. Rasmussen, Z. Physik 107, 741 (1937).
149. D. A. Jackson and H. Kuhn, Proc. Roy. Soc. 167, 205 (1938).
150. I. I. Rabi, S. Millman, P. Kusch and J. R. Zacharias, Phys. Rev. 55, 526 (1939).
151. J. M. B. Kellogg, I. I. Rabi, N. F. Ramsey and J. R. Zacharias, Phys. Rev. 56, 728 (1939).
152. S. Millman and P. Kusch, Phys. Rev. 60, 91 (1941).
153. L. H. Henrich, Astrophys. Journ. 99, 59 (1944).
154. K. J. McCallum and J. E. Mayer, J. Chem. Phys. 11, 56 (1943).
155. H. B. Weissblatt, Dissertation, Johns Hopkins University, 1938.
156. P. P. Sutton and J. E. Mayer, J. Chem. Phys. 3, 20 (1935).
157. D. T. Vier and J. E. Mayer, J. Chem. Phys. 12, 28 (1944).
158. S. Mrozowski, Z. Physik 108, 204 (1938).
159. G. Breit and E. Teller, Astrophys. Journ. 91, 215 (1940).

INDEX

Index

Italic page numbers refer to a detailed discussion of the subject. Section numbers are included when the reference covers the entire section.

Boldface page numbers refer to figures.

The individual elements are given only under their respective symbols (for example, "Hydrogen fine structure" is listed under "H fine structure").

A

A (Argon), 140, 147, 200
A IV, V, 158
Absorption, intensity of, 152
Absorption spectra, series in, 3, 5, 25, 54, 169 ff., 218 ff.
Ac (Actinium), 141
Action integral, 17·
Activated states, 228 ff.
Addition:
  of J and I to F, **187**
  of L and S to J, 87
  of magnetic moments in an atom, 109, 111
  of the l_i to L, 82
  of the s_i to S, 92
Adiabatic law, Ehrenfest, 86, 114, 121, 133
Affinity, electron, 216 ff.
Ag (Silver), 140, 150, 195, 201
AgCl, 222
Al (Aluminum), 140, 147, 195, **198**, 200, 220
Al II, **170** ff.
Alkali atoms (see also each alkali), 54 ff. (I, 5), 71 ff., 92, 94, 162, 215 ff., 225
Alkali ions (see also each alkali), 92
Alkali-like ions (spark spectra), 59 ff.
Alkaline-earth-like ions, 70
Alkaline earths (see also each alkaline earth), 69 ff., 75 ff., 92, 94, 156, 216, 226
Alternation:
  of multiplicities, 81 ff., 94, 227
  of valences, 227

Analysis of multiplets, 177 ff. (IV, 4)
Angstrom unit, 8
Angular momentum, 16 ff., 19, 47 ff., 58, 82 ff., 92, 96, 101 ff., 109 ff., 120
  magnitude, according to quantum mechanics, 101 ff.
  of the electron (spin), 93 ff., 108 ff., 120 ff., 128 ff., 224 ff.
  of the nucleus, 182, 185 ff. (V, 2)
  orbital, 17 ff., 47 ff., 58, 82 ff., 153
Anomalous terms, 141, 164 ff.
Anomalous triplet, 76, 164, **165** ff.
Anomalous Zeeman effect, 93, **97**, 106 ff.
Antisymmetric eigenfunctions, or states, 67 ff., 123 ff., 224 ff.
Applications, chemical, 213 ff. (VI, 3)
A priori probability, 119, 160, 193
Arc spectra, 59, 81
As (Arsenic), 140, 149, 195, 200
Atom collision, excitation by, 229
Atomic binding, 215, 221, 223 ff.
Atomic compounds (atom molecule), 215, 221 ff., 223 ff.
Atomic core, 58 ff., 62, 70, 92 ff.
Atomic model:
  interpretation of the alkali series, 56
  Rutherford-Bohr, 13 ff.
  wave mechanical, **44**
Atomic nucleus:
  deviation from spherical symmetry, 196
  influence on the spectrum, 182 ff. (V, 1 and 2)

CATALOG OF DOVER BOOKS

Relativity, quantum theory, nuclear physics

THE PRINCIPLE OF RELATIVITY, A. Einstein, H. Lorentz, M. Minkowski, H. Weyl. These are the 11 basic papers that founded the general and special theories of relativity, all translated into English. Two papers by Lorentz on the Michelson experiment, electromagnetic phenomena. Minkowski's SPACE & TIME, and Weyl's GRAVITATION & ELECTRICITY. 7 epoch-making papers by Einstein: ELECTROMAGNETICS OF MOVING BODIES, INFLUENCE OF GRAVI-TATION IN PROPAGATION OF LIGHT, COSMOLOGICAL CONSIDERATIONS, GENERAL THEORY, and 3 others. 7 diagrams. Special notes by A. Sommerfeld. 224pp. 5⅜ x 8.
S81 Paperbound **$1.75**

SPACE TIME MATTER, Hermann Weyl. "The standard treatise on the general theory of relativity," (Nature), written by a world-renowned scientist, provides a deep clear discussion of the logical coherence of the general theory, with introduction to all the mathematical tools needed: Maxwell, analytical geometry, non-Euclidean geometry, tensor calculus, etc. Basis is classical space-time, before absorption of relativity. Partial contents: Euclidean space, mathematical form, metrical continuum, relativity of time and space, general theory. 15 diagrams. Bibliography. New preface for this edition. xviii + 330pp. 5⅜ x 8.
S267 Paperbound **$1.85**

PRINCIPLES OF QUANTUM MECHANICS, W. V. Houston. Enables student with working knowl-edge of elementary mathematical physics to develop facility in use of quantum mechanics, understand published work in field. Formulates quantum mechanics in terms of Schroedinger's wave mechanics. Studies evidence for quantum theory, for inadequacy of classical me-chanics, 2 postulates of quantum mechanics; numerous important, fruitful applications of quantum mechanics in spectroscopy, collision problems, electrons in solids; other topics. "One of the most rewarding features . . . is the interlacing of problems with text," Amer. J. of Physics. Corrected edition. 21 illus. Index. 296pp. 5⅜ x 8.   S524 Paperbound **$1.85**

PHYSICAL PRINCIPLES OF THE QUANTUM THEORY, Werner Heisenberg. A Nobel laureate dis-cusses quantum theory; Heisenberg's own work, Compton, Schroedinger, Wilson, Einstein, many others. Written for physicists, chemists who are not specialists in quantum theory, only elementary formulae are considered in the text; there is a mathematical appendix for specialists. Profound without sacrifice of clarity. Translated by C. Eckart, F. Hoyt. 18 figures. 192pp. 5⅜ x 8.   S113 Paperbound **$1.25**

SELECTED PAPERS ON QUANTUM ELECTRODYNAMICS, edited by **J. Schwinger.** Facsimiles of papers which established quantum electrodynamics, from initial successes through today's position as part of the larger theory of elementary particles. First book publication in any language of these collected papers of Bethe, Bloch, Dirac, Dyson, Fermi, Feynman, Heisen-berg, Kusch, Lamb, Oppenheimer, Pauli, Schwinger, Tomonoga, Weisskopf, Wigner, etc. 34 papers in all, 29 in English, 1 in French, 3 in German, 1 in Italian. Preface and historical commentary by the editor. xvii + 423pp. 6⅛ x 9¼.   S444 Paperbound **$2.45**

THE FUNDAMENTAL PRINCIPLES OF QUANTUM MECHANICS, WITH ELEMENTARY APPLICATIONS, E. C. Kemble. An inductive presentation, for the graduate student or specialist in some other branch of physics. Assumes some acquaintance with advanced math; apparatus neces-sary beyond differential equations and advanced calculus is developed as needed. Although a general exposition of principles, hundreds of individual problems are fully treated, with applications of theory being interwoven with development of the mathematical structure. The author is the Professor of Physics at Harvard Univ. "This excellent book would be of great value to every student . . . a rigorous and detailed mathematical discussion of all of the principal quantum-mechanical methods . . . has succeeded in keeping his presenta-tions clear and understandable," Dr. Linus Pauling, J. of the American Chemical Society. Appendices: calculus of variations, math. notes, etc. Indexes. 611pp. 5⅜ x 8.
S472 Paperbound **$2.95**

ATOMIC SPECTRA AND ATOMIC STRUCTURE, G. Herzberg. Excellent general survey for chemists, physicists specializing in other fields. Partial contents: simplest line spectra and elements of atomic theory, building-up principle and periodic system of elements, hyperfine structure of spectral lines, some experiments and applications. Bibilography. 80 figures. Index. xii + 257pp. 5⅜ x 8.   S115 Paperbound **$1.95**

THE THEORY AND THE PROPERTIES OF METALS AND ALLOYS, N. F. Mott, H. Jones. Quantum methods used to develop mathematical models which show interrelationship of basic chem-ical phenomena with crystal structure, magnetic susceptibility, electrical, optical properties. Examines thermal properties of crystal lattice, electron motion in applied field, cohesion, electrical resistance, noble metals, para-, dia-, and ferromagnetism, etc. "Exposition . . . clear . . . mathematical treatment . . . simple," Nature. 138 figures. Bibliography. Index. xiii + 320pp. 5⅜ x 8.   S456 Paperbound **$1.85**

FOUNDATIONS OF NUCLEAR PHYSICS, edited by **R. T. Beyer.** 13 of the most important papers on nuclear physics reproduced in facsimile in the original languages of their authors: the papers most often cited in footnotes, bibliographies. Anderson, Curie, Joliot, Chadwick, Fermi, Lawrence, Cockcroft, Hahn, Yukawa. UNPARALLELED BIBLIOGRAPHY. 122 double-columned pages, over 4,000 articles, books classified. 57 figures. 288pp. 6⅛ x 9¼.
S19 Paperbound **$1.75**

MESON PHYSICS, R. E. Marshak. Traces the basic theory, and explicitly presents results of experiments with particular emphasis on theoretical significance. Phenomena involving mesons as virtual transitions are avoided, eliminating some of the least satisfactory predictions of meson theory. Includes production and study of π mesons at nonrelativistic nucleon energies, contrasts between π and μ mesons, phenomena associated with nuclear interaction of π mesons, etc. Presents early evidence for new classes of particles and indicates theoretical difficulties created by discovery of heavy mesons and hyperons. Name and subject indices. Unabridged reprint. viii + 378pp. 5⅜ x 8.　　　　S500 Paperbound **$1.95**

See also: **STRANGE STORY OF THE QUANTUM,** B. Hoffmann; **FROM EUCLID TO EDDINGTON,** E. Whittaker; **MATTER AND LIGHT, THE NEW PHYSICS,** L. de Broglie; **THE EVOLUTION OF SCIENTIFIC THOUGHT FROM NEWTON TO EINSTEIN,** A. d'Abro; **THE RISE OF THE NEW PHYSICS,** A. d'Abro; **THE THEORY OF GROUPS AND QUANTUM MECHANICS,** H. Weyl; **SUBSTANCE AND FUNCTION, & EINSTEIN'S THEORY OF RELATIVITY,** E. Cassirer; **FUNDAMENTAL FORMULAS OF PHYSICS,** D. H. Menzel.

Hydrodynamics

HYDRODYNAMICS, H. Dryden, F. Murnaghan, Harry Bateman. Published by the National Research Council in 1932 this enormous volume offers a complete coverage of classical hydrodynamics. Encyclopedic in quality. Partial contents: physics of fluids, motion, turbulent flow, compressible fluids, motion in 1, 2, 3 dimensions; viscous fluids rotating, laminar motion, resistance of motion through viscous fluid, eddy viscosity, hydraulic flow in channels of various shapes, discharge of gases, flow past obstacles, etc. Bibliography of over 2,900 items. Indexes. 23 figures. 634pp. 5⅜ x 8.　　　　S303 Paperbound **$2.75**

A TREATISE ON HYDRODYNAMICS, A. B. Basset. Favorite text on hydrodynamics for 2 generations of physicists, hydrodynamical engineers, oceanographers, ship designers, etc. Clear enough for the beginning student, and thorough source for graduate students and engineers on the work of d'Alembert, Euler, Laplace, Lagrange, Poisson, Green, Clebsch, Stokes, Cauchy, Helmholtz, J. J. Thomson, Love, Hicks, Greenhill, Besant, Lamb, etc. Great amount of documentation on entire theory of classical hydrodynamics. Vol I: theory of motion of frictionless liquids, vortex, and cyclic irrotational motion, etc. 132 exercises. Bibliography. 3 Appendixes. xii + 264pp. Vol II: motion in viscous liquids, harmonic analysis, theory of tides, etc. 112 exercises. Bibliography. 4 Appendixes. xv + 328pp. Two volume set. 5⅜ x 8.
S724 Vol I Paperbound **$1.75**
S725 Vol II Paperbound **$1.75**
The set **$3.50**

HYDRODYNAMICS, Horace Lamb. Internationally famous complete coverage of standard reference work on dynamics of liquids & gases. Fundamental theorems, equations, methods, solutions, background, for classical hydrodynamics. Chapters include Equations of Motion, Integration of Equations in Special Gases, Irrotational Motion, Motion of Liquid in 2 Dimensions, Motion of Solids through Liquid-Dynamical Theory, Vortex Motion, Tidal Waves, Surface Waves, Waves of Expansion, Viscosity, Rotating Masses of liquids. Excellently planned, arranged; clear, lucid presentation. 6th enlarged, revised edition. Index. Over 900 footnotes, mostly bibliographical. 119 figures. xv + 738pp. 6⅛ x 9¼.　　　　S256 Paperbound **$2.95**

See also: **FUNDAMENTAL FORMULAS OF PHYSICS,** D. H. Menzel; **THEORY OF FLIGHT,** R. von Mises; **FUNDAMENTALS OF HYDRO- AND AEROMECHANICS,** L. Prandtl and O. G. Tietjens; **APPLIED HYDRO- AND AEROMECHANICS,** L. Prandtl and O. G. Tietjens; **HYDRAULICS AND ITS APPLICATIONS,** A. H. Gibson; **FLUID MECHANICS FOR HYDRAULIC ENGINEERS,** H. Rouse.

Acoustics, optics, electromagnetics

ON THE SENSATIONS OF TONE, Hermann Helmholtz. This is an unmatched coordination of such fields as acoustical physics, physiology, experiment, history of music. It covers the entire gamut of musical tone. Partial contents: relation of musical science to acoustics, physical vs. physiological acoustics, composition of vibration, resonance, analysis of tones by sympathetic resonance, beats, chords, tonality, consonant chords, discords, progression of parts, etc. 33 appendixes discuss various aspects of sound, physics, acoustics, music, etc. Translated by A. J. Ellis. New introduction by Prof. Henry Margenau of Yale. 68 figures. 43 musical passages analyzed. Over 100 tables. Index. xix + 576pp. 6⅛ x 9¼.
S114 Paperbound **$2.95**

THE THEORY OF SOUND, Lord Rayleigh. Most vibrating systems likely to be encountered in practice can be tackled successfully by the methods set forth by the great Nobel laureate, Lord Rayleigh. Complete coverage of experimental, mathematical aspects of sound theory. Partial contents: Harmonic motions, vibrating systems in general, lateral vibrations of bars, curved plates or shells, applications of Laplace's functions to acoustical problems, fluid friction, plane vortex-sheet, vibrations of solid bodies, etc. This is the first inexpensive edition of this great reference and study work. Bibliography. Historical introduction by R. B. Lindsay. Total of 1040pp. 97 figures. 5⅜ x 8.
S292, S293, Two volume set, paperbound, **$4.00**

THE DYNAMICAL THEORY OF SOUND, H. Lamb. Comprehensive mathematical treatment of the physical aspects of sound, covering the theory of vibrations, the general theory of sound, and the equations of motion of strings, bars, membranes, pipes, and resonators. Includes chapters on plane, spherical, and simple harmonic waves, and the Helmholtz Theory of Audition. Complete and self-contained development for student and specialist; all fundamental differential equations solved completely. Specific mathematical details for such important phenomena as harmonics, normal modes, forced vibrations of strings, theory of reed pipes, etc. Index. Bibliography. 86 diagrams. viii + 307pp. 5⅜ x 8.
S655 Paperbound **$1.50**

WAVE PROPAGATION IN PERIODIC STRUCTURES, L. Brillouin. A general method and application to different problems: pure physics, such as scattering of X-rays of crystals, thermal vibration in crystal lattices, electronic motion in metals; and also problems of electrical engineering. Partial contents: elastic waves in 1-dimensional lattices of point masses. Propagation of waves along 1-dimensional lattices. Energy flow. 2 dimensional, 3 dimensional lattices. Mathieu's equation. Matrices and propagation of waves along an electric line. Continuous electric lines. 131 illustrations. Bibliography. Index. xii + 253pp. 5⅜ x 8.
S34 Paperbound **$1.85**

THEORY OF VIBRATIONS, N. W. McLachlan. Based on an exceptionally successful graduate course given at Brown University, this discusses linear systems having 1 degree of freedom, forced vibrations of simple linear systems, vibration of flexible strings, transverse vibrations of bars and tubes, transverse vibration of circular plate, sound waves of finite amplitude, etc. Index. 99 diagrams. 160pp. 5⅜ x 8.
S190 Paperbound **$1.35**

LOUD SPEAKERS: THEORY, PERFORMANCE, TESTING AND DESIGN, N. W. McLachlan. Most comprehensive coverage of theory, practice of loud speaker design, testing; classic reference, study manual in field. First 12 chapters deal with theory, for readers mainly concerned with math. aspects; last 7 chapters will interest reader concerned with testing, design. Partial contents: principles of sound propagation, fluid pressure on vibrators, theory of moving-coil principle, transients, driving mechanisms, response curves, design of horn type moving coil speakers, electrostatic speakers, much more. Appendix. Bibliography. Index. 165 illustrations, charts. 411pp. 5⅜ x 8.
S588 Paperbound **$2.25**

MICROWAVE TRANSMISSION, J. S. Slater. First text dealing exclusively with microwaves, brings together points of view of field, circuit theory, for graduate student in physics, electrical engineering, microwave technician. Offers valuable point of view not in most later studies. Uses Maxwell's equations to study electromagnetic field, important in this area. Partial contents: infinite line with distributed parameters, impedance of terminated line, plane waves, reflections, wave guides, coaxial line, composite transmission lines, impedance matching, etc. Introduction. Index. 76 illus. 319pp. 5⅜ x 8.
S564 Paperbound **$1.50**

THE ANALYSIS OF SENSATIONS, Ernst Mach. Great study of physiology, psychology of perception, shows Mach's ability to see material freshly, his "incorruptible skepticism and independence." (Einstein). Relation of problems of psychological perception to classical physics, supposed dualism of physical and mental, principle of continuity, evolution of senses, will as organic manifestation, scores of experiments, observations in optics, acoustics, music, graphics, etc. New introduction by T. S. Szasz, M. D. 58 illus. 300-item bibliography. Index. 404pp. 5⅜ x 8.
S525 Paperbound **$1.75**

APPLIED OPTICS AND OPTICAL DESIGN, A. E. Conrady. With publication of vol. 2, standard work for designers in optics is now complete for first time. Only work of its kind in English; only detailed work for practical designer and self-taught. Requires, for bulk of work, no math above trig. Step-by-step exposition, from fundamental concepts of geometrical, physical optics, to systematic study, design, of almost all types of optical systems. Vol. 1: all ordinary ray-tracing methods; primary aberrations; necessary higher aberration for design of telescopes, low-power microscopes, photographic equipment. Vol. 2: (Completed from author's notes by R. Kingslake, Dir. Optical Design, Eastman Kodak.) Special attention to high-power microscope, anastigmatic photographic objectives. "An indispensable work," J., Optical Soc. of Amer. "As a practical guide this book has no rival," Transactions, Optical Soc. Index. Bibliography. 193 diagrams. 852pp. 6⅛ x 9¼.
Vol. 1 T611 Paperbound **$2.95**
Vol. 2 T612 Paperbound **$2.95**

THE THEORY OF OPTICS, Paul Drude. One of finest fundamental texts in physical optics, classic offers thorough coverage, complete mathematical treatment of basic ideas. Includes fullest treatment of application of thermodynamics to optics; sine law in formation of images, transparent crystals, magnetically active substances, velocity of light, apertures, effects depending upon them, polarization, optical instruments, etc. Introduction by A. A. Michelson. Index. 110 illus. 567pp. 5⅜ x 8.
S532 Paperbound **$2.45**

OPTICKS, Sir Isaac Newton. In its discussions of light, reflection, color, refraction, theories of wave and corpuscular theories of light, this work is packed with scores of insights and discoveries. In its precise and practical discussion of construction of optical apparatus, contemporary understandings of phenomena it is truly fascinating to modern physicists, astronomers, mathematicians. Foreword by Albert Einstein. Preface by I. B. Cohen of Harvard University. 7 pages of portraits, facsimile pages, letters, etc. cxvi + 414pp. 5⅜ x 8.
S205 Paperbound **$2.00**

OPTICS AND OPTICAL INSTRUMENTS: AN INTRODUCTION WITH SPECIAL REFERENCE TO PRACTICAL APPLICATIONS, B. K. Johnson. An invaluable guide to basic practical applications of optical principles, which shows how to set up inexpensive working models of each of the four main types of optical instruments—telescopes, microscopes, photographic lenses, optical projecting systems. Explains in detail the most important experiments for determining their accuracy, resolving power, angular field of view, amounts of aberration, all other necessary facts about the instruments. Formerly "Practical Optics." Index. 234 diagrams. Appendix. 224pp. 5⅜ x 8.
S642 Paperbound **$1.65**

PRINCIPLES OF PHYSICAL OPTICS, Ernst Mach. This classical examination of the propagation of light, color, polarization, etc. offers an historical and philosophical treatment that has never been surpassed for breadth and easy readability. Contents: Rectilinear propagation of light. Reflection, refraction. Early knowledge of vision. Dioptrics. Composition of light. Theory of color and dispersion. Periodicity. Theory of interference. Polarization. Mathematical representation of properties of light. Propagation of waves, etc. 279 illustrations, 10 portraits. Appendix. Indexes. 324pp. 5⅜ x 8.
S178 Paperbound **$1.75**

FUNDAMENTALS OF ELECTRICITY AND MAGNETISM, L. B. Loeb. For students of physics, chemistry, or engineering who want an introduction to electricity and magnetism on a higher level and in more detail than general elementary physics texts provide. Only elementary differential and integral calculus is assumed. Physical laws developed logically, from magnetism to electric currents, Ohm's law, electrolysis, and on to static electricity, induction, etc. Covers an unusual amount of material; one third of book on modern material: solution of wave equation, photoelectric and thermionic effects, etc. Complete statement of the various electrical systems of units and interrelations. 2 Indexes. 75 pages of problems with answers stated. Over 300 figures and diagrams. xix +669pp. 5⅜ x 8.
S745 Paperbound **$2.75**

THE ELECTROMAGNETIC FIELD, Max Mason & Warren Weaver. Used constantly by graduate engineers. Vector methods exclusively: detailed treatment of electrostatics, expansion methods, with tables converting any quantity into absolute electromagnetic, absolute electrostatic, practical units. Discrete charges, ponderable bodies, Maxwell field equations, etc. Introduction. Indexes. 416pp. 5⅜ x 8.
S185 Paperbound **$2.00**

ELECTRICAL THEORY ON THE GIORGI SYSTEM, P. Cornelius. A new clarification of the fundamental concepts of electricity and magnetism, advocating the convenient m.k.s. system of units that is steadily gaining followers in the sciences. Illustrating the use and effectiveness of his terminology with numerous applications to concrete technical problems, the author here expounds the famous Giorgi system of electrical physics. His lucid presentation and well-reasoned, cogent argument for the universal adoption of this system form one of the finest pieces of scientific exposition in recent years. 28 figures. Index. Conversion tables for translating earlier data into modern units. Translated from 3rd Dutch edition by L. J. Jolley. x + 187pp. 5½ x 8¾.
S909 Clothbound **$6.00**

THEORY OF ELECTRONS AND ITS APPLICATION TO THE PHENOMENA OF LIGHT AND RADIANT HEAT, H. Lorentz. Lectures delivered at Columbia University by Nobel laureate Lorentz. Unabridged, they form a historical coverage of the theory of free electrons, motion, absorption of heat, Zeeman effect, propagation of light in molecular bodies, inverse Zeeman effect, optical phenomena in moving bodies, etc. 109 pages of notes explain the more advanced sections. Index. 9 figures. 352pp. 5⅜ x 8.
S173 Paperbound **$1.85**

TREATISE ON ELECTRICITY AND MAGNETISM, James Clerk Maxwell. For more than 80 years a seemingly inexhaustible source of leads for physicists, mathematicians, engineers. Total of 1082pp. on such topics as Measurement of Quantities, Electrostatics, Elementary Mathematical Theory of Electricity, Electrical Work and Energy in a System of Conductors, General Theorems, Theory of Electrical Images, Electrolysis, Conduction, Polarization, Dielectrics, Resistance, etc. "The greatest mathematical physicist since Newton," Sir James Jeans. 3rd edition. 107 figures, 21 plates. 1082pp. 5⅜ x 8.
S636-7, 2 volume set, paperbound **$4.00**

See also: **FUNDAMENTAL FORMULAS OF PHYSICS, D. H. Menzel; MATHEMATICAL ANALYSIS OF ELECTRICAL & OPTICAL WAVE MOTION, H. Bateman.**

Mechanics, dynamics, thermodynamics, elasticity

MECHANICS VIA THE CALCULUS, P. W. Norris, W. S. Legge. Covers almost everything, from linear motion to vector analysis: equations determining motion, linear methods, compounding of simple harmonic motions, Newton's laws of motion, Hooke's law, the simple pendulum, motion of a particle in 1 plane, centers of gravity, virtual work, friction, kinetic energy of rotating bodies, equilibrium of strings, hydrostatics, sheering stresses, elasticity, etc. 550 problems. 3rd revised edition. xii + 367pp. 6 x 9.
S207 Clothbound **$3.95**

MECHANICS, J. P. Den Hartog. Already a classic among introductory texts, the M.I.T. professor's lively and discursive presentation is equally valuable as a beginner's text, an engineering student's refresher, or a practicing engineer's reference. Emphasis in this highly readable text is on illuminating fundamental principles and showing how they are embodied in a great number of real engineering and design problems: trusses, loaded cables, beams, jacks, hoists, etc. Provides advanced material on relative motion and gyroscopes not usual in introductory texts. "Very thoroughly recommended to all those anxious to improve their real understanding of the principles of mechanics." MECHANICAL WORLD. Index. List of equations. 334 problems, all with answers. Over 550 diagrams and drawings. ix + 462pp. 5⅜ x 8.
S754 Paperbound **$2.00**

THEORETICAL MECHANICS: AN INTRODUCTION TO MATHEMATICAL PHYSICS, J. S. Ames, F. D. Murnaghan. A mathematically rigorous development of theoretical mechanics for the advanced student, with constant practical applications. Used in hundreds of advanced courses. An unusually thorough coverage of gyroscopic and baryscopic material, detailed analyses of the Corilis acceleration, applications of Lagrange's equations, motion of the double pendulum, Hamilton-Jacobi partial differential equations, group velocity and dispersion, etc. Special relativity is also included. 159 problems. 44 figures. ix + 462pp. 5⅜ x 8.
S461 Paperbound **$2.00**

THEORETICAL MECHANICS: STATICS AND THE DYNAMICS OF A PARTICLE, W. D. MacMillan. Used for over 3 decades as a self-contained and extremely comprehensive advanced undergraduate text in mathematical physics, physics, astronomy, and deeper foundations of engineering. Early sections require only a knowledge of geometry; later, a working knowledge of calculus. Hundreds of basic problems, including projectiles to the moon, escape velocity, harmonic motion, ballistics, falling bodies, transmission of power, stress and strain, elasticity, astronomical problems. 340 practice problems plus many fully worked out examples make it possible to test and extend principles developed in the text. 200 figures. xvii + 430pp. 5⅜ x 8.
S467 Paperbound **$2.00**

THEORETICAL MECHANICS: THE THEORY OF THE POTENTIAL, W. D. MacMillan. A comprehensive, well balanced presentation of potential theory, serving both as an introduction and a reference work with regard to specific problems, for physicists and mathematicians. No prior knowledge of integral relations is assumed, and all mathematical material is developed as it becomes necessary. Includes: Attraction of Finite Bodies; Newtonian Potential Function; Vector Fields. Green and Gauss Theorems; Attractions of Surfaces and Lines; Surface Distribution of Matter; Two-Layer Surfaces; Spherical Harmonics; Ellipsoidal Harmonics; etc. "The great number of particular cases . . . should make the book valuable to geophysicists and others actively engaged in practical applications of the potential theory." Review of Scientific Instruments. Index. Bibliography. xiii + 469pp. 5⅜ x 8.
S486 Paperbound **$2.25**

THEORETICAL MECHANICS: DYNAMICS OF RIGID BODIES, W. D. MacMillan. Theory of dynamics of a rigid body is developed, using both the geometrical and analytical methods of instruction. Begins with exposition of algebra of vectors, it goes through momentum principles, motion in space, use of differential equations and infinite series to solve more sophisticated dynamics problems. Partial contents: moments of inertia, systems of free particles, motion parallel to a fixed plane, rolling motion, method of periodic solutions, much more. 82 figs. 199 problems. Bibliography. Indexes. xii + 476pp. 5⅜ x 8.
S641 Paperbound **$2.00**

MATHEMATICAL FOUNDATIONS OF STATISTICAL MECHANICS, A. I. Khinchin. Offering a precise and rigorous formulation of problems, this book supplies a thorough and up-to-date exposition. It provides analytical tools needed to replace cumbersome concepts, and furnishes for the first time a logical step-by-step introduction to the subject. Partial contents: geometry & kinematics of the phase space, ergodic problem, reduction to theory of probability, application of central limit problem, ideal monatomic gas, foundation of thermo-dynamics, dispersion and distribution of sum functions. Key to notations. Index. viii + 179pp. 5⅜ x 8.
S147 Paperbound **$1.35**

ELEMENTARY PRINCIPLES IN STATISTICAL MECHANICS, J. W. Gibbs. Last work of the great Yale mathematical physicist, still one of the most fundamental treatments available for advanced students and workers in the field. Covers the basic principle of conservation of probability of phase, theory of errors in the calculated phases of a system, the contributions of Clausius, Maxwell, Boltzmann, and Gibbs himself, and much more. Includes valuable comparison of statistical mechanics with thermodynamics: Carnot's cycle, mechanical definitions of entropy, etc. xvi + 208pp. 5⅜ x 8.
S707 Paperbound **$1.45**

THE DYNAMICS OF PARTICLES AND OF RIGID, ELASTIC, AND FLUID BODIES; BEING LECTURES ON MATHEMATICAL PHYSICS, A. G. Webster. The reissuing of this classic fills the need for a comprehensive work on dynamics. A wide range of topics is covered in unusually great depth, applying ordinary and partial differential equations. Part I considers laws of motion and methods applicable to systems of all sorts; oscillation, resonance, cyclic systems, etc. Part 2 is a detailed study of the dynamics of rigid bodies. Part 3 introduces the theory of potential; stress and strain, Newtonian potential functions, gyrostatics, wave and vortex motion, etc. Further contents: Kinematics of a point; Lagrange's equations; Hamilton's principle; Systems of vectors; Statics and dynamics of deformable bodies; much more, not easily found together in one volume. Unabridged reprinting of 2nd edition. 20 pages of notes on differential equations and the higher analysis. 203 illustrations. Selected bibliography. Index. xi + 588pp. 5⅜ x 8.
S522 Paperbound **$2.35**

A TREATISE ON DYNAMICS OF A PARTICLE, E. J. Routh. Elementary text on dynamics for beginning mathematics or physics student. Unusually detailed treatment from elementary definitions to motion in 3 dimensions, emphasizing concrete aspects. Much unique material important in recent applications. Covers impulsive forces, rectilinear and constrained motion in 2 dimensions, harmonic and parabolic motion, degrees of freedom, closed orbits, the conical pendulum, the principle of least action, Jacobi's method, and much more. Index. 559 problems, many fully worked out, incorporated into text. xiii + 418pp. 5⅜ x 8.
$$\text{S696 Paperbound } \mathbf{\$2.25}$$

DYNAMICS OF A SYSTEM OF RIGID BODIES (Elementary Section), E. J. Routh. Revised 7th edition of this standard reference. This volume covers the dynamical principles of the subject, and its more elementary applications: finding moments of inertia by integration, foci of inertia, d'Alembert's principle, impulsive forces, motion in 2 and 3 dimensions, Lagrange's equations, relative indicatrix, Euler's theorem, large tautochronous motions, etc. Index. 55 figures. Scores of problems. xv + 443pp. 5⅜ x 8.
$$\text{S664 Paperbound } \mathbf{\$2.35}$$

DYNAMICS OF A SYSTEM OF RIGID BODIES (Advanced Section), E. J. Routh. Revised 6th edition of a classic reference aid. Much of its material remains unique. Partial contents: moving axes, relative motion, oscillations about equilibrium, motion. Motion of a body under no forces, any forces. Nature of motion given by linear equations and conditions of stability. Free, forced vibrations, constants of integration, calculus of finite differences, variations, precession and nutation, motion of the moon, motion of string, chain, membranes. 64 figures. 498pp. 5⅜ x 8.
$$\text{S229 Paperbound } \mathbf{\$2.35}$$

DYNAMICAL THEORY OF GASES, James Jeans. Divided into mathematical and physical chapters for the convenience of those not expert in mathematics, this volume discusses the mathematical theory of gas in a steady state, thermodynamics, Boltzmann and Maxwell, kinetic theory, quantum theory, exponentials, etc. 4th enlarged edition, with new material on quantum theory, quantum dynamics, etc. Indexes. 28 figures. 444pp. 6⅛ x 9¼.
$$\text{S136 Paperbound } \mathbf{\$2.45}$$

FOUNDATIONS OF POTENTIAL THEORY, O. D. Kellogg. Based on courses given at Harvard this is suitable for both advanced and beginning mathematicians. Proofs are rigorous, and much material not generally avialable elsewhere is included. Partial contents: forces of gravity, fields of force, divergence theorem, properties of Newtonian potentials at points of free space, potentials as solutions of Laplace's equations, harmonic functions, electrostatics, electric images, logarithmic potential, etc. One of Grundlehren Series. ix + 384pp. 5⅜ x 8.
$$\text{S144 Paperbound } \mathbf{\$1.98}$$

THERMODYNAMICS, Enrico Fermi. Unabridged reproduction of 1937 edition. Elementary in treatment; remarkable for clarity, organization. Requires no knowledge of advanced math beyond calculus, only familiarity with fundamentals of thermometry, calorimetry. Partial Contents: Thermodynamic systems; First & Second laws of thermodynamics; Entropy; Thermodynamic potentials: phase rule, reversible electric cell; Gaseous reactions: van't Hoff reaction box, principle of LeChatelier; Thermodynamics of dilute solutions: osmotic & vapor pressures, boiling & freezing points; Entropy constant. Index. 25 problems. 24 illustrations. x + 160pp. 5⅜ x 8
$$\text{S361 Paperbound } \mathbf{\$1.75}$$

THE THERMODYNAMICS OF ELECTRICAL PHENOMENA IN METALS and A CONDENSED COLLECTION OF THERMODYNAMIC FORMULAS, P. W. Bridgman. Major work by the Nobel Prizewinner: stimulating conceptual introduction to aspects of the electron theory of metals, giving an intuitive understanding of fundamental relationships concealed by the formal systems of Onsager and others. Elementary mathematical formulations show clearly the fundamental thermodynamical relationships of the electric field, and a complete phenomenological theory of metals is created. This is the work in which Bridgman announced his famous "thermomotive force" and his distinction between "driving" and "working" electromotive force. We have added in this Dover edition the author's long unavailable tables of thermodynamic formulas, extremely valuable for the speed of reference they allow. Two works bound as one. Index. 33 figures. Bibliography. xviii + 256pp. 5⅜ x 8. S723 Paperbound **$1.65**

REFLECTIONS ON THE MOTIVE POWER OF FIRE, by Sadi Carnot, and other papers on the 2nd law of thermodynamics by E. Clapeyron and R. Clausius. Carnot's "Reflections" laid the groundwork of modern thermodynamics. Its non-technical, mostly verbal statements examine the relations between heat and the work done by heat in engines, establishing conditions for the economical working of these engines. The papers by Clapeyron and Clausius here reprinted added further refinements to Carnot's work, and led to its final acceptance by physicists. Selections from posthumous manuscripts of Carnot are also included. All papers in English. New introduction by E. Mendoza. 12 illustrations. xxii + 152pp. 5⅜ x 8.
$$\text{S661 Paperbound } \mathbf{\$1.50}$$

TREATISE ON THERMODYNAMICS, Max Planck. Based on Planck's original papers this offers a uniform point of view for the entire field and has been used as an introduction for students who have studied elementary chemistry, physics, and calculus. Rejecting the earlier approaches of Helmholtz and Maxwell, the author makes no assumptions regarding the nature of heat, but begins with a few empirical facts, and from these deduces new physical and chemical laws. 3rd English edition of this standard text by a Nobel laureate. xvi + 297pp. 5⅜ x 8.
$$\text{S219 Paperbound } \mathbf{\$1.75}$$

THE THEORY OF HEAT RADIATION, Max Planck. A pioneering work in thermodynamics, providing basis for most later work. Nobel Laureate Planck writes on Deductions from Electrodynamics and Thermodynamics, Entropy and Probability, Irreversible Radiation Processes, etc. Starts with simple experimental laws of optics, advances to problems of spectral distribution of energy and irreversibility. Bibliography. 7 illustrations, xiv + 224pp. 5⅜ x 8.
S546 Paperbound **$1.50**

A HISTORY OF THE THEORY OF ELASTICITY AND THE STRENGTH OF MATERIALS, I. Todhunter and K. Pearson. For over 60 years a basic reference, unsurpassed in scope or authority. Both a history of the mathematical theory of elasticity from Galileo, Hooke, and Mariotte to Saint Venant, Kirchhoff, Clebsch, and Lord Kelvin and a detailed presentation of every important mathematical contribution during this period. Presents proofs of thousands of theorems and laws, summarizes every relevant treatise, many unavailable elsewhere. Practically a book apiece is devoted to modern founders: Saint Venant, Lame, Boussinesq, Rankine, Lord Kelvin, F. Neumann, Kirchhoff, Clebsch. Hundreds of pages of technical and physical treatises on specific applications of elasticity to particular materials. Indispensable for the mathematician, physicist, or engineer working with elasticity. Unabridged, corrected reprint of original 3-volume 1886-1893 edition. Three volume set. Two indexes. Appendix to Vol. I. Total of 2344pp. 5⅜ x 8⅜.
S914-916 The set, Clothbound **$12.50**

THE MATHEMATICAL THEORY OF ELASTICITY, A. E. H. Love. A wealth of practical illustration combined with thorough discussion of fundamentals—theory, application, special problems and solutions. Partial Contents: Analysis of Strain & Stress, Elasticity of Solid Bodies, Elasticity of Crystals, Vibration of Spheres, Cylinders, Propagation of Waves in Elastic Solid Media, Torsion, Theory of Continuous Beams, Plates. Rigorous treatment of Volterra's theory of dislocations, 2-dimensional elastic systems, other topics of modern interest. "For years the standard treatise on elasticity," AMERICAN MATHEMATICAL MONTHLY. 4th revised edition. Index. 76 figures. xviii + 643pp. 6⅛ x 9¼.
S174 Paperbound **$2.95**

RAYLEIGH'S PRINCIPLE AND ITS APPLICATIONS TO ENGINEERING, G. Temple & W. Bickley. Rayleigh's principle developed to provide upper and lower estimates of true value of fundamental period of a vibrating system, or condition of stability of elastic systems. Illustrative examples; rigorous proofs in special chapters. Partial contents: Energy method of discussing vibrations, stability. Perturbation theory, whirling of uniform shafts. Criteria of elastic stability. Application of energy method. Vibrating systems. Proof, accuracy, successive approximations, application of Rayleigh's principle. Synthetic theorems. Numerical, graphical methods. Equilibrium configurations, Ritz's method. Bibliography. Index. 22 figures. ix + 156pp. 5⅜ x 8.
S307 Paperbound **$1.50**

INVESTIGATIONS ON THE THEORY OF THE BROWNIAN MOVEMENT, Albert Einstein. Reprints from rare European journals. 5 basic papers, including the Elementary Theory of the Brownian Movement, written at the request of Lorentz to provide a simple explanation. Translated by A. D. Cowper. Annotated, edited by R. Fürth. 33pp. of notes elucidate, give history of previous investigations. Author, subject indexes. 62 footnotes. 124pp. 5⅜ x 8.
S304 Paperbound **$1.25**

See also: **FUNDAMENTAL FORMULAS OF PHYSICS, D. H. Menzel.**

ENGINEERING

THEORY OF FLIGHT, Richard von Mises. Remains almost unsurpassed as balanced, well-written account of fundamental fluid dynamics, and situations in which air compressibility effects are unimportant. Stressing equally theory and practice, avoiding formidable mathematical structure, it conveys a full understanding of physical phenomena and mathematical concepts. Contains perhaps the best introduction to general theory of stability. "Outstanding," Scientific, Medical, and Technical Books. New introduction by K. H. Hohenemser. Bibliographical, historical notes. Index. 408 illustrations. xvi + 620pp. 5⅜ x 8⅜. S541 Paperbound **$2.85**

THEORY OF WING SECTIONS, I. H. Abbott, A. E. von Doenhoff. Concise compilation of subsonic aerodynamic characteristics of modern NASA wing sections, with description of their geometry, associated theory. Primarily reference work for engineers, students, it gives methods, data for using wing-section data to predict characteristics. Particularly valuable: chapters on thin wings, airfoils; complete summary of NACA's experimental observations, system of construction families of airfoils. 350pp. of tables on Basic Thickness Forms, Mean Lines, Airfoil Ordinates, Aerodynamic Characteristics of Wing Sections. Index. Bibliography. 191 illustrations. Appendix. 705pp. 5⅜ x 8. S558 Paperbound **$2.95**

SUPERSONIC AERODYNAMICS, E. R. C. Miles. Valuable theoretical introduction to the supersonic domain, with emphasis on mathematical tools and principles, for practicing aerodynamicists and advanced students in aeronautical engineering. Covers fundamental theory, divergence theorem and principles of circulation, compressible flow and Helmholtz laws, the Prandtl-Busemann graphic method for 2-dimensional flow, oblique shock waves, the Taylor-Maccoll method for cones in supersonic flow, the Chaplygin method for 2-dimensional flow, etc. Problems range from practical engineering problems to development of theoretical results. "Rendered outstanding by the unprecedented scope of its contents . . . has undoubtedly filled a vital gap," AERONAUTICAL ENGINEERING REVIEW. Index. 173 problems, answers. 106 diagrams. 7 tables. xii + 255pp. 5⅜ x 8. S214 Paperbound **$1.45**

WEIGHT-STRENGTH ANALYSIS OF AIRCRAFT STRUCTURES, F. R. Shanley. Scientifically sound methods of analyzing and predicting the structural weight of aircraft and missiles. Deals directly with forces and the distances over which they must be transmitted, making it possible to develop methods by which the minimum structural weight can be determined for any material and conditions of loading. Weight equations for wing and fuselage structures. Includes author's original papers on inelastic buckling and creep buckling. "Particularly successful in presenting his analytical methods for investigating various optimum design principles," AERONAUTICAL ENGINEERING REVIEW. Enlarged bibliography. Index. 199 figures. xiv + 404pp. 5⅝ x 8⅜.
S660 Paperbound **$2.45**

INTRODUCTION TO THE STATISTICAL DYNAMICS OF AUTOMATIC CONTROL SYSTEMS, V. V. Solodovnikov. First English publication of text-reference covering important branch of automatic control systems—random signals; in its original edition, this was the first comprehensive treatment. Examines frequency characteristics, transfer functions, stationary random processes, determination of minimum mean-squared error, of transfer function for a finite period of observation, much more. Translation edited by J. B. Thomas, L. A. Zadeh. Index. Bibliography. Appendix. xxii + 308pp. 5⅜ x 8.
S420 Paperbound **$2.25**

TENSORS FOR CIRCUITS, Gabriel Kron. A boldly original method of analysing engineering problems, at center of sharp discussion since first introduced, now definitely proved useful in such areas as electrical and structural networks on automatic computers. Encompasses a great variety of specific problems by means of a relatively few symbolic equations. "Power and flexibility . . . becoming more widely recognized," Nature. Formerly "A Short Course in Tensor Analysis." New introduction by B. Hoffmann. Index. Over 800 diagrams. xix + 250pp. 5⅜ x 8.
S534 Paperbound **$1.85**

DESIGN AND USE OF INSTRUMENTS AND ACCURATE MECHANISM, T. N. Whitehead. For the instrument designer, engineer; how to combine necessary mathematical abstractions with independent observation of actual facts. Partial contents: instruments & their parts, theory of errors, systematic errors, probability, short period errors, erratic errors, design precision, kinematic, semikinematic design, stiffness, planning of an instrument, human factor, etc. Index. 85 photos, diagrams. xii + 288pp. 5⅜ x 8.
S270 Paperbound **$1.95**

APPLIED ELASTICITY, J. Prescott. Provides the engineer with the theory of elasticity usually lacking in books on strength of materials, yet concentrates on those portions useful for immediate application. Develops every important type of elasticity problem from theoretical principles. Covers analysis of stress, relations between stress and strain, the empirical basis of elasticity, thin rods under tension or thrust; Saint Venant's theory, transverse oscillations of thin rods, stability of thin plates, cylinders with thin walls, vibrations of rotating disks, elastic bodies in contact, etc. "Excellent and important contribution to the subject, not merely in the old matter which he has presented in new and refreshing form, but also in the many original investigations here published for the first time," NATURE. Index. 3 Appendixes. vi + 672pp. 5⅜ x 8.
S726 Paperbound **$2.95**

STRENGTH OF MATERIALS, J. P. Den Hartog. Distinguished text prepared for M.I.T. course, ideal as introduction, refresher, reference, or self-study text. Full clear treatment of elementary material (tension, torsion, bending, compound stresses, deflection of beams, etc.), plus much advanced material on engineering methods of great practical value: full treatment of the Mohr circle, lucid elementary discussions of the theory of the center of shear and the "Myosotis" method of calculating beam deflections, reinforced concrete, plastic deformations, photoelasticity, etc. In all sections, both general principles and concrete applications are given. Index. 186 figures (160 others in problem section). 350 problems, all with answers. List of formulas. viii + 323pp. 5⅜ x 8.
S755 Paperbound **$1.95**

PHOTOELASTICITY: PRINCIPLES AND METHODS, H. T. Jessop, F. C. Harris. For the engineer, for specific problems of stress analysis. Latest time-saving methods of checking calculations in 2-dimensional design problems, new techniques for stresses in 3 dimensions, and lucid description of optical systems used in practical photoelasticity. Useful suggestions and hints based on on-the-job experience included. Partial contents: strained and stress-strain relations, circular disc under thrust along diameter, rectangular block with square hole under vertical thrust, simply supported rectangular beam under central concentrated load, etc. Theory held to minimum, no advanced mathematical training needed. Index. 164 illustrations. viii + 184pp. 6⅛ x 9¼.
S137 Clothbound **$3.75**

MECHANICS OF THE GYROSCOPE, THE DYNAMICS OF ROTATION, R. F. Deimel, Professor of Mechanical Engineering at Stevens Institute of Technology. Elementary general treatment of dynamics of rotation, with special application of gyroscopic phenomena. No knowledge of vectors needed. Velocity of a moving curve, acceleration to a point, general equations of motion, gyroscopic horizon, free gyro, motion of discs, the damped gyro, 103 similar topics. Exercises. 75 figures. 208pp. 5⅜ x 8.
S66 Paperbound **$1.65**
S144 Paperbound **$1.98**

A TREATISE ON GYROSTATICS AND ROTATIONAL MOTION: THEORY AND APPLICATIONS, Andrew Gray. Most detailed, thorough book in English, generally considered definitive study. Many problems of all sorts in full detail, or step-by-step summary. Classical problems of Bour, Lottner, etc.; later ones of great physical interest. Vibrating systems of gyrostats, earth as a top, calculation of path of axis of a top by elliptic integrals, motion of unsymmetrical top, much more. Index. 160 illus. 550pp. 5⅜ x 8.
S589 Paperbound **$2.75**

FUNDAMENTALS OF HYDRO- AND AEROMECHANICS, L. Prandtl and O. G. Tietjens. The well-known standard work based upon Prandtl's lectures at Goettingen. Wherever possible hydro-dynamics theory is referred to practical considerations in hydraulics, with the view of unifying theory and experience. Presentation is extremely clear and though primarily physical, mathematical proofs are rigorous and use vector analysis to a considerable extent. An Enginering Society Monograph, 1934. 186 figures. Index. xvi + 270pp. 5⅜ x 8.

S374 Paperbound **$1.85**

APPLIED HYDRO- AND AEROMECHANICS, L. Prandtl and O. G. Tietjens. Presents, for the most part, methods which will be valuable to engineers. Covers flow in pipes, boundary layers, airfoil theory, entry conditions, turbulent flow in pipes, and the boundary layer, determining drag from measurements of pressure and velocity, etc. "Will be welcomed by all students of aerodynamics," NATURE. Unabridged, unaltered. An Engineering Society Monograph, 1934. Index. 226 figures, 28 photographic plates illustrating flow patterns. xvi + 311pp. 5⅜ x 8.

S375 Paperbound **$1.85**

HYDRAULICS AND ITS APPLICATIONS, A. H. Gibson. Excellent comprehensive textbook for the student and thorough practical manual for the professional worker, a work of great stature in its area. Half the book is devoted to theory and half to applications and practical prob-lems met in the field. Covers modes of motion of a fluid, critical velocity, viscous flow, eddy formation, Bernoulli's theorem, flow in converging passages, vortex motion, form of effluent streams, notches and weirs, skin friction, losses at valves and elbows, siphons, erosion of channels, jet propulsion, waves of oscillation, and over 100 similar topics. Final chapters (nearly 400 pages) cover more than 100 kinds of hydraulic machinery: Pelton wheel, speed regulators, the hydraulic ram, surge tanks, the scoop wheel, the Venturi meter, etc. A special chapter treats methods of testing theoretical hypotheses: scale models of rivers, tidal estuaries, siphon spillways, etc. 5th revised and enlarged (1952) edition. Index. Ap-pendix. 427 photographs and diagrams. 95 examples, answers. xv + 813pp. 6 x 9.

S791 Clothbound **$8.00**

FLUID MECHANICS FOR HYDRAULIC ENGINEERS, H. Rouse. Standard work that gives a coherent picture of fluid mechanics from the point of view of the hydraulic engineer. Based on courses given to civil and mechanical engineering students at Columbia and the California Institute of Technology, this work covers every basic principle, method, equation, or theory of interest to the hydraulic engineer. Much of the material, diagrams, charts, etc., in this self-contained text are not duplicated elsewhere. Covers irrotational motion, conformal map-ping, problems in laminar motion, fluid turbulence, flow around immersed bodies, transporta-tion of sediment, general charcteristics of wave phenomena, gravity waves in open channels, etc. Index. Appendix of physical properties of common fluids. Frontispiece + 245 figures and photographs. xvi + 422pp. 5⅜ x 8.

S729 Paperbound **$2.25**

THE MEASUREMENT OF POWER SPECTRA FROM THE POINT OF VIEW OF COMMUNICATIONS ENGINEERING, R. B. Blackman, J. W. Tukey. This pathfinding work, reprinted from the "Bell System Technical Journal," explains various ways of getting practically useful answers in the measurement of power spectra, using results from both transmission theory and the theory of statistical estimation. Treats: Autocovariance Functions and Power Spectra; Direct Analog Computation; Distortion, Noise, Heterodyne Filtering and Pre-whitening; Aliasing; Rejection Filtering and Separation; Smoothing and Decimation Procedures; Very Low Fre-quencies; Transversal Filtering; much more. An appendix reviews fundamental Fourier tech-niques. Index of notation. Glossary of terms. 24 figures. XII tables. Bibliography. General index. 192pp. 5⅜ x 8.

S507 Paperbound **$1.85**

MICROWAVE TRANSMISSION DESIGN DATA, T. Moreno. Originally classified, now rewritten and enlarged (14 new chapters) for public release under auspices of Sperry Corp. Material of immediate value or reference use to radio engineers, systems designers, applied physicists, etc. Ordinary transmission line theory; attenuation; capacity; parameters of coaxial lines; higher modes; flexible cables; obstacles, discontinuities, and injunctions; tuneable wave guide impedance transformers; effects of temperature and humidity; much more. "Enough theoretical discussion is included to allow use of data without previous background," Electronics. 324 circuit diagrams, figures, etc. Tables of dielectrics, flexible cable, etc., data. Index. Ix + 248pp. 5⅜ x 8.

S459 Paperbound **$1.50**

GASEOUS CONDUCTORS: THEORY AND ENGINEERING APPLICATIONS, J. D. Cobine. An indis-pensable text and reference to gaseous conduction phenomena, with the engineering view-point prevailing throughout. Studies the kinetic theory of gases, ionization, emission phe-nomena; gas breakdown, spark characteristics, glow, and discharges; engineering applica-tions in circuit interrupters, rectifiers, light sources, etc. Separate detailed treatment of high pressure arcs (Suits); low pressure arcs (Langmuir and Tonks). Much more. "Well organized, clear, straightforward," Tonks, Review of Scientific Instruments. Index. Bibliog-raphy. 83 practice problems. 7 appendices. Over 600 figures. 58 tables. xx + 606pp. 5⅜ x 8.

S442 Paperbound **$2.85**

See also: BRIDGES AND THEIR BUILDERS, D. Steinman, S. R. Watson; A DIDEROT PICTORIAL ENCYCLOPEDIA OF TRADES AND INDUSTRY; MATHEMATICS IN ACTION, O. G. Sutton; THE THEORY OF SOUND, Lord Rayleigh; RAYLEIGH'S PRINCIPLE AND ITS APPLICATION TO ENGI-NEERING, G. Temple, W. Bickley; APPLIED OPTICS AND OPTICAL DESIGN, A. E. Conrady; HYDRODYNAMICS, Dryden, Murnaghan, Bateman; LOUD SPEAKERS, N. W. McLachlan; HIS-TORY OF THE THEORY OF ELASTICITY AND OF THE STRENGTH OF MATERIALS, I. Todhunter,

K. Pearson; THEORY AND OPERATION OF THE SLIDE RULE, J. P. Ellis; DIFFERENTIAL EQUA-
TIONS FOR ENGINEERS, P. Franklin; MATHEMATICAL METHODS FOR SCIENTISTS AND ENGI-
NEERS, L. P. Smith; APPLIED MATHEMATICS FOR RADIO AND COMMUNICATIONS ENGINEERS,
C. E. Smith; MATHEMATICS OF MODERN ENGINEERING, E. G. Keller, R. E. Doherty; THEORY
OF FUNCTIONS AS APPLIED TO ENGINEERING PROBLEMS, R. Rothe, F. Ollendorff, K. Pohlhausen.

CHEMISTRY AND PHYSICAL CHEMISTRY

ORGANIC CHEMISTRY, F. C. Whitmore. The entire subject of organic chemistry for the practicing chemist and the advanced student. Storehouse of facts, theories, processes found elsewhere only in specialized journals. Covers aliphatic compounds (500 pages on the properties
and synthetic preparation of hydrocarbons, halides, proteins, ketones, etc.), alicyclic compounds, aromatic compounds, heterocyclic .compounds, organophosphorus and organometallic
compounds. Methods of synthetic preparation analyzed critically throughout. Includes much of
biochemical interest. "The scope of this volume is astonishing," INDUSTRIAL AND ENGINEER-
ING CHEMISTRY. 12,000-reference index. 2387-item bibliography. Total of x + 1005pp. $5\frac{3}{8}$ x 8.
Two volume set.
S700 Vol I Paperbound **$2.00**
S701 Vol II Paperbound **$2.00**
The set **$4.00**

THE PRINCIPLES OF ELECTROCHEMISTRY, D. A. MacInnes. Basic equations for almost every
subfield of electrochemistry from first principles, referring at all times to the soundest and
most recent theories and results; unusually useful as text or as reference. Covers coulometers
and Faraday's Law, electrolytic conductance, the Debye-Hueckel method for the theoretical
calculation of activity coefficients, concentration cells, standard electrode potentials, thermodynamic ionization constants, pH, potentiometric titrations, irreversible phenomena, Planck's
equation, and much more. "Excellent treatise," AMERICAN CHEMICAL SOCIETY JOURNAL.
"Highly recommended," CHEMICAL AND METALLURGICAL ENGINEERING. 2 Indices. Appendix.
585-item bibliography. 137 figures. 94 tables. ii + 478pp. $5\frac{5}{8}$ x $8\frac{3}{8}$.
S52 Paperbound **$2.35**

**THE CHEMISTRY OF URANIUM: THE ELEMENT, ITS BINARY AND RELATED COMPOUNDS, J. J. Katz
and E. Rabinowitch.** Vast post-World War II collection and correlation of thousands of AEC
reports and published papers in a useful and easily accessible form, still the most complete
and up-to-date compilation. Treats "dry uranium chemistry," occurrences, preparation, properties, simple compounds, isotopic composition, extraction from ores, spectra, alloys, etc. Much
material available only here. Index. Thousands of evaluated bibliographical references. 324
tables, charts, figures. xxi + 609pp. $5\frac{3}{8}$ x 8.
S757 Paperbound **$2.95**

KINETIC THEORY OF LIQUIDS, J. Frenkel. Regarding the kinetic theory of liquids as a generalization and extension of the theory of solid bodies, this volume covers all types of
arrangements of solids, thermal displacements of atoms, interstitial atoms and ions,
orientational and rotational motion of molecules, and transition between states of matter.
Mathematical theory is developed close to the physical subject matter. 216 bibliographical
footnotes. 55 figures. xi + 485pp. $5\frac{3}{8}$ x 8.
S94 Clothbound **$3.95**
S95 Paperbound **$2.45**

POLAR MOLECULES, Pieter Debye. This work by Nobel laureate Debye offers a complete guide
to fundamental electrostatic field relations, polarizability, molecular structure. Partial contents: electric intensity, displacement and force, polarization by orientation, molar polarization and molar refraction, halogen-hydrides, polar liquids, ionic saturation, dielectric constant, etc. Special chapter considers quantum theory. Indexed. 172pp. $5\frac{3}{8}$ x 8.
S64 Paperbound **$1.50**

ELASTICITY, PLASTICITY AND STRUCTURE OF MATTER, R. Houwink. Standard treatise on
rheological aspects of different technically important solids such as crystals, resins, textiles,
rubber, clay, many others. Investigates general laws for deformations; determines divergences
from these laws for certain substances. Covers general physical and mathematical aspects
of plasticity, elasticity, viscosity. Detailed examination of deformations, internal structure
of matter in relation to elastic and plastic behavior, formation of solid matter from a fluid,
conditions for elastic and plastic behavior of matter. Treats glass, asphalt, gutta percha,
balata, proteins, baker's dough, lacquers, sulphur, others. 2nd revised, enlarged edition.
Extensive revised bibliography in over 500 footnotes. Index. Table of symbols. 214 figures.
xviii + 368pp. 6 x $9\frac{1}{4}$.
S385 Paperbound **$2.45**

THE PHASE RULE AND ITS APPLICATION, Alexander Findlay. Covering chemical phenomena
of 1, 2, 3, 4, and multiple component systems, this "standard work on the subject"
(NATURE, London), has been completely revised and brought up to date by A. N. Campbell
and N. O. Smith. Brand new material has been added on such matters as binary, tertiary
liquid equilibria, solid solutions in ternary systems, quinary systems of salts and water.
Completely revised to triangular coordinates in ternary systems, clarified graphic representation, solid models, etc. 9th revised edition. Author, subject indexes. 236 figures. 505
footnotes, mostly bibliographic. xii + 494pp. $5\frac{3}{8}$ x 8.
S91 Paperbound **$2.45**

TERNARY SYSTEMS: INTRODUCTION TO THE THEORY OF THREE COMPONENT SYSTEMS, G. Masing. Furnishes detailed discussion of representative types of 3-components systems, both in solid models (particularly metallic alloys) and isothermal models. Discusses mechanical mixture without compounds and without solid solutions; unbroken solid solution series; solid solutions with solubility breaks in two binary systems; iron-silicon-aluminum alloys; allotropic forms of iron in ternary system; other topics. Bibliography. Index. 166 illustrations. 178pp. 5⅝ x 8⅜.   S631 Paperbound **$1.45**

THE STORY OF ALCHEMY AND EARLY CHEMISTRY, J. M. Stillman. An authoritative, scholarly work, highly readable, of development of chemical knowledge from 4000 B.C. to downfall of phlogiston theory in late 18th century. Every important figure, many quotations. Brings alive curious, almost incredible history of alchemical beliefs, practices, writings of Arabian Prince Oneeyade, Vincent of Beauvais, Geber, Zosimos, Paracelsus, Vitruvius, scores more. Studies work, thought of Black, Cavendish, Priestley, Van Helmont, Bergman, Lavoisier, Newton, etc. Index. Bibliography. 579pp. 5⅜ x 8.   S628 Paperbound **$2.45**

See also: **ATOMIC SPECTRA AND ATOMIC STRUCTURE, G. Herzberg; INVESTIGATIONS ON THE THEORY OF THE BROWNIAN MOVEMENT, A. Einstein; TREATISE ON THERMODYNAMICS, M. Planck.**

ASTRONOMY AND ASTROPHYSICS

AN ELEMENTARY SURVEY OF CELESTIAL MECHANICS, Y. Ryabov. Elementary exposition of gravitational theory and celestial mechanics. Historical introduction and coverage of basic principles, including: the elliptic, the orbital plane, the 2- and 3-body problems, the discovery of Neptune, planetary rotation, the length of the day, the shapes of galaxies, satellites (detailed treatment of Sputnik I), etc. First American reprinting of successful Russian popular exposition. Elementary algebra and trigonometry helpful, but not necessary; presentation chiefly verbal. Appendix of theorem proofs. 58 figures. 165pp. 5⅜ x 8.
                                                                    T756 Paperbound **$1.25**

THE SKY AND ITS MYSTERIES, E. A. Beet. One of most lucid books on mysteries of universe; deals with astronomy from earliest observations to latest theories of expansion of universe, source of stellar energy, birth of planets, origin of moon craters, possibility of life on other planets. Discusses effects of sunspots on weather; distances, ages of several stars; master plan of universe; methods and tools of astronomers; much more. "Eminently readable book," London Times. Extensive bibliography. Over 50 diagrams. 12 full-page plates, fold-out star map. Introduction. Index, 238pp. 5¼ x 7½.   T627 Clothbound **$3.00**

THE REALM OF THE NEBULAE, E. Hubble. One of the great astronomers of our time records his formulation of the concept of "island universes," and its impact on astronomy. Such topics are covered as the velocity-distance relation; classification, nature, distances, general field of nebulae; cosmological theories; nebulae in the neighborhood of the Milky Way. 39 photos of nebulae, nebulae clusters, spectra of nebulae, and velocity distance relations shown by spectrum comparison. "One of the most progressive lines of astronomical research," The Times (London). New introduction by A. Sandage. 55 illustrations. Index. iv + 201pp. 5⅜ x 8.   S455 Paperbound **$1.50**

OUT OF THE SKY, H. H. Nininger. A non-technical but comprehensive introduction to "meteoritics", the young science concerned with all aspects of the arrival of matter from outer space. Written by one of the world's experts on meteorites, this work shows how, despite difficulties of observation and sparseness of data, a considerable body of knowledge has arisen. It defines meteors and meteorites; studies fireball clusters and processions, meteorite composition, size, distribution, showers, explosions, origins, craters, and much more. A true connecting link between astronomy and geology. More than 175 photos, 22 other illustrations. References. Bibliography of author's publications on meteorites. Index. viii + 336pp. 5⅜ x 8.   T519 Paperbound **$1.85**

SATELLITES AND SCIENTIFIC RESEARCH, D. King-Hele. Non-technical account of the manmade satellites and the discoveries they have yielded up to the spring of 1959. Brings together information hitherto published only in hard-to-get scientific journals. Includes the life history of a typical satellite, methods of tracking, new information on the shape of the earth, zones of radiation, etc. Over 60 diagrams and 6 photographs. Mathematical appendix. Bibliography of over 100 items. Index. xii + 180pp. 5⅜ x 8½.   T703 Clothbound **$4.00**

HOW TO MAKE A TELESCOPE, Jean Texereau. Enables the most inexperienced to choose, design, and build an f/6 or f/8 Newtonian type reflecting telescope, with an altaizmuth Couder mounting, suitable for lunar, planetary, and stellar observation. A practical step-by-step course covering every operation and every piece of equipment. Basic principles of geometric and physical optics are discussed (though unnecessary to construction), and the merits of reflectors and refractors compared. A thorough discussion of eyepieces, finders, grinding, installation, testing, using the instrument, etc. 241 figures and 38 photos show almost every operation and tool. Potential errors are anticipated as much as possible. Foreword by A. Couder. Bibliography and sources of supply listing. Index. xiii + 191pp. 6¼ x 10.   T464 Clothbound **$3.50**

AN INTRODUCTORY TREATISE ON DYNAMICAL ASTRONOMY, H. C. Plummer. Unusually wide connected and concise coverage of nearly every significant branch of dynamical astronomy, stressing basic principles throughout: determination of orbits, planetary theory, lunar theory, precession and nutation, and many of their applications. Hundreds of formulas and theorems worked out completely, important methods thoroughly explained. Covers motion under a central attraction, orbits of double stars and spectroscopic binaries, the libration of the moon, and much more. Index. 8 diagrams. xxi + 343pp. 5⅝ x 8⅜. S689 Paperbound **$2.35**

A COMPENDIUM OF SPHERICAL ASTRONOMY, S. Newcomb. Long a standard collection of basic methods and formulas most useful to the working astronomer, and clear full text for students. Includes the most important common approximations; 40 pages on the method of least squares; general theory of spherical coordinates; parallax; aberration; astronomical refraction; theory of precession; proper motion of the stars; methods of deriving positions of stars; and much more. Index. 9 Appendices of tables, formulas, etc. 36 figures. xviii + 444pp. 5⅜ x 8.
S690 Paperbound **$2.25**

AN INTRODUCTORY TREATISE ON THE LUNAR THEORY, E. W. Brown. Indispensable for all scientists and engineers interested in orbital calculation, satellites, or navigation of space. Only work in English to explain in detail 5 major mathematical approaches to the problem of 3 bodies, those of Laplace, de Pontécoulant, Hansen, Delaunay, and Hill. Covers expressions for mutual attraction, equations of motion, forms of solution, variations of the elements in disturbed motion, the constants and their interpretations, planetary and other disturbing influences, etc. Index. Bibliography. Tables. xvi + 292pp. 5⅝ x 8⅜.
S666 Paperbound **$2.00**

LES METHODES NOUVELLES DE LA MECANIQUE CELESTE, H. Poincaré. Complete text (in French) of one of Poincaré's most important works. This set revolutionized celestial mechanics: first use of integral invariants, first major application of linear differential equations, study of periodic orbits, lunar motion and Jupiter's satellites, three body problem, and many other important topics. "Started a new era . . . so extremely modern that even today few have mastered his weapons," E. T. Bell. Three volumes. Total 1282pp. 6⅛ x 9¼.
Vol. 1. S401 Paperbound **$2.75**
Vol. 2. S402 Paperbound **$2.75**
Vol. 3. S403 Paperbound **$2.75**
The set **$7.50**

SPHERICAL AND PRACTICAL ASTRONOMY, W. Chauvenet. First book in English to apply mathematical techniques to astronomical problems is still standard work. Covers almost entire field, rigorously, with over 300 examples worked out. Vol. 1, spherical astronomy, applications to nautical astronomy; determination of hour angles, parallactic angle for known stars; interpolation; parallax; laws of refraction; predicting eclipses; precession, nutation of fixed stars; etc. Vol. 2, theory, use, of instruments; telescope; measurement of arcs, angles in general; electro-chronograph; sextant, reflecting circles; zenith telescope; etc. 100-page appendix of detailed proof of Gauss' method of least squares. 5th revised edition. Index. 15 plates, 20 tables. 1340pp. 5⅜ x 8. Vol. 1 S618 Paperbound **$2.75**
Vol. 2 S619 Paperbound **$2.75**
The set **$5.50**

THE INTERNAL CONSTITUTION OF THE STARS, Sir A. S. Eddington. Influence of this has been enormous; first detailed exposition of theory of radiative equilibrium for stellar interiors, of all available evidence for existence of diffuse matter in interstellar space. Studies quantum theory, polytropic gas spheres, mass-luminosity relations, variable stars, etc. Discussions of equations paralleled with informal exposition of intimate relationship of astrophysics with great discoveries in atomic physics, radiation. Introduction. Appendix. Index. 421pp. 5⅜ x 8.
S563 Paperbound **$2.25**

ASTRONOMY OF STELLAR ENERGY AND DECAY, Martin Johnson. Middle level treatment of astronomy as interpreted by modern atomic physics. Part One is non-technical, examines physical properties, source of energy, spectroscopy, fluctuating stars, various models and theories, etc. Part Two parallels these topics, providing their ·mathematical foundation. "Clear, concise, and readily understandable," American Library Assoc. Bibliography. 3 indexes. 29 illustrations. 216pp. 5⅜ x 8. S537 Paperbound **$1.50**

RADIATIVE TRANSFER, S. Chandrasekhar. Definitive work in field provides foundation for analysis of stellar atmospheres, planetary illumination, sky radiation; to physicists, a study of problems analogous to those in theory of diffusion of neutrons. Partial contents: equation of transfer, isotropic scattering, H-functions, diffuse reflection and transmission, Rayleigh scattering, X, Y functions, radiative equilibrium of stellar atmospheres. Extensive bibliography. 3 appendices. 35 tables. 35 figures. 407pp. 5⅝ x 8⅜. S599 Paperbound **$2.25**

AN INTRODUCTION TO THE STUDY OF STELLAR STRUCTURE, Subrahmanyan Chandrasekhar. Outstanding treatise on stellar dynamics by one of world's greatest astrophysicists. Uses classical & modern math methods to examine relationship between loss of energy, the mass, and radius of stars in a steady state. Discusses thermodynamic laws from Caratheodory's axiomatic standpoint; adiabatic, polytropic laws; work of Ritter, Emden, Kelvin, others; Stroemgren envelopes as starter for theory of gaseous stars; Gibbs statistical mechanics (quantum); degenerate stellar configuration & theory of white dwarfs, etc. "Highest level of scientific merit," BULLETIN, AMER. MATH. SOC. Bibliography. Appendixes. · Index. 33 figures. 509pp. 5⅜ x 8. S413 Paperbound **$2.75**

PRINCIPLES OF STELLAR DYNAMICS, S. Chandrasekhar. A leading astrophysicist here presents the theory of stellar dynamics as a branch of classical dynamics, clarifying the fundamental issues and the underlying motivations of the theory. He analyzes the effects of stellar encounters in terms of the classical 2-body problem, and investigates problems centering about Liouville's theorem and the solutions of the equations of continuity. This edition also includes 4 important papers by the author published since "Stellar Dynamics," and equally indispensable for all workers in the field: "New Methods in Stellar Dynamics" and "Dynamical Friction," Parts I, II, and III. Index. 3 Appendixes. Bibliography. 50 illustrations. x + 313pp. 5⅜ x8.
S659 Paperbound **$2.00**

A SHORT HISTORY OF ASTRONOMY, A. Berry. Popular standard work for over 50 years, this thorough and accurate volume covers the science from primitive times to the end of the 19th century. After the Greeks and the Middle Ages, individual chapters analyze Copernicus, Brahe, Galileo, Kepler, and Newton, and the mixed reception of their discoveries. Post-Newtonian achievements are then discussed in unusual detail: Halley, Bradley, Lagrange, Laplace, Herschel, Bessel, etc. 2 Indexes. 104 illustrations, 9 portraits. xxxi + 440pp. 5⅜ x 8.
T210 Paperbound **$2.00**

THREE COPERNICAN TREATISES, translated with notes by Edward Rosen. 3 papers available nowhere else in English: "The. Commentariolus" and "Letter against Werner" of Copernicus; the "Narratio prima" of Rheticus. The "Commentariolus" is Copernicus's most lucid exposition of his system. The "Letter against Werner" throws light on development of Copernicus's thought. The "Narratio prima" is earliest printed presentation of the new astronomy. "Educational and enjoyable," Astrophysical Journal. Corrected edition. Biographical introduction. 877-item bibliography of virtually every book, article, on Copernicus published 1939-1958. Index. 19 illustrations. 218pp. 5⅜ x 8.
S585 Paperbound **$1.75**

EARTH SCIENCES

PRINCIPLES OF STRATIGRAPHY, A. W. Grabau. Classic of 20th century geology, unmatched in scope and comprehensiveness. Nearly 600 pages cover the structure and origins of every kind of sedimentary, hydrogenic, oceanic, pyroclastic, atmoclastic, hydroclastic, marine hydroclastic, and bioclastic rock; metamorphism; erosion; etc. Includes also the constitution of the atmosphere; morphology of oceans, rivers, glaciers; volcanic activities; faults and earthquakes; and fundamental principles of paleontology (nearly 200 pages). New introduction by Prof. M. Kay, Columbia U. 1277 bibliographical entries. 264 diagrams. Tables, maps, etc. Two volume set. Total of xxxii + 1185pp. 5⅜ x 8.
S686 Vol I Paperbound **$2.50**
S687 Vol II Paperbound **$2.50**
The set **$5.00**

THE GEOLOGICAL DRAMA, H. and G. Termier. Unusual work by 2 noted French geologists: not the usual survey of geological periods, but general principles; continent formation, the influence of ice-ages and earth movements in shaping the present-day land masses, the creation and advance of life, the position of man. Readable and authoritative survey for the layman; excellent supplement for the student of geology; important collection of recent European theories for the American geologist. Much material appears here for the first time in a non-technical work. Index. 30 photographs, 5 diagrams. 5 maps. 144pp. 6 x 9.   T702 Clothbound **$3.95**

THE EVOLUTION OF THE IGNEOUS ROCKS, N. L. Bowen. Invaluable serious introduction applies techniques of physics and chemistry to explain igneous rock diversity in terms of chemical composition and fractional crystallization. Discusses liquid immiscibility in silicate magmas, crystal sorting, liquid lines of descent, fractional resorption of complex minerals, petrogenesis, etc. Of prime importance to geologists & mining engineers, also to physicists, chemists working with high temperatures and pressures. "Most important," TIMES, London. 3 indexes. 263 bibliographic notes. 82 figures. xviii + 334pp. 5⅜ x 8.   S311 Paperbound **$1.85**

INTERNAL CONSTITUTION OF THE EARTH, edited by **Beno Gutenberg.** Completely revised. Brought up-to-date, reset. Prepared for the National Research Council this is a complete & thorough coverage of such topics as earth origins, continent formation, nature & behavior of the earth's core, petrology of the crust, cooling forces in the core, seismic & earthquake material, gravity, elastic constants, strain characteristics and similar topics. "One is filled with admiration . . . a high standard . . . there is no reader who will not learn something from this book," London, Edinburgh, Dublin, Philosophic Magazine. Largest bibliography in print: 1127 classified items. Indexes. Tables of constants. 43 diagrams. 439pp. 6⅛ x 9¼.
S414 Paperbound **$2.45**

HYDROLOGY, edited by Oscar E. Meinzer. Prepared for the National Research Council. Detailed complete reference library on precipitation, evaporation, snow, snow surveying, glaciers, lakes, infiltration, soil moisture, ground water, runoff, drought, physical changes produced by water, hydrology of limestone terranes, etc. Practical in application, especially valuable for engineers. 24 experts have created "the most up-to-date, most complete treatment of the subject," AM. ASSOC. of PETROLEUM GEOLOGISTS. Bibliography. Index. 165 illustrations. xi + 712pp. 6⅛ x 9¼.
S191 Paperbound **$2.95**

THE BIRTH AND DEVELOPMENT OF THE GEOLOGICAL SCIENCES, F. D. Adams. Most thorough history of the earth sciences ever written. Geological thought from earliest times to the end of the 19th century, covering over 300 early thinkers & systems: fossils & their explanation, vulcanists vs. neptunists, figured stones & paleontology, generation of stones, dozens of similar topics. 91 illustrations, including medieval, renaissance woodcuts, etc. Index. 632 footnotes, mostly bibliographical. 511pp. 5⅜ x 8.   T5 Paperbound **$2.00**

DE RE METALLICA, Georgius Agricola. 400-year old classic translated, annotated by former President Herbert Hoover. The first scientific study of mineralogy and mining, for over 200 years after its appearance in 1556, it was the standard treatise. 12 books, exhaustively annotated, discuss the history of mining, selection of sites, types of deposits, making pits, shafts, ventilating, pumps, crushing machinery; assaying, smelting, refining metals; also salt, alum, nitre, glass making. Definitive edition, with all 289 16th century woodcuts of the original. Biographical, historical introductions, bibliography, survey of ancient authors. Indexes. A fascinating book for anyone interested in art, history of science, geology, etc. Deluxe edition. 289 illustrations. 672pp. 6¾ x 10¾. Library cloth.   S6 Clothbound **$10.00**

GEOGRAPHICAL ESSAYS, William Morris Davis. Modern geography & geomorphology rest on the fundamental work of this scientist. 26 famous essays presenting most important theories, field researches. Partial contents: Geographical Cycle, Plains of Marine and Subaerial Denudation, The Peneplain, Rivers and Valleys of Pennsylvania, Outline of Cape Cod, Sculpture of Mountains by Glaciers, etc. "Long the leader & guide," ECONOMIC GEOGRAPHY. "Part of the very texture of geography . . . models of clear thought," GEOGRAPHIC REVIEW. Index. 130 figures. vi + 777pp. 5⅜ x 8.   S383 Paperbound **$2.95**

A HISTORY OF ANCIENT GEOGRAPHY, E. H. Bunbury. Standard study, in English, of ancient geography; never equalled for scope, detail. First full account of history of geography from Greeks' first world picture based on mariners, through Ptolemy. Discusses every important map, discovery, figure, travel, expedition, war, conjecture, narrative, bearing on subject. Chapters on Homeric geography, Herodotus, Alexander expedition, Strabo, Pliny, Ptolemy, would stand alone as exhaustive monographs. Includes minor geographers, men not usually regarded in this context: Hecataeus, Pythea, Hipparchus, Artemidorus, Marinus of Tyre, etc. Uses information gleaned from military campaigns such as Punic wars, Hannibal's passage of Alps, campaigns of Lucullus, Pompey, Caesar's wars, the Trojan war. New introduction by W. H. Stahl, Brooklyn College. Bibliography. Index. 20 maps. 1426pp. 5⅜ x 8.
                                                      T570-1, clothbound, 2 volume set **$12.50**

URANIUM PROSPECTING, H. L. Barnes. For immediate practical use, professional geologist considers uranium ores, geological occurrences, field conditions, all aspects of highly profitable occupation. Index. Bibliography. x + 117pp. 5⅜ x 8.   T309 Paperbound **$1.00**

BIOLOGICAL SCIENCES

THE ORIGIN OF LIFE, A. I. Oparin. A classic of biology. This is the first modern statement of the theory of gradual evolution of life from nitrocarbon compounds. A brand-new evaluation of Oparin's theory in light of later research, by Dr. S. Morgulis, University of Nebraska. xxv +270pp. 5⅜ x8.   S213 Paperbound **$1.75**

HEREDITY AND YOUR LIFE, A. M. Winchester. Authoritative, concise explanation of human genetics, in non-technical terms. What factors determine characteristics of future generations, how they may be altered; history of genetics, application of knowledge to control health, intelligence, number of entire populations. Physiology of reproduction, chromosomes, genes, blood types, Rh factor, dominant, recessive traits, birth by proxy, sexual abnormalities, radiation, much more. Index. 75 illus. 345pp. 5⅜ x 8.   T598 Paperbound **$1.45**

Dover publishes books on art, music, philosophy, literature, languages, history, social sciences, psychology, handcrafts, orientalia, puzzles and entertainments, chess, pets and gardens, books explaining science, intermediate and higher mathematics mathematical physics, engineering, biological sciences, earth sciences, classics of science, etc. Write to:

Dept. catrr.
Dover Publications, Inc.
180 Varick Street, N. Y. 14, N. Y.